Congratulations to

Karan Mahajan

Winner of the

2017 Bard Fiction Prize

Karan Mahajan, author of *The Association of Small Bombs*, joins previous winners Nathan Englander, Emily Barton, Monique Truong, Paul La Farge, Edie Meidav, Peter Orner, Salvador Plascencia, Fiona Maazel, Samantha Hunt, Karen Russell, Benjamin Hale, Brian Conn, Bennett Sims, Laura van den Berg, and Alexandra Kleeman.

The Bard Fiction Prize is awarded annually to a promising emerging writer who is an American citizen aged thirty-nine years or younger at the time of application. In addition to a monetary award of $30,000, the winner receives an appointment as writer in residence at Bard College for one semester without the expectation that he or she will teach traditional courses. The recipient will give at least one public lecture and meet informally with students.

For more information, please contact:

Bard Fiction Prize
Bard College
PO Box 5000
Annandale-on-Hudson, NY 12504-5000

COMING UP IN THE SPRING

Conjunctions:68
INSIDE OUT:
ARCHITECTURES OF EXPERIENCE

Edited by Bradford Morrow

The structures that surround us inform and sometimes define who we are. Humans, animals, even viruses dwell somewhere, and that somewhere is often central to their existence, as lasting or ephemeral as it may be.

Inside Out: Architectures of Experience collects writings in which the vast range of architectures crucial to our being is investigated. The issue comprises a narrative map of lives lived or imagined in domestic spaces such as mansions, shanties, trailers, high-rise flats, cliff dwellings; public edifices such as hotels, motels, old-age homes, dorms, train stations; temporary zones like tents, deer stands, pillow forts, cardboard shelters; replicas such as dolls' houses, dioramas, scale models; animal environments like beehives, bird nests, and anthills. Other possible architectures include everything from caves to film sets, cages to monasteries, sewer tunnels to symbolic spaces like the infamous glass house.

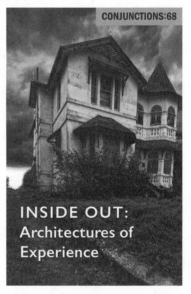

While the stories, poems, and essays gathered in *Conjunctions:68* will be about a multitude of experiences, each will center around a habitat, an existential structure. Architectural spaces will be built, divided, destroyed. Will be broken into and out of. Homes will be invaded and run away from, but they will also be where the heart is. Where we are born, live, and die—these focal locations will constitute *Inside Out: Architectures of Experience.*

Robert Coover, Elaine Equi, Lance Olsen, Frederic Tuten, and many others will be featured in this issue.

CONJUNCTIONS:68

INSIDE OUT:
Architectures of
Experience

One-year individual US subscriptions to *Conjunctions* are only $18 (two years for $32) for today's most fearlessly imagined, immaculately conceived fiction, poetry, and narrative nonfiction. To read dangerously, subscribe or renew at conjunctions.com, or mail your check to *Conjunctions*, Bard College, Annandale-on-Hudson, NY 12504. For e-book editions of current and selected past issues, visit openroadmedia.com/conjunctions. If you have questions or wish to request an invoice, e-mail conjunctions@bard.edu or call (845) 758-7054.

CONJUNCTIONS

Bi-Annual Volumes of New Writing

Edited by
Bradford Morrow

Contributing Editors
John Ashbery
Martine Bellen
Mei-mei Berssenbrugge
Mary Caponegro
Brian Evenson
William H. Gass
Peter Gizzi
Robert Kelly
Ann Lauterbach
Norman Manea
Rick Moody
Howard Norman
Karen Russell
Joanna Scott
David Shields
Peter Straub
John Edgar Wideman

Published by Bard College

EDITOR: Bradford Morrow
MANAGING EDITOR: Micaela Morrissette
SENIOR EDITORS: Jedediah Berry, Benjamin Hale, Joss Lake, J. W. McCormack, Edie Meidav, Nicole Nyhan, Pat Sims
COPY EDITOR: Pat Sims
ASSISTANT EDITORS: Matthew Balik, Ari Braverman, Nicholas Wetherell
PUBLICITY: Darren O'Sullivan, Mark R. Primoff
EDITORIAL ASSISTANTS: Janet Barrow, Kaitlynn Buchbaum, Brigid Fister, Adela Foo, Gilad Jaffe, Kelsey Johnson, Tessa Menatien, Charles Noyes, Chloe Reimann, Zoe Rohrich, Jay Rosenstein, Chloe Scala, Anna Sones

CONJUNCTIONS is published in the Spring and Fall of each year by Bard College, Annandale-on-Hudson, NY 12504.

SUBSCRIPTIONS: Use our secure online ordering system at conjunctions.com, or send subscription orders to CONJUNCTIONS, Bard College, Annandale-on-Hudson, NY 12504. Single year (two volumes): $18.00 for individuals; $40.00 for institutions and non-US. Two years (four volumes): $32.00 for individuals; $80.00 for institutions and non-US. For information about subscriptions, back issues, and advertising, contact us at (845) 758-7054 or conjunctions@bard.edu. *Conjunctions* is listed and indexed in JSTOR and Humanities International Complete and included in EBSCO*host*.

Editorial communications should be sent to Bradford Morrow, *Conjunctions*, 21 East 10th Street, 3E, New York, NY 10003. Unsolicited manuscripts cannot be returned unless accompanied by a stamped, self-addressed envelope. Electronic and simultaneous submissions will not be considered. If you are submitting from outside the United States, contact conjunctions@bard.edu for instructions.

Cover design by Jerry Kelly, New York. Cover art by Joseba Elorza (miraruido.com): *Invasion*, digital collage, 2013. © Joseba Elorza 2016; all rights reserved by the artist.

Conjunctions e-books of current and selected past issues are distributed by Open Road Integrated Media (openroadmedia.com/conjunctions) and available for purchase in all e-reader formats from Amazon, Apple, B&N, Google, Indiebound, Kobo, Overdrive, and elsewhere.

Retailers can order print issues directly from *Conjunctions* or via Ubiquity Distributors, Inc., ubiquitymags.com, 607 Degraw Street, Brooklyn, NY 11217. Telephone: (718) 875-5491. Fax: (718) 875-8047.

Printers: Edwards Brothers Malloy, Circle Press

Typesetter: Bill White, Typeworks

ISSN 0278-2324

ISBN 978-0-941964-83-8

Manufactured in the United States of America.

TABLE OF CONTENTS

OTHER ALIENS

Coedited by Bradford Morrow and Elizabeth Hand

EDITORS' NOTE. 7

Leena Krohn, *Two Stories* (translated from Finnish by
Eva Buchwald) 8

Jeffrey Ford, *Not Without Mercy* 22

Julia Elliott, *Clouds* 31

John Crowley, *The Million Monkeys of M. Borel* 57

Laura Sims, *Walking Dead Love Songs* 61

Valerie Martin, *Bromley Hall* 67

Lavie Tidhar, *Tinkerers* 86

Samuel R. Delany, *An Interview* (conducted by
Brian Evenson) 99

Matthew Baker, *The Transition* 115

Paul Park, *Blind Spot* 133

James Tiptree, Jr., *Favored by Strange Gods: A Selection of
Letters to Joanna Russ* (with an introductory note by
Nicole Nyhan) 137

Michael Parrish Lee, *The Showroom Variations* 196

Peter Straub, *The Process Is a Process All Its Own* 207

Kelly Link, *An Interview* (conducted by Elizabeth Hand) 227

Madeline Bourque Kearin, *Fallout* 238

Jean Muno, *Cartoon* (translated from French by
Edward Gauvin) 254

Jonathan Thirkield, *Two Poems* 265

John Clute and John Crowley, *Mysterious Strangers:*
A Conversation 275

Joyce Carol Oates, *Undocumented Alien* 286

S. P. Tenhoff, *The Unrivaled Happiness of Otters* 309

Brian Evenson, *Smear* 322

Jessica Reed, *Four Atomic Poems* 329

E. G. Willy, *Radio City* 337

James Morrow, *Noh Exit* 351

NOTES ON CONTRIBUTORS 374

EDITORS' NOTE

WHO OR WHAT IS AN ALIEN? Someone or something whose profound otherness stirs in us terror, even dread? Or perhaps a healthy—sometimes dangerous—curiosity? In Joseba Elorza's cover art for this issue, are the aliens those commandeering the descending saucers or are they the three conspicuously nonchalant figures in the foreground, interrupted on their way to work? On the other hand, are both UFOs and metropolitan pedestrians somehow alien?

Aliens are, by definition, Other. They are the stuff of science and speculative fiction, of Fantastika and fantasy, yes, but they are also traditional literary figures whom society, however unfairly, has labeled misfits, nonpersons, the Ishmaels of the world. When Frankenstein's monster stalks the countryside, an ill-fated product of human genius and hubris, he is the alien, the Other. But those who misjudge him and seek his destruction are also the Others in Shelley's story.

In *The New Wave Fabulists* issue of *Conjunctions*, nominally "genre" writers tested literary boundaries in risky and exciting ways. In *Betwixt the Between*, "literary" authors explored the terrains of genre fiction. Having thus established a discourse between the literary and genre worlds, we felt compelled in *Other Aliens* to further unsettle the precincts of genre and literary writing, push for even more freedom to define what alienation and otherness is about.

Joyce Carol Oates's chilling experiment turns the mind of an immigrant alien into that of an alien in the interplanetary sense. Matthew Baker explores a new body dysmorphia. Peter Straub's synesthetic serial killer inhales the odors of languages. Michael Parrish Lee markets human products. Madeline Bourque Kearin's marooned heroine sits still in the middle of time. Laura Sims writes odes of love to zombies. A host of other aliens can also be discovered here.

To be able to offer interviews with Samuel R. Delany, Kelly Link, John Crowley, and John Clute, along with a generous selection of previously unpublished letters by James Tiptree, Jr., who knew better than most what it is like to feel *other*, is for us a distinct honor. In these glimpses into the writerly mind, as in all the imaginative worlds this issue contains, we pursue a definition of the indefinable.

—Bradford Morrow and Elizabeth Hand
October 2016
New York City and Lincolnville, Maine

7

Two Stories
Leena Krohn

—Translated from Finnish by Eva Buchwald

IN THE QUIET OF THE GARDENS

THE SHALLOW CLAY POT CONTAINED white sand and a black stone. Around the stone, there were rings in the sand traced by Sylvia's fingertip. This was one of Sylvia's miniature landscapes, a kind of zen garden. She named all her gardens, as one does with works of art. This garden was called "Cause and Effect." The white sand was taken from the city's public beach, where Sylvia had spooned it into a plastic bag. She suspected this was an unlawful activity, so she had gone to the beach late in the evening, once all the sun worshippers had gone home. The round black stone was from one of Sylvia's trips abroad, plucked from a Greek graveyard.

The stone was action, any action, or prime cause. The sand was water, and its rings, traveling far beyond the rim of the pot, were the result of the stone being flung into the water.

Sylvia had made her first miniature garden for her niece. She thought Anja might feel inspired to create her own landscapes, which would take the girl's mind off the maelstrom of her parents' divorce and her subsequent move. But it seemed that Anja joined in the game only for her aunt's sake. She managed to put together one landscape in a glass-domed pot that Sylvia gave her, using a little moss and a pebble for a boulder. It seemed to Sylvia that Anja didn't even choose the pebble very carefully, it was just a random pebble of suitable size that happened to catch Anja's eye in the local playground. The mirror in Sylvia's compact served as a lake. And that was that. Having reached the ripe old age of nine, Anja had grown out of playing; nowadays she practiced competitive dance, went downhill skiing, and tweeted with her friends. But Sylvia began spending more and more time in her little worlds. This turned out to be Sylvia's own way of playing.

Small is beautiful, this had always been Sylvia's motto in her youth, but as she grew older she became increasingly convinced of how true

8

it was. Small became more than a mere hobby; it turned into a passion, a new calling.

Possibly it was a notion that had its roots in Sylvia's childhood. Back then, she'd had moments when she'd see everything around her as if it were small and far away. This had happened especially when she was tired. She would be playing hopscotch in the yard, or eating dinner with her mom and dad, and suddenly everything would come to a standstill. She would stop hopping and be left standing on one leg, or if she'd been eating, her spoon would come to a halt between her bowl and her mouth. When she looked around, her friends, her mom and dad, objects, rooms, houses appeared ever so small, as if she were looking through the wrong end of a pair of binoculars, as if they had receded so far into the distance that it was barely possible to make them out. This would last about a minute, if that, then the world would return to normal. Only her mother would sometimes ask her: "What are you looking at?," to which Sylvia would bluntly retort: "Nothing!"

This only happened once during Sylvia's adulthood, one autumn day when she had climbed to the top of a viewing tower with a friend, in order to watch the migrating birds as they left. The melancholic autumn landscape that lay before her—the island, the birch grove with its turning leaves, the suburban tower blocks beyond—all shrank suddenly into a kind of toy land. She could still clearly perceive every single detail, however, and the view seemed more and more beautiful and fascinating. She didn't know whether it was something to do with her eyes or whether it was a sort of fit, like epilepsy, or some other neurological complaint. But these moments didn't frighten her; rather, she almost longed for them. They were crystal clear and yet dreamlike, almost magical.

The world was repeatedly thrown into turmoil, both the world at large and Sylvia's own private world. After being diagnosed with rheumatism, Sylvia retired early on sickness benefit from the bank where she worked, losing her friends and her daily routine. She would very gladly have taken care of her own real garden, but she didn't have one. She did have a balcony, however, facing east, in her one-room, already mortgage-free apartment in a clean, modern suburb. She was very happy about that. It was on her balcony, which got the morning sun, that she drank her coffee in the summertime, and it was there she built her first few miniature gardens.

In her youth, and even in later years, Sylvia had been something of an activist, in her own modest way. She had donated to several

9

humanitarian organizations, first out of her student loan and later out of her modest wage. She had participated in demonstrations against war and nuclear power and private car ownership and poor mining regulations and animal abuse, not only in her hometown but also in far-flung reaches of the world, saving up for months on end for the privilege of demonstrating. Both her own problems and other people's tragedies made her sad. She took matters, both near and far, to heart: devastated environments she'd never seen, strangers who lived on the other side of the globe hungry, homeless, and oppressed. She didn't know them, but to them she extended her sorrow and pity. Of course they were completely unaware of this. Their hunger persisted, wars continued, mines collapsed, the landscape grew uglier, and animals and people suffered.

Now Sylvia applied her rheumatically deformed fingers to the creation of meticulously designed landscapes over which she had unique control. When the scale of things changes, everything changes. The smaller, the better, was how Sylvia thought. Her toy lands were free from suffering. No one could spoil them. They were not only landscapes but also fantasies, like the models for set designs in a theater. But they didn't require actors.

Sylvia ordered miniature equipment over the Internet, preferably on a scale of one to twenty-four, even though the range was more limited than in the more popular dollhouse scale of one to twelve. Sometimes she combined both sizes in the same landscape. It gave a surrealistic touch to her work. In winter, her toy worlds had to be brought in from the balcony. They filled her windowsills but the space wasn't enough. By taking a lot of her books to a secondhand bookstore, Sylvia managed to clear off a whole long shelf to accommodate her landscapes.

Sylvia gathered moss and lichens from the local woods, she picked sprigs of blueberry and lingonberry, heather and coralbells, all of which turned into meadows and copses and coniferous forests in her landscapes. The winter stalks, which Sylvia planted in the sand, became exotic trees. Occasionally Sylvia went to the nursery to buy precious bonsai plants such as myrtle, hornbeam, and Chinese juniper.

One of her gardens was called "Laundry Day." The pot contained a roof-covered wooden well, in front of which lay a tin basin. Sylvia had stretched a piece of thread between two bonsai for a washing line, and from it she hung handkerchiefs cut into quarters, representing sheets. They were attached to the line with minuscule clothespins.

Another garden was called "Road to America." For this she had acquired succulent plants of various shapes and sizes: mistletoe cactus, *Haworthia*, pebble plants. A dirt road ran through the desert and on it Sylvia had drawn the footsteps of a wanderer in boots. They led to a bright red drinks dispenser with its door slightly ajar. It was full of Coca-Cola bottles.

A square pot, which Sylvia had placed on the bookshelf, was called "Author's Garden." Sylvia had tried to make it resemble an English cottage garden. The little star-shaped flowers of the yarrow impersonated white roses. The landscape included a little house that was surrounded by a picket fence made of matches. The house was, in fact, a music box that Sylvia had been given as a child, a souvenir from Switzerland. When the box was opened, it played *Es ist für uns eine Zeit angekommen*. The author lived in the music box house. He was not visible, but his typewriter, a wad of paper, and a stack of books lay on the garden table along with a telephone, wine bottle, and glass. A slim wooden chair stood facing the typewriter, and on the chair Sylvia had placed her own hand-sewn cushion. The chair was a miniature model of Charles Dickens's chair. It had slender armrests and crafted legs, and its backrest was wicker. It was the most expensive piece of miniature furniture Sylvia had ever bought.

One garden had been built into a basket. It was rimmed with a low brushwood fence that Sylvia wove from birch twigs. There was a gate in the fence and, beyond the gate, a tree and a well. The tree was a small bonsai that had been trained from a linden shoot. This piece depicted the landscape in one of Sylvia's favorite songs from Schubert, "Der Lindenbaum."

There was a long, narrow pot, the longest clay pot Sylvia had managed to find, in which she created a park boulevard. It led to Rodin's statue *The Thinker*. She was thrilled to have found a miniature of the statue through a commercial website. The trees in the park were created from the blueberry sprigs Sylvia had collected. Between the sprigs she placed small green iron benches, and the boulevard was surfaced with aquarium gravel. At one end of the gravel stretch, there was a red bicycle and at the other, a black car. This garden was called "I Think I Am."

Sylvia's friend Irene, a former colleague from the credit department of the bank, commented after seeing the gardens; "You're regressing into childhood."

And it was true, Sylvia played like a child, intensely focused, forgetting all else. Creating her miniature worlds gave her enormous satisfaction. Her aches and pains subsided, and she forgot to worry about the madness and injustice of the world. If her hobby did not improve the world, at least it didn't harm it, Sylvia reflected.

Her niece said: "They're nice, Auntie Sylvia. But you could do one with a beach and parasols and lots of people."

But Sylvia's world was devoid of people or dolls representing them, and devoid of animals. They were deserted landscapes, where living presence was only indicated by some object, piece of furniture, clothespins, or just footsteps in the sand.

Sylvia had become devoted to her new solitary hobby for some time, and was relatively content with her life. Then one day her gardens, in which peace and harmony had reigned, showed signs of strange goings-on. At first Sylvia could only wonder at them.

The first landscape to change was "Cause and Effect." The black stone vanished, and the sand, in which she had drawn three concentric rings, lay flat and even, as if someone had smoothed them out. Sylvia searched for the stone for a long time, going through her desk, her bookshelf, the floor, her whole apartment. She thought perhaps her niece, who had been visiting on the weekend, had fiddled with it for some reason and forgotten to replace the stone. It was smooth and round and pleasant to handle. But then it occurred to her to search in the sand, and eventually, deep down in the bottom of the pot, her fingertips touched the stone. It had sunk into the sand representing water, as if it really were water.

Sylvia didn't dwell on the matter; she soon put it out of her mind. Until, one day, one of the white sheets in her "Laundry Day" piece was ripped in the middle. It looked as though some creature had flown through the cloth. She couldn't understand it. Perhaps a bird, a starling or a sparrow, had pecked at it when the pot was on the balcony? Instead of changing the ripped sheet for a fresh one, she renamed the landscape. It might as well be called "Who Ruined the Laundry," she decided.

A change also took place in the garden called "I Think I Am." The black car at the end of the avenue had driven to the other end and knocked over the bicycle, mounting the handlebars with its front wheel. The Thinker sat staring pensively at the sight, which Sylvia did not readjust. She left the bike where it was, partially under the car, and renamed the work "Guilty."

In the "Author's Garden," Charles Dickens's beautiful chair had been knocked over and the wine bottle had fallen from the table onto the ground. The receiver of the old-fashioned telephone, which had previously rested in its cradle, was now hanging from its wire over the edge of the table, as if the speaker had just let it drop. She re-named this work too: "Bad News."

Sylvia could not conceive of any explanation other than that Anja, who had a key to her place, had come over while Sylvia was at the shops or library or out walking. She asked Anja on three occasions whether she had been playing with her landscapes. "It's absolutely fine if you have," said Sylvia. "I'm happy for you to play with them. But I'd like you to tell me."

After the third time, Anja lost her temper.

"I wouldn't lay a finger on your crazy pots, not even if you paid me. It's a stupid game. Stupid! No other adults play games like that."

After that, Sylvia believed Anja was telling the truth. She apologized to her niece for wrongly suspecting her. But it left her even more baffled as to what was happening to her creations. Her little worlds, formerly so peaceful, seats of quiet and harmony, were turn-ing into riddles, theaters of the absurd, stages of dramatic or criminal events. But the reason for their transformation was still as impercep-tible as the black stone that had sunk to the bottom of the sand.

Nevertheless, Sylvia felt there was something exciting about the transformations. She accepted them. They brought suspense to her otherwise uneventful life. Until one day "Der Lindenbaum" was ruined. Sylvia was really upset by its fate. Her handsome, slender bonsai linden had broken and fallen—no, it had been felled. Its delicate trunk had been cut about halfway down. When she looked closely at the stump, she had the impression it had been chopped down with an ax. For the first time, she felt a shudder of fear. Her niece would never have been capable of such a monstrous act.

Sylvia rang Irene and asked her to come over.

"I have something important to tell you," she said.

Sylvia once again showed all her landscapes to Irene, and carefully described all the recent changes that had taken place in them. She said she suspected someone had managed to make a copy of her key or Anja's, and entered her apartment when she was away. This person had not stolen anything, however, only destroyed her artworks. Why on earth someone would do such a thing, she could not fathom. It was probably simply vandalism. She had decided to report it to the police.

Her friend was pensive and unusually silent as she observed the sorry-looking gardens. She left soon after drinking her coffee, with-out her usual chitchat on the latest developments at work.

"Don't report this to the police just yet," she turned to advise Sylvia at the door.

The next day Irene rang to say: "Sylvia, I've booked you an appointment with my therapist. She helped me a lot after my divorce. I'm worried about you. Go and talk to her about your problems. They seem serious to me."

Sylvia was astonished. "I'm not sure I understand. It is a problem, yes, that there's some vandal secretly entering my apartment, creating trouble, and destroying my artworks. But it's a matter for the police, not a therapist. I mean there's no point in me discussing it with a therapist; it's a different matter if the person is apprehended. Then they should definitely start having therapy."

"Go and see her anyway, for my sake," said Irene. "Tell her everything just the way you told me. Please! I'll come and see you tomorrow. We can think it over together."

When Irene arrived, Sylvia was pale and unsettled.

"Come and see," she said, and led Irene over to the windowsill.

Sylvia's latest landscape was on the windowsill. It was built into a long copper baking tin, and its theme was "River of Death." The water was made of cobalt-blue shards of mosaic glass, and a black glass swan swam on the river. Sylvia had found the swan at the local flea market. The banks of the river were lined with dark-green haircap moss. But the swan's long neck was broken. Its head lay on the mossy bank.

"When did this happen?" Irene asked.

"I found it this morning," said Sylvia morosely, placing the swan's head on her palm. "Someone must have come in during the night. I will have to install a chain and safety locks."

"Sylvia, dear, no one has been here. No one!" said Irene.

"What are you saying? What do you mean?" Sylvia asked, at first surprised, then angry.

She turned the swan's head over in her fingers. Irene didn't answer, but Sylvia had begun to understand. Her face grew dark and she pursed her lips.

"Don't be afraid, it'll all be sorted out," said Irene, and she tried to hug her. "I'll come with you, we'll make you well again."

"Why should I go anywhere? It wasn't me who did it," said Sylvia, pushing Irene away. "That's ridiculous. Why would I damage my own artworks?"

"I don't know. But who else could it be?" asked Irene.

Sylvia squeezed the little piece of glass in her right fist so hard that a drop of blood swelled up between her index and ring fingers.

"They can all be fixed. You can glue the swan's neck back together, and redesign the gardens, make them even more beautiful than before," Irene comforted her.

"But what if—," Sylvia began and then fell silent. She opened her fist and placed the head back on the hairy moss of "River of Death."

"That's it! How could I not have understood it earlier?" she said, and stroked the moss with her bloodstained finger.

"Understood what?" asked Irene.

"What if there is no vandal?"

"That's what I've been trying to tell you," said Irene.

"You were trying to tell me that I am the vandal," said Sylvia drily, in a voice that was not at all kind. "But it's not me. This is about something else altogether. I've only just begun to see."

"What's it about then?" Irene asked, frustrated by now.

"It's about my landscapes transforming themselves, from the inside. It has to be. Because it's time for them to change. Because they're not islands. I always thought they were. I believed they would remain intact, exactly as I made them. But of course they can't. And it's no one's fault. It's just something I have to accept."

Sylvia distractedly opened the music box and the author's house began playing *Es ist für uns eine Zeit angekommen.*

"That's absolutely insane," said Irene, and this time it was she who lost her temper. "Be reasonable now! And stop that plinking noise!"

Amid the tiny, changing landscapes the two of them glared at one another like enemies. The swan swam along the river headless. The laundry was ruined. The linden was felled. The author had received some bad news in the garden and his manuscript lay unfinished.

If the Thinker had any thoughts, he kept them to himself, as always.

THE LIGHT IN THE GUEST ROOM

The shallow bay was slowly becoming overgrown. A belt of wetland rushes ran along its banks, every summer encroaching further upon the bay and providing shelter for both the Eurasian bittern and the grey heron. The call of the Eurasian bittern sounded like the foghorn of a distant ship, but the bleak cry of the grey heron sometimes made Essi jump. It sounded like the wail of someone at death's door. Essi never saw the great birds, only heard their calls.

When it was windy, the rustle of the rushes carried right up to

15

the old white-stucco house. Essi knew that the rushes were technically common reeds. On windy days she recalled Pascal, who once wrote that a human being was a thinking reed. Essi herself firmly believed that every reed, of which there were billions growing in a curve along the shoreline, was a sentient being in its own way. If they didn't think, they were thoughts in themselves, and the rustle in the rushes resembled a murmur so remote that it was impossible to make out the words.

The house was on the north shore and it was always cool, even in a heat wave. During the summer, the yard rested in the damp shade of the tall deciduous trees, and under their cover, the house's roof tiles had gathered plenty of moss.

When there were no leaves on the trees, the view stretched as far as the strait. The room was wallpapered in a slightly powdery bluish gray, and just below the ceiling ran a white border printed with blue sailboats. The bookshelves were stacked with books inherited from Bert's father, law books, dictionaries, and nonfiction that no one had needed in years, as well as annuals from the Philosophical Society. It was rare for anyone to stay overnight in this room. The children, who had long since moved away from home, slept there two or three times a year. Essi sometimes used the room to write letters, sometimes simply to lie down for a moment in the narrow wooden bed, with her eyes closed, as free from thought as possible. A Buddha from Nepal was placed on the windowsill, as well as a blue-glass vase that currently contained bulrushes. In the spring and summer, if someone was coming to stay in the room, Essi would put wildflowers in the vase, or peonies and hollyhocks from the garden if they were already in bloom.

Sometimes Essi spent the night in the room, or at least part of the night. She would climb upstairs whenever Bert, who suffered from asthma, was snoring with exceptional gusto and failed to stop even after obediently turning over at his wife's request.

This was the very reason Essi had climbed the stairs after midnight that night. She was hoping to spend the rest of the night in peace and quiet in the guest room, and she wanted a lie-in the next morning. That's why she had hung a dark sheet in front of the thin white curtains, even though it was a moonless, cloudy night. If the clouds dispersed in the morning, the rays of the rising sun would shine straight onto her bed. The additional layer also cut out the glimmer of the distant streetlamp on the harbor road, and so the room was pitch-dark when Essi went to bed. After turning off the lamp on the bedside table, Essi noticed there wasn't the slightest gleam of light in the room, not even so much as a wisp emanating from the cracks around the curtain or the door. It was the kind of obscurity that the eye never gets used to. No matter how long you stared into it, no shape emerged from beneath its tenebrous weight, no hint of color or contour, not the vaguest shadow of a shadow. Darkness like that is not simply the absence of light, it is a substance, a mass of its own. Its pull had sucked in all the color, shapes, and dimensions of the entire guest room with all its books and sailboats and vases. Essi felt she had never before seen such absolute darkness. Except that you can't see darkness.

Essi had always imagined that blindness must be the same kind of coal blackness. But someone she knew who had gone blind in later years had corrected her misconception. She had pointed out that it was quite the opposite. That blindness, at least as far as her blindness was concerned, was not black at all. It was a brume cloud, shreds, dark patches, flickering membranes that shifted as the eyes moved.

Essi had never been afraid of the dark anyway; she fell asleep easily and succumbed to a deep, dreamless slumber. Nevertheless, in the small hours, when it was still just as dark as when she had gone to bed, Essi was awake again, and she couldn't understand why. She was sure she hadn't even slept for an hour. As always, she had fallen asleep with her left hand under her ear and her right arm along her side, with her face to the wall, but as she woke she turned onto her back. As usual, Essi was fully awake at once and aware that she wasn't in her own bed but in the guest room.

The darkness in the room was unbroken except for one spot. Below Essi's left breast, on the blue-and-white-checked bedspread, which Essi used as an extra blanket because the room was cold, there was a bright splash of light. This was surely what had woken her. Where did it come from, this splash of light? There was no television in the room, no computer or even a phone charger. There was an old portable radio that had stood on the dresser for years, but its batteries were dead. Essi couldn't think of any source of energy capable of casting such a light effect onto her bed. The sheet was still tightly stretched over the window just as she had hung it. This bright, crisply defined light shining just below her breast didn't seem to come from anywhere, and neither did it illuminate its surroundings. It was an evenly distributed, pure white glow, a carefully delineated perfect circle, as if a torch were being held close under the cover. If the light were coming from a different direction it would never have been as round.

17

It was still and steady, about five or six centimeters in diameter. Essi lifted the checked coverlet, which was lined with dark-blue fabric. In between was a thin layer of cotton padding that the light penetrated. The snow-white luster made the threads in the fabric stand out. The light wasn't on the coverlet, it seemed to be inside it. It came from nowhere, not from within the room or from without; it had no source. It was just a glow, a light of its own, a spirit creature. It was like a miniature full moon, but its luminosity was not borrowed light, like that of the moon in the sky.

Essi lifted and lowered the coverlet over and over, looking at the round glow from above, through the coverlet's checked fabric, and below, through the lining. Even though she moved the coverlet around, the silver medallion stayed firmly in place.

So far, Essi had simply marveled at the manifestation, now she was afraid. Fear shot through her diaphragm, right at the point where the strange moonlight glow lingered, and it numbed her arms and legs. Her petrified limbs were an indication that the light was an unnatural, abnormal phenomenon, one that should not exist. Although it didn't move, it seemed alive in some way. It was like some creature that had descended upon her in her sleep and had perhaps been watching her for hours. Or perhaps it was sucking energy from her heart?

Essi sat bolt upright and fumbled for the light switch on her bedside lamp. Once the ordinary electric light had reclaimed the familiar room from the dark, along with all its objects well-worn by human hand, she calmed down. There was no longer any gratuitous glow visible on or in the coverlet. But Essi didn't dare turn off the light. She got up and switched on the desk lamp as well and began reading the letter she had left on the desk the day before, which she hadn't yet had time to answer. It was from her friend Hiroko, who had just gotten married to Mr. White Stone. Hiroko wrote:

> We spent our honeymoon in Shikoku, three days in the Kagawa Prefecture on Naoshima Island, one day visiting the Konpira temple in Kagawa, and a couple of days visiting the hot springs of Ehime in Dogo-onsen, following the Shimanami Ocean Road, through the archipelago of the Seto Inland Sea. The islands grew ever more beautiful in the changing landscapes created by the light, the stars, the wind, and the surf. The evening shifted gradually from burnt orange to lilac, the morning from glowing red to bluish white. As I watched the changing landscapes of the inland sea, I also saw something unchanging. The horizon.

When Essi had finished reading, she dimmed the light on her bed-side table by placing over the lampshade a colorful silk scarf she had received from the writer of the letter. It cast patches of yellow, red, and green across the wall, and none of pure white. Essi finally managed to fall asleep to the colors and the thought of the horizon's eternity.

Over morning coffee, she told Bert about the incident.

"There must be some explanation," said Bert.

"I think so too," said Essi. "Perhaps some kind of electromagnetic phenomenon?"

Later that day, Essi went upstairs to examine the bedspread. There was nothing remarkable about it; it was a thinly lined polyester coverlet, whose label indicated it was to be washed at 40 degrees. Over the following nights Essi used earplugs long before Bert started snoring, to be on the safe side. She wasn't keen on the idea of climbing upstairs at midnight.

When her stepson, Max, a student of energy technology, came over the following weekend, she described the night's incident to him.

"I suppose it could have been static electricity," he said doubtfully.

"Do you think that's possible?"

"What fabric is the bedspread made of?"

"Polyester, hundred percent, I checked," Essi answered.

"Hmm," said Max, "polyester has a negative electrical charge and a human body has positive. That can create static electricity. Were you touching the cover?"

"Yes, I was, I was twisting and turning it every which way. But I don't remember touching the light itself. Which is a shame, because now I don't know if it was hot or cold."

"It wasn't just a flash of light?" asked Max.

"No, nothing like a flash of light. It was a persistent light, which stayed in one place. I think it must have been lying on my chest for goodness knows how long before I woke up."

"I don't understand," said Max. "Then it can't have been static electricity. That kind of force discharges in a split second. There may be a buzzing sound and small sparks if it's a strong charge. Not a persistent light, that's impossible."

"I saw what I saw," said Essi.

"I don't doubt it," said Max, "but perhaps what you saw was a dream."

The incident troubled Essi for a long time and she also told her childhood friend Irinja about it. Irinja was Orthodox by religion. Irinja said that a pure white light is holy, sacred light, and that there were certain churches where similar manifestations had been witnessed. In Irinja's view, Essi should be glad that such a light had visited her room, in a perfectly ordinary house. Essi felt this was a beautiful, comforting thought, but she couldn't understand why a holy light would have chosen her, a nonbeliever.

But her cousin Kirsti, who claimed to have a lot of experience of the other side, had a completely different view.

"If you see it again, turn all the lights on immediately," she urged, "and whatever you do, don't try and make contact with it. Never have anything to do with that kind of thing."

"What kind of thing?"

"The demonic," said Kirsti gravely.

Even though she was amused by Kirsti's warning, Essi couldn't help feeling a flutter of fear. She felt it especially between her shoulder blades, as if someone were pressing an icy hand to her back. Her husband by contrast merely snorted and repeated that of course there was a rational explanation for the light.

"You tell us what it is then," Essi suggested.

And he did, he said exactly the same thing as his son. Essi was amazed that a dream was the only rational explanation they could come up with. She guessed, however, that another theory they had the delicacy not to mention was that she was hallucinating. To them a dream or a hallucination seemed logical, but not to Essi. She knew she had been completely awake and alert as she examined the little light. Why had it visited her? If it was a message, a premonition, a warning, or a promise, she failed to comprehend it. What was the point of a message, if its recipient couldn't fathom it? It still lay there in her memory, lingering on her chest, near her heart, round and unblemished as a shiny silver coin, peaceful and almost fond, but as strange as ever.

Perhaps it was ridiculous, but on a couple of winter nights Essi plucked up the courage to climb the stairs to the guest room once again and she slept under the checked coverlet. She lay awake for quite some time before she could fall asleep, dozing off lightly only to awake with a start every now and then, wondering whether the light had returned. She both hoped and feared the unwavering moon would reappear, and her breathing quickened at the very thought of its manifestation on one of the longest, darkest nights, when cloud cover along the shoreline rested like a roof over the treetops. It was as if she were waiting for something forbidden but long missed. But it was all in vain, as the light never appeared.

The next spring, there were unusual halo effects in the sky. When Essi was driving along the highway from town, an immense spiral-shaped cloud hovered over the verdant fields and the edge of the forest. There was a clear glow at its center, from which a pillar-shaped rainbow stretched to the ground. She saw a number of cars parked by the roadside, and many people got out of their cars to stare at the horizon and take pictures with their smartphones of the rapidly fading phenomenon.

Later, one sunny April day, Bert called her into the garden to see something. When she came out, Bert was pointing silently up at the sky. Essi could see a rainbow-colored ring glistening around the spring sun and another, broader white misty belt that seemed to run through the sun. It was like a wheel of light encompassing the middle of the sky, and where the two rings met, there were two smaller suns glowing on either side of the real sun. Essi could distinguish all the colors of the spectrum in them too.

Three suns! She had never seen anything like it before. But for all its exceptionality, the magnificent geometry of the sky had an explanation. It was reported in the press and on the news and many people witnessed it, whereas the light in the guest room was hers alone. Whenever Essi remembered it, she wondered whether the little moon had woken her on purpose, or whether she had simply chanced upon the glow, which had no more sense or purpose than a mirage on a hot day or a will-o'-the-wisp flickering over the marshlands.

As evening approached and Essi was once again startled by the cry of an invisible bird whose life remained a mystery to her, she began to ponder that whatever knowledge one person possesses can easily be learned by another. But there are also things that no one knows, and these things can't be learned and don't belong to the realm of human knowledge but to some other realm. The memory of the circular light rested on Essi's chest like a glowing pendant that had been placed there by a stranger; it was a gift at once perilous and immeasurably precious.

Not Without Mercy
Jeffrey Ford

THE SNOW ANGLED DOWN fiercely out of the west, filling the parking lot and road and fields beyond. Amy stood at the office window
and peered into the storm, trying to spot the headlights of Harry's old
truck coming up Sossey Road. She shut off the lamps and signs out
by the pumps in order to see better. Her boss, Fareed, had called earlier and told her not to shut down the gas in case someone traveling
through the storm might need fuel. "Cash, they're out of luck," he'd
said. "But a debit card, yes. Travelers in need." He'd laughed and so
had she, but now she was worried. It was a ten-mile drive from the
edge of town out to the gas station and it looked to her like there was
already eight inches on the ground, no sign of letup. Drifts were
forming in the road.

She took out her cell phone and dialed Harry. Three rings later, he
answered. "Have you left yet?" she asked. "I was just thinking I
could stay here on the cot and you could come out tomorrow morning and get me. It looks really shitty out there."

"Too late," said Harry. "I'm here."

She peered again and now saw the headlights and the silhouette of
falling snow they cast. "OK," she said and hung up.

Harry pulled into the darkened parking lot. Amy put on her coat
and locked the garage and office doors. She left the office light on as
a gesture to lonely passersby. He stayed in the truck and rolled his
window down as she approached.

"How's Sossey?" she asked.

"Bad. We'll have to take it slow and hope we don't get stuck."

She walked around to the passenger side of the truck, clasping closed
the top of her coat with her right hand. The door of the truck squealed
miserably and she shook her head. "How old is this rolling pile?"

"Shhh," he said, patted the dashboard, and then lit the two cigarettes he held between his lips. She got situated in the seat, shut the
door, and he handed her one.

"How are the kids?" she asked and took a long drag, closing her
eyes like she was praying.

"They're in bed, asleep. Your old man is listening for them."

"Good," she said, and he put the truck in gear and crept out of the parking lot.

Amy tapped the pocket of her coat on the left side. "Oh, I thought I'd left it in the office."

"What?" He opened the window a slit to flick his ash.

"Fareed's wife, Susan, brought by that necklace this morning that I paid her to make for Becky. It's beautiful. Fake diamonds and a real sapphire."

"Shit, that's right, her birthday's next week."

"She's gonna be fourteen."

"Ain't that a kick in the head," said Harry, and a deafening roar pounced from above. The truck vibrated and swerved across the road. He did everything he could to keep it from going into the drainage ditch.

"What the . . . ," said Amy, and her words were cut off by the appearance from over the truck roof of something on fire, whistling down against the storm. In a moment it was out of sight behind the trees. Then they heard it hit, felt it, and saw an eruption of sparks shoot up in all directions. Harry managed to keep the truck on the road and swerved around the bend ahead, which brought them closer to the field that had been brimming with soybeans not three months earlier and now was home to whatever had dropped from the sky.

They saw the thing, the size of their garden shed, glowing in the distance. Harry slowed to a stop. "What do we do?" he asked.

"It doesn't look like a plane," said Amy.

"That's no plane."

"Is it a meteor?

"Doesn't look like that either."

"Well, forget it," she said. "I don't want to find out."

He pushed down on the gas, the wheels spun and smoke billowed out of the exhaust pipe, but they sat pretty much where they were.

"Oh, bullshit," she said.

"Yeah." He revved the engine and spun the tires a few more times until finally she said, "OK, that's enough. Is that shovel in the back?"

"Yeah."

"I'll dig the ice out from under the tires and maybe we can grab some road." She zipped up her coat, flipped the hood on without securing it, and got out.

Harry left the lights on and kept it running. The residual glow from the high beams faintly lit the area around the sides of the truck.

23

He found a flare in the bed, lit it, and set it up a few yards behind where they'd stopped. The wind had abated considerably since they'd left the station. Snow still came down but not quite as furiously. "I've got some sand in the back too," he said.

Amy asked him for another cigarette. He lit it in his cupped hands for her. With the butt in the corner of her lips she went to work, chipping and scraping at the frozen slush. Harry resorted to carrying handfuls of sand and throwing them under the tires.

"Hey," she said. "Let me shovel a little first, otherwise I'm shoveling the sand away." She shook her head.

"Oh, sorry."

"You're an idiot," she said and they both laughed.

She dug for a while and he watched. He said, "Whatever came down in the storm has gone out. It's just dark there now."

"If it was a nicer night we could walk out and see," she said. She handed him the shovel and motioned for him to take a turn. While he went at it, she peered across the field and saw nothing but snow falling and that eventually disappearing a few yards beyond into black. She thought of that field in summer with the moon shining over it.

"I've hit road under three tires," Harry eventually called. "I'll get some sand with the shovel, throw it on there, and we'll be out of here in a minute."

"Christ, I'm freezing," said Amy.

They both heard a very odd sound coming up from the ditch at the side of the road. "Do you hear that?" he said.

"Yeah, what is it?"

"Like burbling, right?" she said.

They looked down into the ditch and something was crawling up the side of it.

"What is that?" he said.

"A possum or skunk?"

"Nah."

The thing pulled itself up the snowy embankment and stood to its full height.

"No fucking way," he said.

"I never saw anything like it."

"A three-foot block of scrapple?" said Harry.

"And three tentacles."

He cocked the shovel over his shoulder, wanting to hit the thing back into the ditch, but he was stunned by the sight of it. The creature had a thousand little legs under the bottom side of that bad meat block. Those tiny legs had to scrabble like mad for it to scuttle only half a foot. It had no eyes, just two holes at seemingly random spots on the right side of its front. One was oozing a glistening drool. The hole at the top of the left side of the body, somewhat larger than the two on the other side, poorly hid sharp teeth in a lipless hole.

Amy yelled, "Get it away."

He swung with all his might and the shovel head hit the thing with an echoing slap and thud. The blow sent it sliding down the side of the ditch. Although it sank out of sight, they could hear it still burbling, and now sputtering, choking, and giving off a whispered growl like a demon purring.

"What kind of deal was that?"

"Let's get out of here."

They jumped into the truck and as they shut the doors it stalled out with a shudder. She turned the key but there was only a click. Three more times she tried to start it.

"Don't flood it," he said.

"Will you shut the fuck up." She tried it again.

"The battery's brand-new," said Harry. "I just had the whole thing checked out."

"The lights are still on," she said.

"That thing's got a brain lock on us." He opened the glove compartment and pulled out a Colt pistol. "We'll see about this," he said.

As Harry was climbing back onto the road, the thing was coming up out of the ditch again. Amy jumped across the console in the middle of the seats to watch from the open passenger door. The thing waved its tentacles at Harry and advanced, albeit slowly. He raised the gun, said, "Fuck you," and fired, once, twice. Harry and Amy blinked with the noise of each round. The first bullet put a neat hole through the thing, so instead of having two maybe eye sockets it now had three. The second shot chipped a rounded corner of scrapple off the rumbling brick of alien and brought a reedy scream from the thing. It toppled over at the edge of the incline.

Harry advanced gingerly to kick it into the ditch, only 50 percent sure it was dead. As he inched closer, one of the three tentacles popped up and, quick as a blink, shot a golden seed into his forehead. It happened too fast for Amy to see it. A moment later, one flew out and hit her in the forehead as well. He staggered backward toward the cab of the pickup, and she reached for him from the passenger seat. They both knew the instant the golden seeds entered their heads, breaking tiny holes in their skulls and burrowing into the gray matter, that they were somehow transformed. The universe whirled in his mind's eye—planets and stars and clusters, weaving in and out and around, spinning like a top. In her thoughts the ground leaped up into her through her shoes. As she reached out to touch his shoulder, the two of them turned to pink dust and blew away.

Eight minutes later, the thing was at the side of the truck. It lifted the empty clothes off Amy and Harry and inspected the pockets. In them, among other things, it found a cheap pen, the lighter, a peppermint candy stuck to the lining, a sapphire necklace. It kept the necklace and the lighter. Using its tentacles as hands, it tossed the remainder of belongings into the cab. It scuttled away through the snow, bullet wounds slowly healing beneath the action of a laving ten-inch-long sky-blue tongue that darted from the lipless hole in front. As it moved and healed, it inserted both the gun and the necklace into another large, lipless hole, only this one was in the rear. It shoved two tentacles into two face holes and moaned low through its back hole. A second later there was an audible popping noise and the pickup vanished, snow filling the place it had been.

The creature traveled on through the night, drooling, burbling, scuttling. It moved through the storm. It moved across a field, its tracks being slowly covered, and rested in a windbreak of trees. Snow swirled around it and it was cold. Its bottom half, dragged through every snowdrift on the way, was frigid, but the thousand legs never ceased moving. Tentacles wiggled and swooped through the air like escaped fire hoses, and it sharpened its concentration on the circle of blue within the circle of black that dominated its thoughts. In among the towering white oaks, the sun now up and shining in a blue sky onto pure white, the creature found a comfortable spot and fell over, face-first.

The wind swept in among the trees and rearranged the snow to cover the gray meat package. A week later it thawed out and then proceeded to lie there beneath the trees, in the weeds, a platform for insects, a curious scent for coyotes. Seasons upon seasons passed— sun shining, rain falling, snow blowing, leaves turning. Its tentacles eventually rotted off and broke down to the point where field mice could chew them and they did. Its thousand legs went to sod, like so many miniature cigars left out in a downpour. When the temperature climbed, gleaming liquid drizzled out and left a lavender crewcut moss growing across the ground. The spot was so peaceful and quiet, just the wind passing through the leaves of the old trees and the padding of squirrels along the boughs.

In the midst of a very virulent spring in which the beetles made lace of leaves and yellow flowers grew throughout the thicket, there came without warning a sudden blip of air from the creature's back hole, and a mote of an idea was loosed into the atmosphere. That minuscule pink dot caught the wind and was up and out over the field in a moment. As insignificant as it seemed, it contained multitudes, the information for a command that upon contact with a human's nasal lining would download into the host to be run. The virus replaced DNA with strands of alien spun sugar and initiated through mitochondrial transcendence in the host the conception of a story.

The virus instructed the subject to tell a long, involved tale in a certain manner, with a certain rhythm, tone, and character. In fact, the host had no choice but to perform the story for a listener the way its programmers intended. To begin listening to it meant that one couldn't stop. Those who heard it became infected with it and were able to tell it exactly the same way as the initial host. When that story ran in a mind for seven days, all thoughts became irreparably corrupted and seized like a pickup engine run out of oil. The imagery of the story toppled and jumbled and choked the byways of thought till all became less and less unto nothing. Even the merest notion stalled, withered, and died.

Don't worry, this story isn't that story. The reason you know it isn't that story is because in that story Becky never got her necklace. In this story, she does. Here's how it happened.

Becky was in her midforties by then, married with three kids, all girls. Five nights after Christmas, she woke up around 2:00 a.m. to find a strange man standing at the foot of her bed, holding a lit cigarette lighter in one hand and proffering forth a sparkling necklace with the other. She cleared her eyes, believing it a dream, but there he was—a stooped old man with straggly white hair parted in the middle. He was dressed in a threadbare jacket and trousers with cigarette holes in the lap, zipper half open. She was instantly numb with fear.

The intruder leaned forward toward her from the bottom of the bed, whispering, "We are not without mercy. Take what is yours." The third time he said it, Becky nudged her husband and said, "Tim, Tim, there's someone in the room."

He pretended to still be asleep, but slowly snaked his arm up the side of the nightstand and slipped his hand into the second drawer from the bottom. He got a grip on the gun inside and once it was firmly in his hand, he lunged upward, spun, and squeezed off five rounds. Three of them hit the old man and sent him sprawling against the closet door. One had taken out his eye, one shattered his chin, and the third was a bull's-eye to the Adam's apple. He slumped down into a sitting position, croaked, "Mercy," fell into a dream of the peaceful spot beneath the white oaks in the soybean field where he had found the lighter and necklace the voice in his head demanded he retrieve. He fell into the lavender fuzz that spread across the ground and passed through to the next world.

The police reported the break-in at Becky and Tim's place as a burglary. A week after the medics had come and carted the old man's body away, a police officer who'd arrived that night to answer the 9-1-1 call Tim had made as the gun smoke cleared showed up at the front door. He had the necklace and lighter and was returning them, assuming they had been stolen by the intruder that night. Becky liked the looks of the necklace so she went along with his scenario and figured she might as well get something out of the horrible incident. Tim wasn't home, which was good, because she was sure if she tried to lie to the officer in his presence, he'd have corrected her that the items weren't theirs.

Before he left, the officer told her something about the "perpetrator," as he called the burglar. "That old guy just basically disintegrated over a period of a few days. I mean a body usually sticks around till they can find relatives and bury it, but not this perp. He came apart like overcooked salmon. Just rotted away in the morgue drawer. The guys down there told me they'd never seen anything like it. Said he stank to high heaven."

"Right," said Becky, not really wanting to listen to descriptions of the demise of the horrid old pervert. The officer had more to say, but she wiggled her fingers at him in a casual goodbye and shut the front door before he could go on. That afternoon, she wore the necklace without the slightest idea that it had been made specifically for her years earlier. While she sat drinking a cup of coffee, staring through the sliding-glass door to the backyard, she noticed the sapphire pendant of the thing had begun to glow a deep-space indigo.

She was astonished when a blue beam shot out of the precious stone and projected a moving image on the glass door. If she could have, she'd have gotten up and run, she'd have ripped the necklace off, she'd have screamed, although the house was empty. As it was, though, she was paralyzed. All she could do was watch. The scene, through which she could see the white oak and the garden and shed, was of a kindly looking old man with white hair and a white walrus mustache. He wore khaki pants, sandals, a V-neck sweater, powder green, with a short-sleeved white shirt under it, and he could have been the nicer brother of the man who'd broken into the house.

He sat under a tree projected upon the glass just about where the real tree could be seen through it. "Greetings," said the old man and smiled. "Call me Uncle Gribnob. I'm appearing to you in a familiar form so as not to frighten you. I'm here to offer a sort of explanation as to why your planet is being invaded and your species is being wiped out. We're not without mercy. We thought you deserved an explanation. Just keep your peace for a few minutes while I explain and then feel free to ask questions. I'll answer anything you like. Do you understand? You may nod if you do."

Becky nodded.

"OK," said the old man. "Here's the long and short of it. We take no pleasure in wiping your kind out. It's not usually our way. We're doing this for the greater good of the universe. Somebody has to do it, and since we're the most culturally and morally advanced and have the most cutting-edge technology, we've taken it upon ourselves to do the deed. Believe me, it's not without the consent, no, approval, of the other civilizations. Even the reptile people were unanimously for it.

"You see, we've all had to deal with your kind before. And what I mean by your kind is, you have a distinctive aberration in your minds that can't be healed or manipulated or fixed. And that one small mistake, that single knot in the works, so to speak, makes your species so dangerous. We've seen the results. You're not sophisticated enough yet to be a problem to the universe at large, but who wants to let things get to that point?

"Your defective brains persist in insisting, even through a faulty mathematics that makes your error magically vanish, that the ratio of the circumference of a circle to its diameter is an endless number. You no doubt heard of pi in school? The ratio, in reality, is simply 3, but your lack of sense dares to claim it is a number with endless decimal places. It would be funny if it weren't for what we know peoples who have this deviant psycho structure are capable of. How can anything be endless in a limited universe? Dangerously delusional. So we're going to ease you out of existence. Questions?"

Becky could barely follow what had been said. She thought she was having a stroke or that Tim had dropped a hit of acid into her coffee before he left for work. All she managed to get out was, "What can I do?"

Jeffrey Ford

"Well," said Uncle Gribnob. His image wavered in and out. Finally he vanished from the glass, and she could see clearly into the backyard where the wind was blowing end-of-summer leaves. The necklace continued to glow and his voice continued to sound in her head. "You can do me a favor and listen to this story."

She did and that night at dinner she told it to Tim and the kids. Becky noticed her younger daughter's eyes shone with pleasure at the descriptions of gunplay. A few days later, the whole family shut down within a few hours of each other, and a few days after that the alien squadron drifted in for a landing at the Home Depot parking lot.

Clouds
Julia Elliott

ON FOGGY SUMMER DAYS, when the sky seemed to descend, filling
the streets with clouds, satellite people came down from their floating worlds, though they avoided those hours between late morning
and early evening when sunlight suffused the haze. From a distance
they looked almost normal: dining in restaurants, browsing in shops,
strolling through parks at dusk in their wispy goat-silk clothes. But
when you got close enough, you could see muscles flexing beneath
their transparent skin, glimmers of glands, veins, and bones. Like
glass frogs, their skin had a gelatinous sheen. For many generations
their aircraft had hovered in the densest parts of the troposphere,
enveloped in vapor, and direct sunlight never touched their skin.

I ran an organic blueberry farm in West Virginia, on the Tygarts
Valley River, and sometimes, when the berries ripened and the
weather turned hazy, satellite people came to buy fruit. They showed
up near dusk to eat at Orphic Grape Vineyard, farm-to-table fare
served in lavish gardens. They usually traveled in groups, so I was
surprised to see a sky-man loitering in my orchard one June evening.
He wore elastic gauze leggings, a raw silk tunic, a nitrile rubber backpack. Aerogel gave them rashes. Lots of things gave them allergies.
They obsessed over the purity of their food.

The man smiled, a complex configuration of skeletal muscle, a
glint of bone beneath his salmon-colored flesh. His irises were a
weird metallic gray like sharkskin, and I could see the reddish contours of his inner eyeballs, the muscles that rotated them. Though
the back of his cranium was concealed by pale lilac hair, I could
make out his frontal skull, gleaming and opaque beneath two strands
of muscle. Sky-people were careful to keep their torsos covered.

"Are you still open?" When he smiled, I could see the roots of his
teeth.

I nodded. I took him to the rustic shed where I sold fresh berries
and jam. He hung around, and I felt a thrumming in the air, as
though invisible birds flitted around the room.

"Doing some camping," he said.

31

"Alone?" I asked.

"Trying to find my spirit animal." He laughed. "I think it might be the chipmunk."

Satellite people seldom joked with me, kept their transactions polite but terse. I couldn't help but smile.

He bought some blueberries, pressed his index finger onto my print pad, and squinted into the iris scanner. A hologram of his head rotated in the air. I scanned his features, ascertaining that the image matched the man.

Red Wolf Tavern, tucked into Valley Falls State Park, was mostly a locals hangout, a dark cabin draped with pelts, adorned with skulls, lit with old-fashioned LED lanterns. They had a deck with a mountain view, but a storm had swept in. Rain pattered the solar shingles. And I sat at the end of the bar drinking red wine, trying not to think about my ex-husband, whose memory always haunted me on rainy nights.

The cabin seemed to pitch like a ship in the storm, drunkards struggling to hold their footing. Hunter, the bartender, smiled at Mamie, a flash of yellow teeth in his wolfman beard. Mamie, who ran the wildlife rescue shelter, had a baby squirrel tucked into her shirt. Some kind of chant played on the ancient music streamer—perhaps medieval, perhaps Native American—the buzz of multiple voices made it hard to tell. I was on my third glass, the world deepening, pulsing with mystery that would soon morph into insomnia, headache, depression. But I'd hit a sweet spot. And there stood the sky-man on the rough-hewn floor.

He glanced around, recognized me, approached.

"Hi," he said, slipping onto the stool next to me. "Remember me?"

In the darkness of the tavern he looked almost normal, his skin more opaque, which highlighted the prettiness of his features: large eyes, sharp nose, lips like pink grapes, a hint of transparency, a glimpse of the lush pulp within.

"How's the camping going?" I asked.

"Lovely weather for it."

He wasn't joking. Cloud-people relished rain.

He smiled. He ordered organic, biodynamic wine from a local vineyard where they buried bull horns crammed with cow manure. Their brochure described full-moon harvest rituals, the purification of fermentation vessels, wine as the blood of gods.

We drank. We talked about organic farming. The sky-man, who told me to call him Xander, said my blueberries were the best he'd ever tasted.

"What's your secret?"

"Whistlepig manure."

He laughed.

"What's a whistlepig?"

"Old term for groundhog. I've always preferred it. Lends a certain whimsy to the chubby underground rodents."

"I've always found them fascinating. Especially their hibernation habits."

We talked about winter on earth, animals tucked into holes, nestled into burrows, dreaming in the fragrant, woody darkness of tree hollows. We discussed fat stores, slowing heart rates, frogs with iced skin, tiny livers pumping out glucose to keep cells moist and plump.

"Their hearts literally stop," we said at the same time.

I had the paranoid feeling that sky-people were telepathic, that he was reading my thoughts. But I took another sip of wine. I shed the qualm like an amphibian molting a crinkly, ashen skin, emerging all the greener.

"All their organs do. But what about their brains?" I asked.

"I don't really know. Do you think they dream?"

"Or are their heads full of eerie static?"

"I've seen a scan of an Arctic squirrel's brain during hibernation," he said. "I think the brain waves stop."

"So, sky-man, why do you know so much about hibernation?"

"I've been curious about it since I was a kid. Plus I suffer from insomnia, so lots of late-night Internet immersion, wandering in virtual forests, scrambling down into animal dens with all five sensors turned up."

"Which makes it even harder to sleep," I chimed in, a fellow insomniac. We'd probably scrambled down some of the same illusory holes.

I laughed. I regarded his eyeballs again, the visible contours, the gleam of socket bone and metallic irises. I had the urge to see them in the sun. To literally gaze down into them, witness delicate contractions, crystalline lenses morphing into different shapes. But sunlight was poison to him.

The sky-man sighed, said he missed the earth.

"Every summer I feel an aching hunger—bone-deep, hopeless—for grass and trees and soil. A stint of camping usually does the trick."

Julia Elliott

"Slumming on earth," I joked, "and then you fly back up into the clouds."

"Have you ever been up there?"

I remembered a camping trip from my girlhood. Sprawled around a fire, stargazing, we'd seen a ship float by—blue light, flashes of silver in the dark sky. One girl, whose father worked at a military port where supply ships landed, whispered of kidnappings, of young girls getting snatched up into the clouds.

"No," I said.

"You ought to visit."

"Isn't it practically impossible for ordinary people like me?"

"There are ways," he said. "And you don't seem ordinary."

"You smell like the earth," he whispered.

In the dark he almost felt like a normal man, though his body temperature was noticeably low, not cold exactly, but not warm. And his skin felt slick, as though lubricated with petroleum jelly. He gave off a sweet smell like synthetic apples, redolent of aerosol air-freshening sprays. Otherwise, his anatomy was familiar: a firm chest with nipples that stiffened to my touch, chill bumps all over, a moist nest of groin hair featuring an uncircumcised erection.

The sex was fine, mammalian, with satisfying crescendos on both sides. But the miracle came afterward, sliding into endless tunnels of conversation. Two insomniacs, awake in the darkness, talking our throats sore, words mingling, whirling in the breathy air above our faces.

The next morning he turned his back to me as he dressed in a panic, the floor-to-ceiling windows of my old aluminum prefab lit with morning sun.

"It was supposed to rain today." He groaned. "And I wanted to walk in the woods. I could talk to you forever."

"I know!" I said. I pictured us in the cabin, drinking guayusa tea, talking and talking as mist shrouded the windows. But the bald sun glared.

His rump muscles tensed, reminding me of high-school anatomy holograms, adolescents chuckling over the term gluteus maximus.

He slipped into an elastic bodysuit that resembled cycling apparel, pulled a Mylar sun hat and a UV face shield from his backpack.

"Sorry I have to leave like this," he said, lips cool against my cheek. He rushed out into the morning sunlight, glanced back once before jogging down my dirt drive.

Summer deepened, reaching a giddy pitch—insects screaming in the humid green, a sudden spate of copperheads, gnats, and mosquitoes hovering in dirty swarms. My throat itched. My brain burned. Yes, I missed the kisses of the sky-man, but I really wanted to talk to him. Especially when, by early August, I had to admit that I was pregnant, two missed periods, my belly already puffed out, nausea seething in my gut. I had Xander's contact information in my data system, but I had too much pride to text him. Now the seriousness of the situation called for face time, and I didn't want him to see me like this: cheeks broken out from the surge of hormones, skin strangely bloodless, eyes baggy as from an allergy attack.

Of course I craved strange foods—cow liver with currant jelly, roasted beets with blood sausage, mushrooms stuffed with red roe. The mealy smell of boiled pasta made me gag. I couldn't stomach bread, rice, or cereal. Fetid green gasses seemed to waft from blocks of cheese. The toilet had a pond-like tang. But I loved the blunt, waxy smell of raw beef.

One afternoon, walking alone in the forest, I felt a rash urge to pounce on a rabbit and skin it, bite into its warm flesh. I hurried home, my face flushed, and stood in the orchard gazing up into the sky, trying to spot a ship. I sat in the grass, drained of energy, and sipped from a bottle of cranberry juice. At dusk a sky-craft appeared, a brief twinkle, and then it burrowed like a sperm into a fat, round cloud. I had no idea whose ship this was, but I pictured Xander standing on the deck, staring into glowing fog, breathing the strange, gassy air. I pictured the interior of his skull, brain steeped in cerebrospinal fluid, bright as coral, extending tentacles of thought to catch prey.

By the time tourists came back for leaf season, I was wearing maternity tops, my belly blown out like a woman on the verge of birth.
    —*I'm huge already*, I texted Lydia, a college friend, whose son was now two.
    —*Some women show early.*
    —*But I'm enormous.*
    —*You just feel enormous.*

35

Julia Elliott

I sent her a pic.

—*OMG. Have you been to a doctor? You might have a fibroid. They feed on estrogen and swell up fast. Largest on record weighed 140 pounds.*

—*I've been to a midwife,* I lied. *But I'm due for a checkup.*

—*You need to see a fucking doctor fast.*

Lydia didn't know about the sky-man. She didn't know I'd finally broken down and started eating raw meat—grass fed, biodynamic, butchered ritualistically at Sacred Cow Farm. The French ate raw meat, as did Paleo fanatics. And some holistic doctors prescribed it for anemia. There were still nomadic people in Africa who gently sliced the jugulars of their cows, filled bowls with blood, and drank it raw. The cows went on with their business unfazed. The people were healthy, vibrant, and suffered no tooth decay. They lived on a nature preserve whose borders were contracting.

—*But I feel great,* I texted. *No more nausea. Plenty of energy.*

—*Second trimester. Quickening. Have you felt the baby kick?*

The first electrical swishes had come early, at the beginning of month three, and with them a feeling of dreamy serenity. My ovaries were in overdrive, pumping out estrogen, a natural antidepressant, but perhaps the being curled within my belly contributed to the hormonal brew—changing my brain chemistry. Every night, from midnight to three, the child kicked—I could feel the full-bodied heft of the fetus, squirming like a worm in a cocoon, no longer content to stew in a subaquatic dream. I'd crawl out of bed, pull on a cardigan and boots, and walk the old logging trail that ran behind my cabin until the creature calmed.

One November night the baby kicked and kicked. I hiked all the way up a small mountain, skeletal trees silvered with moonlight, the sky clear. The rich family who owned the mountain had put up a cluster of Kevlar-coated living pods on its south side, and their children had built a miniature Stonehenge on top.

I sat down by the toy monument and snacked on packaged beef jerky. A weasel-like snout poked out of a bush. I tossed it a twist of dried meat. Sniffing, the animal crept closer—glistening, elegant—a mink. It plucked up the morsel and turned it in its tiny paws. Without a thought, I pounced, grabbed the mammal, felt muscles tensing beneath soft fur. Claws pricked through my flannel jacket. Fangs bit into my leather gloves. The mink's scream was like a sharp hiss of

36

industrial steam. I snapped its neck. Gnawed at its throat. Licked a trickle of musky blood, delicious at first, but then metallic, bitter, tainted with fur and fear. There was liquid dung all over my clothes.

I retched, tossed the small carcass into the brush, and ran down the mountain.

In the shower I felt a spasm like a bad menstrual cramp—probably a Braxton-Hicks, a practice contraction. When I stepped onto the bath mat another convulsion seized me, worse than before. I pulled on my robe, curled up in my bed, eyes on the clock, counting. Another contraction ten minutes later. Maybe I did have a fibroid, which could cause a tightening of uterine muscles. But then a certainty bloomed in my head like a poison flower: preterm labor, induced by running down a mountain in a panic.

According to the Internet, my fetus was the size of a squirrel, its organs not fully ripe. Fresh taste buds stippled its tongue. It had no fingernails. Its skin was fluffed with lanugo, its central nervous system still developing, tiny brain growing, sprouting obscure neurons, etching intricate webs of thought and function. I pictured the infant snatched out into alien air, its face scrunched with rage as it struggled to breathe, raw lungs working behind its rib cage, tiny as moth wings. I felt another spasm. This one had me rushing to the dresser, where I'd left my phone. But it wasn't there. And now snow whirled outside my window, flecks aglow in the orb of my security light, the orchard beyond it dark.

I paced. I squatted. Tossed in bed. Got up. Repeatedly sat on the toilet, calling my dead mother's name. Nothing soothed the raw throbs, the glowing red pain. I staggered back to the bathroom again, sat on the commode, breathing pond odors and lavender-scented shampoo. Clutching myself, I huffed in thick whirls of air, sick to the gills from the life burrowed in me. Nausea beyond nausea.

Something trickled out of me. I crawled back to bed, gazed at the brutal obtuseness of my holographic clock: floating blue segments of lines, Arabic numerals, runes. I pictured my cervix opening, fat, veiny petals of meat. I heard chanting now, coming from the forest. I pictured spectral women, larger than trees, crouched over my house. I pressed my fingers into the wet ache again, felt a spongy firmness, red splits of pain as the curd-smeared skull pressed at outer air.

37

*

I woke up. Wan sun. Dove-colored sky. Thick clouds floating beyond my big windows.

Snow covered the orchard, trees glittering with ice. I felt a surge of elation as I drank in the beauty, but then a pulse of pain brought back the endless night. The first thing I saw was a veiny blob of gelatinous meat stuck to my left thigh, blood all over the sheets. *The baby*, I thought, *dead*, and my heart plummeted. But the newborn, slathered with white vernix that looked like mineral sunscreen, lay curled between my knees, its umbilical cord attached to the blob. The other thing was my placenta, I realized, recalling a second series of contractions, pushing something out—a twin, I'd thought, a reasonable explanation for my hugeness. And then I'd passed out.

Now I sat up, heart pounding, afraid to touch the baby, expecting the chill of dead flesh. The newborn was the size of a rabbit, not dangerously small, its head elongated into an alien cone by the birth canal, pale hair greased to its soft skull. Arms. Legs. Feet. Fists. Eye slits encased in puffy bags. Swollen labia. A girl.

"Adelaide," I whispered as I touched her cheek.

Her rosebud mouth opened and emitted a warm wheeze of breath.

Adelaide's birthday snow did not thaw. More snow fell, and I was anxious to have her checked by a doctor, even though she appeared to be a fully developed newborn. I also needed to address the legal complexities of her origins and acquire a birth certificate—all of which meant contacting Xander. Instead, I settled into hibernation mode, stationed on the couch with my feeding pillow, a jug of spring water, my tablet chock-full of gothic romances. I still dreaded the moment when Adelaide latched on—the burning nipples, the raw sear of pain that ran up my milk ducts with her first fierce suck. And then I felt hot prickles on my areolas, probably from the rash that had flared the day after she was born. But the pain subsided as I settled into an oxytocin dream, gazing down at the glowing face, her skin peachy and semisheer, a hint of muscle tissue flexing like goldfish under ice.

I kept the woodstove blazing, and when I looked out at the snowy orchard, I imagined live creatures buried under snow: bears snoring in underground dens, whistlepigs curled in musky holes, frogs burrowed into the muddy depths of ponds, their blood frozen. I remembered that endless conversation with Xander in the bar, thoughts zagging between us like lightning from cloud to earth.

Why didn't I contact him? Why didn't he contact me?

I lay listening to the *drip drip drip* of thawing snow, Adelaide curled against my belly, snuffling for my teat. She mewled as she wormed her way up my abdomen. She was strangely strong for three months, her gray eyes glossy and alert as she zeroed in on her target, my tender areolas, inflamed with a fresh rash. I'd read on the Internet that some women suffered from overly sensitive breasts, that it sometimes took a month for them to toughen up, that all the lanolin in the world wouldn't help—but I was three months into feeding. I worried that I was allergic to Adelaide's saliva, some alien chemical from her father's DNA, and that she was allergic to something in my milk that stippled her cheeks with tiny bumps. I knew that infants were born with all of their teeth, beastly little choppers buried beneath their rosy gums. Some babies broke them early; others were born with a few teeth in their mouths. I slid my finger along her dental ridge, looking for nubbins of bone. Drool spilled from her bottom lip as she smiled.

Adelaide nosed my nipple. I braced myself as she opened her mouth wide like a snake unhinging its jaw. Enveloping half my breast, she latched on. I winced, gripping a pillow. First came a sensation of stinging nettles. Next came a tingling burn, deep in my breast tissue, that worked its way up my milk ducts and through my nipple. And then, at last, an opiate burst of love, infant fused to my body like some glowing celestial appendage.

I would kill for her. I would pinch off pieces of my own heart and drop them into her adorable, gaping mouth.

I massaged her plump shoulders, felt crusty patches of eczema. I ran my fingers along the delicate knobs of her spine and took a deep, drunken whiff of her musk-sweet hair. Melting icicles sparkled on the eaves. A single hawk spiraled in the flame-blue sky.

Adelaide unlatched, cooed, lifted her head from my bosom, and smiled. Pink milk dribbled from her mouth, turning darker: red. The color of passion, panic, blood, and love; poppies and rubies and severe terror alerts; communion, fire, mercury, wine. My heart raced. I opened her mouth, searching for wounds. And then I saw a spreading red blot on my T-shirt. I checked my nipples: still intact. But the surrounding skin was crosshatched with tiny cuts, some of them still seeping.

39

*

I put her in a bath to relax her, easing her down into the seat of her aerogel tub. Her wet skin turned opalescent, and I could see the shadowy contours of her organs, dusky pinks and purples. I rubbed her with a warm rag until she glowed with love and grinned. I examined the inside of her mouth in the bright bathroom light. Tracing the ridges of her palate, I felt a prick just behind the dental ridge. I jerked my finger out—the tip bled. Inside the baby's mouth, small serrated gills opened, revealing wavering cilia the color of pomegranate seeds. And then the gills closed. Adelaide pressed her lips together and smiled.

April flowers had bloomed, and I needed to spread blood meal and coffee grounds in the blueberry orchard. I needed to get my shop ready for summer. But I felt exhausted. Adelaide was eating fruit and meat paste, but she still nursed every four hours, still had a rash around her mouth and eczema on her shoulders and the backs of her knees. But she was growing strong, clambering around on four legs ahead of schedule, rolling, climbing. I'd set up an electron-vector play fence beneath a plum tree, and I lazed in a lawn chair in the shade, drinking gallons of water, eating canned sardines and rare roast beef and bits of raw cow's liver that I chopped and stored in cryogenic InstaFreeze.

I'd lost ten pounds. My skin looked splotchy. My hair was falling out in clumps and the roots of my teeth ached. Self-diagnosing anemia, I took iron supplements, stinking doses of cod-liver oil, and a nano-biotic multivitamin engineered for nursing mothers. When the air cooled in the evening, I took Adelaide inside. Cuddling her on the couch, I pulled up story after story on my tablet: sinister fairy tales, beast fables spiked with death, progressive narratives of empowered princesses and self-actualized robots.

Adelaide, eyes bright with intelligence, tried to touch the holograms. I thought of Xander circling the earth in his ship, following the thickest masses of cumulonimbus clouds. Perhaps he had a wife up there. That would explain his silence. Or maybe he'd decided that our differences were unbridgeable. There were conflicting theories on the satellite people: they were aliens who'd spliced human genes into their DNA; they were ancient Sumerian aristocrats who had acquired space technology from an alien race; they were inbred

Romanian royals with a congenital anemia who'd fled the Great Plague of 1738 in steam-powered blimps designed by a court magician. Some people said they'd inexplicably appeared in the middle of the twenty-first century; others said they'd been orbiting our green planet since 4000 BC. Breathtakingly powerful people, richly neurotic, isolated in vast fortresses of dynastic wealth—had they ever really lived on earth?

On a foggy day in May, when Adelaide was six months old, she ambled over to my lawn chair, placed her hand on my chest, and said, *Mickimoo, Mama*. Tall for her age, she'd walked at five months, and soon after started piecing together a rudimentary vocabulary: *Mama, moon, mickimoo, ball, tablet, fan, boob*. She crawled into my lap, pulled my wrap top open, seized her preferred breast (the left), and latched on.

I still winced and gritted my teeth. I still clenched my fists for the first few seconds. I still visualized her feeding apparatus: the opening of serrated gills, the deep-rose cilia burrowing into flesh. But I felt flushed with love when the pain subsided. I kissed her silky head. I'd gotten used to bloodstains on my shirt. I knew that ordinary breast milk was manufactured from proteins, sugars, and fats in mothers' blood, which made Adelaide's evolutionary quirk not so freakish, really.

But I had to admit that I felt depleted. Pale as a parsnip, ninety-eight pounds, I was going bald and had lost a tooth. After the child fed, I fell into a weird doze—half nap, half swoon. I dreamed of Xander floating down to earth in a cloud, and when I woke up, he was there, standing in the mist at the edge of the forest.

"Why didn't you tell me?" He rushed around my cabin in a panic, stuffing clothes into a lab-leather bag. Adelaide lurked behind the couch. Her head popped up, groundhog like, huge eyes studying her father, her cheeks chafed and red. She sucked her bottom lip into her mouth.

"I've been meaning to, but—"

"You'll need a transfusion, fast. But I can't get a shuttle for at least two hours."

"Can't we do it down here?"

"They wouldn't know where to begin."

41

I still hadn't acquired a birth certificate. Adelaide had not been DNA scanned, iris matched, microchipped. Technically, she didn't exist.

But there she was, fat cheeked and lovely, toddling up to me and placing her hand on my breast.

"Mickimoo," she said, a look of yearning mischief in her eyes. Playful. Sweet. Heart melting.

"No." Xander swept her up in his arms. "We can't risk it."

Her face crinkled with rage. A few silent heaves, and then she broke into an animal roar.

At dusk we waited in the field beyond the orchard. I sat in a lawn chair, Adelaide nestled against me, whimpering. Xander paced and studied the sky. I had no strength for words, and he was too anxious to talk. The fog had retreated into the forest, sucked down into its black core. A half-moon floated. Wisps of cloud drifted. Stars materialized. At last, the ship popped up just beyond the horizon. Billowing like a stingray, its tail emitted a blue plume of exhaust.

In seconds it hovered above us, vast, blotting out the moon. A valve opened in its silvery underbelly. A diamond-shaped shuttle spun down and landed in the meadow, poised two feet above the dewy grass.

I woke up in a dim room. Warm tubes snaked around my arms, pumping fluid into my veins. No furniture beyond my medical recliner and some hideous, puffy biotech chair. Nano-engineered jade walls radiated a soothing light—I'd seen walls like this in high-end catalogs, and I had to admit they were beautiful. I heard music—neo-primitive electronica, Sanskrit chanting, echolocating whales, and whispering wind.

How long had I been on Xander's ship? I remembered stepping into the shuttle, feeling woozy when it started up, passing out during its spinning ascent. And Adelaide: where was Adelaide? I tried to sit up, felt resistance—no straps, some kind of force field. I screamed.

Xander rushed in, holding Adelaide. She looked comfortable, relaxing in the crook of his right arm. But when she saw me she erupted into wild twitter, kicking and laughing and flailing to be near me.

"Mama, Mama, mickimoo!" she shrieked.

"Why the fuck am I strapped down?" I hissed.

"Strapped?" Xander smirked, a twitch of orange musculature.
"You know what I mean."
"Calm down," he said. "You have to be perfectly still when you get the juice. That's all."
He studied the monitor attached to my IV.
"Dr. Isabelle says you've got to have 62.3 more NCGs, and then we can unplug."
"Mama, mickimoo!" shouted Adelaide.
"Just a minute, Addy." Xander rubbed her back. "Mama's got to have a few more glugs of Zoblen."
"Which is?"
"Hybrid plasma product. She won't be allergic to your milk anymore, and most importantly, you won't be anemic. Ah, there we go."
"Milk?"
"Essentially." Xander avoided my gaze.
"And it's Ada, not Addy," I said. "The preferred nickname, I mean. Though I usually call her Adelaide."
"Ada, of course. Much prettier." Xander smiled, tapped the touch screen, and I felt the warm tubes uncoil.

We lounged on the front deck at dusk, a vast expanse of engineered obsidian that sparkled with drops of dew. We were in the belly of a cloud. Thick clots of pink vapor floated, obscuring the sky.
"Mother picked out these tasteless chairs." Xander patted the side of his biotech chaise: an ergonomic sweep of engineered flesh upholstered in living beaver fur. Warm, plush, pliable from high lipid concentrations, the chair cradled my spine. "The fur's moisture resistant," he added, "but sometimes gives off a musky smell, even though that gene was supposedly deleted."
"I do detect a hint of moist rodent," I said, "which I actually find comforting, earthy."
We fell into conversation, sank into a bubbling whirl of words. We talked about human pheromones, the gut revulsion we suffered at the sight of certain people, the kinetic connection we'd felt talking in the bar the night after we'd first met, the joys of a truly collaborative conversation, thoughts like tree roots intertwining in arcane depths of soil, branches mingling among clouds. We talked about curdy clouds viewed from earth, sunlight etching gray convolutions with pink glow. About staring down at masses of mist at night, cities shimmering beneath. About moving through the belly of a cloud, the

feel of thick vapor on the skin—an alien feeling for me.

"Does it feel nourishing or oppressive?" he asked.

"A little of both."

"Explain?"

"Nourishing for the skin. Oppressive for the respiratory system."

I tried to describe the onset of an ozone headache, the itch in my throat, the feeling that my lungs were shriveling.

"And sometimes my skin feels soggy. Like I've been in a bath for too long."

I held sleeping Ada in my arms, breathing her sweet scalp scent through my ozone-filter mask. We'd started calling her Ada the week before, when I'd woken up from my transfusion—our first awkward collaboration as parents. And now Xander reached for my hand.

"We're pulling out of the clouds," he said.

I held my breath as the ship swooped down, out of the troposphere. I was drunk, floating six miles above the equator. The sky sparkled with stars. The pocked moon glowed.

"Come on." Xander squeezed my hand. "Walk to the brink with me and have a look at your planet."

"Isn't it your planet too?"

"Technically."

When he stroked my arm, I felt a warm slither of lust in my groin. I wanted to fuck Xander, retract from our illusory physical fusion, and then lie in bed and whisper in the dark until we affected a CG lightning bolt that left us exhausted enough to sleep.

We stood up, wedged Ada into the depths of my chair, and covered her in a blanket.

There was no visible railing at the edge of the deck, only an electron force field, which Xander liked to lean into while I cowered in my chair.

"Come on," he said, pulling me toward the abyss.

Arms wrapped around each other, we walked to the edge. My stomach dropped as I peered down at Ecuador: the glittering of Quito, the darkness of forests, mountains and valleys and swathes of smog.

"See that." Xander pointed at a darkish spot. "That's La Mitad del Mundo, the middle of the world."

He eased down my ozone filter, exposing my nose and mouth.

"You don't need it at this altitude."

He kissed me for a long time.

*

"Mama, mickimoo, now." Ada head-butted my chest.

"Say please," said Xander.

"Pease."

We laughed as she seized my breast. I winced. Gritted my teeth. And then: love, joy, light. Her eczema was gone. She'd grown at least two inches. Her hair had thickened into lilac curls. Xander said it was the rich cloud air, the high humidity, not to mention the nutritionally potent baby food she'd been eating, handmade by his mother's chief chef. Ada's skin glowed with a moist sheen, pearly, slightly more translucent—just as it had looked in the bath at home.

I lay on Xander's bed: a sleek platform of engineered teak, the mattress stuffed with biofeathers. His apartment was organic contemporary. He liked "neonatural" fibers, a mix of nano-engineered stone and wood, lab-leather and horn, textiles from GM animals, and what he called "earth pieces," odds and ends he'd purchased directly on the ground, mostly handmade—a hemp pillowcase from South Africa, jute rugs from India, pottery from Peru. His dining table was a floating disk of turquoise with an invisible electromagnetic base. He had robot domestics; an army of small, supple cleaning units; and an ironic android valet with a cheesy British accent. He complained that his mother still kept human servants. I didn't ask what he meant by "human."

"She's very old-fashioned," he said. "And rather blunt, especially since she's been sick. Don't take it personally."

"You're scaring me."

"It's just dinner. It'll be over quickly."

"I wish we'd done this earlier. It's been, what, a month? And the pressure just keeps building."

"It's not you, promise. She's ill. Father's dead. I'm her only child. She's been pretty isolated over the last decade."

I'd hated his mother ever since he'd told me that she was the one who'd kept him from returning to earth, that she'd suffered a number of fake illnesses while keeping their ship in high-frequency sky-zones that blocked communication with the outside world. A manipulative old hypochondriac, she'd endured faux liver failure, a heart attack that turned out to be hypertension, and an endless series of imaginary gallstones.

Xander approached the bed with a bowl of plums, organic, fresh from a farm in Afghanistan. He wore goat-silk pajama pants and I could see the bony glint of his rib cage, twin pink lungs nestled within it, a flicker of his throbbing heart. I put my hand on his thigh, an easy gesture, and rolled against him, breathing in the smells I craved.

The matriarch sat by a purple lithium fire, wearing a holographic far-thingale, a neo-Elizabethan trend that rich celebs from my mom's generation had sported thirty years ago. Only her face and hands were exposed, her skin crinkled and darkly translucent, flashes of bone and veins and tensed sinews, though she had lush, bioengi-neered lips. She wore a tall fuchsia beehive wig, slightly crooked. Her throne was gilded, upholstered in dirty red velvet. A weaselly hound slunk around her feet. Its head popped up. Its eyes bugged out. An old-fashioned robot.

The room was a weird mix of GM "living furniture," mostly of the furry variety, and ancient pieces of neon 1960s rococo revival that Xander had already complained about. The air smelled of musk, dust, and some weird medicinal odor.

"Come closer, young lady; I don't bite." She motioned for us to sit.

We sat down on the sofa—warm, pungent, like sinking into the flank of a cat. Ada turned her head away from her grandmother and nuzzled my breasts.

The old woman sniggered. I wondered how I could feel an intense revulsion for her while enjoying an effortless kinship with her son.

"Quite the little family already." She simpered.

"Mother, please," Xander hissed.

A servant appeared, a sky-man dressed in a silk tunic, and offered us raw beef wrapped in slivers of pickled beet. He poured wine from a dusty bottle into goblets with snakes etched into the rims.

"Aged four hundred years," said Xander's mother. "And the gob-lets are not nano, but real gold plate from the 1990s."

Xander rolled his eyes, but I savored the thick burgundy, which tasted of figs and copper, some dark mineral I couldn't place.

"Mickimoo, Mama, now, pease," said Ada.

"I'm glad to hear her talking," said Xander's mother, "though I'm surprised she's not using verbs."

"Mother," said Xander.

"Don't you think she's rather small for her age?"

"You know earth children develop more slowly in the early years, but when we hit adulthood, we're all pretty much on par."

Xander's mother snorted at this. "Did the transfusion help?"

"Yes," said Xander. "Both mother and daughter are doing much better."

46

"So you run a blueberry farm?" Absurdly, Xander's mother pulled out a lorgnette and examined me through the glass. "How quaint. Do they still use the term hippie down there?"

"Yes," I said, "though I'm not sure I qualify."

"Mickimoo, mama, pease, pease, now," said Ada.

"Do you mind?" I asked.

"Of course not."

The old woman watched with interest as Ada latched on, smirking when I tried not to wince.

"Well, Xander certainly qualifies as a hippie." She removed her eyepiece. "He has romanticized the earth ever since his father first took him camping. He likes to tromp around in the mud and smell the flowers, but I prefer the clouds." She gestured toward the window, a rectangle of yellow fog.

Ada and her father romped out on the deck while I sulked inside, wheezing into my ozone mask. Something was wrong with the ship's air-filtration system. My lungs felt squeezed. I suffered headaches and nausea. Isabelle, the family doctor, had diagnosed mild ozone poisoning and a sensitivity to the methane emitted by the ship's bacterial mold-cleaning mechanism, along with a vitamin D deficiency. She advised me to avoid the deck, told me to wear my mask inside, urged me to take a trip to earth and pop two D3 capsules per day.

Imagining ripe fruit dropping from bushes, I longed for my blueberry farm, felt panicky about abandoning it, but it was currently too sunny for Xander there, and perhaps for Ada now that she'd adjusted to sky-weather. I had dreams about walking through my orchard, sunlight on my face and arms, dreams of basking naked on the lawn at noon until my freckles glowed like flecks of copper.

We were planning a trip to the Tierra del Fuego National Park, waiting for the right conditions, a solid month of misty weather, and I longed for the feel of soil beneath my feet.

Reclining by the window in a hovering chair, I watched Ada emerge from the clouds, taller and running already, her semisheer skin glistening. Xander jogged after her, leaned in to tickle her one last time, and then they hurried in, careful to close the portals quickly.

Our camping pod perched in the mist beside Lake Roca, distant mountains swathed in gray mist. The days were short and mostly cloudy, sometimes windy and cold. I reclined in a lawn chair, still weak but feeling much better, my hands crawling crab-like through the grass. I pulled up a clump and sniffed the sweet, pungent roots.

Ada came running from the lake, clinking her bucket of magic stones. Xander plodded three feet behind her, smiling but tired.

"I love you! I love you! I love you!" the child shrieked, petting me with her tiny hands.

She'd just learned the word *love*, and she always uttered it ecstatically, caressing our faces, gesturing at mountains, birds, and clouds.

"Poor Mama is sick, but now that we're on earth you're going to get better," Ada said, studying me with her huge, shark-gray eyes.

"That's right," said Xander.

"Mickimoo, Mama," Ada whispered. She crawled into my lap, heavy as a five-year-old, dangling long legs into the grass. Gently, she undid my blouse. Gently, she latched on. Gently, she patted my arm as my body tensed from the pain. She closed her eyes and fell into a trance as she sucked my blood. Her face had thinned out; her neck had grown swannish. Her cheekbones had a lovely, elfin curve. But her eczema was back. Her hair had turned lank and dry. And Xander was exhausted, his skin murky. His organs looked shrunken and dark. Our conversations drooped. He complained that his brain stalled, that sometimes the effort of speaking pained him.

But even so, he wanted to stay two more weeks, and then find another place to camp, the Drift Creek Wilderness on the Oregon Coast, he said, though it would be harder for me to get occasional doses of sun.

The next day was partly cloudy. Though Xander spent the afternoon hunkered down in the pod, portals shut, he urged me to enjoy it.

"Go bask," he said.

The word *bask*, coming from his mouth, sounded delicious, decadent.

I put my chair in a spot of sun and sprawled. I drank beet juice, nibbled chunks of raw lamb liver. As heat infused my body, I felt my muscles relax. I wallowed like a pagan in mystic sunbeams and opened a bottle of chilled chardonnay.

Adelaide, wearing sunscreen and her Mylar hat, watched me from the shade of her UV umbrella. I could feel her sulking as she stabbed at the sand with her little shovel. But I couldn't pull myself out of my chair. The wine, the sun, the glittering lake. Sweet grits of sand between my toes. The inexplicable mystery of big water, creatures patrolling its depths.

I floated. Closed my eyes. Dozed off.

When I woke up, Ada was standing over me, studying me with her metallic eyes, her face inflamed from the sun. My heart pounded. How long had I been asleep? I swept the child up into my arms and ran toward the pod.

Ada moaned on her little foldout bed, her face swollen, covered in red boils. It was high afternoon, the pod shut up against the sun's assault. The air-conditioning smelled pissy.

Frantic, I paced the small space.

Xander didn't blame me; he rubbed my back.

"It's not your fault," he said. "We didn't know she had a sun allergy."

"But we suspected, didn't we? We know it's not good for her. Fuck. Why did I drink that wine? Why did I fall asleep?"

"But I was napping inside the pod myself, completely oblivious."

"But you're not feeling well."

As I rubbed nanobiotic ointment into her skin, Ada's eyes fluttered open.

"Mama," she wheezed. "My tummy hurts."

"Dear God." Xander jumped to his feet, grabbed his phone.

"What?"

"We've got to get her back to the ship fast."

"What's the matter?"

"It's probably nothing, but it could have gotten inside her."

"What do you mean, 'inside her'?"

Xander wouldn't look at me. He coughed. "Into her organs."

I collapsed onto the daybed and then leapt up again, walked over to Ada and stroked her hair.

"Don't worry," said Xander, "our medical team knows exactly what to do for this. And you don't have to come up—Mother still hasn't had the filtration system fixed. You can stay for another week. It would be horrible to snatch you away after the progress you've made. When she's better, we can go to Oregon as planned."

"I can't abandon her."

"You're not abandoning her; you're healing yourself, for your own good and hers. And I'll be with her every second of every day."

Xander touched my face and peered into my eyes, which he often described as *startlingly opaque.*

"Trust me," he said. And I did.

I watched their shuttle whir up into dusky clouds. I could barely make out the ship, hovering beyond a cumulonimbus mass. When I saw it dart over the lake and disappear beyond the horizon, I felt something inside me shrivel, some organ or gland, obscure but essential, drained of vibrant juice. Clutching my gut, I released the deep keening moan of a bereft whale.

I sat on the windswept shore, cormorants circling above the water. My phone bleeped. When I tapped the Real-Deal icon, Xander and Ada popped up on the beach: Ada still in her bed, Xander standing behind her, both of them smiling. Her pustules were drying up. She looked even older than she had yesterday.

"I can almost touch you, Mama." Ada reached toward me. "I can see the lake."

"How are you feeling?" I asked.

"Better and better. The doctor gave me more medicine."

"How's the formula working out?" I couldn't bring myself to say *blood product*.

"She doesn't love it," said Xander, "but it's enough to keep her going until we have you back."

"It's yucky, Mama. I want mickimoo."

I felt flickers of pain in my breasts. I'd been pumping, of course, with an intricate device that extracted trickles of blood.

"How do *you* feel?" Xander asked me.

"Physically OK, I guess. But lonely, depressed."

"What's 'depressed' mean?" asked Ada.

"Kind of a grown-up thing," said Xander.

"I'm grown-up." Ada laughed.

"Just a little sad," I said, "because I miss you two."

"But I'm sending the shuttle for Mama on Wednesday," said Xander, "and we'll all be together again."

"Hip hip hooray," shouted Ada, tossing her robot bunny into the air.

Xander moved closer. In the hologram, his flesh looked even more spectral, but his words came through, warm and thick, and we sank into conversation again, talking of Ada's progress but then drifting off into speculative chatter—his mother's recent rash of illnesses, the morphogenesis of microorganisms, mind-altering bacteria. Though the conversation was grim, we lost ourselves in its intricacies. And then we sat sighing. And then we hung up.

Late Tuesday night, strong winds shook the camping pod, and I thought I heard beasts rustling outside in the night. I imagined storybook wolves in tattered pants, frisking on their hind feet, fangs dripping with cartoonish saliva. I checked the portal: locked. I picked up my laser gun and aimed it at the light fixture.

My phone bleeped. It was Xander. When his face materialized, frowning, my stomach dropped. If Ada had taken a turn for the worse, I'd never forgive myself for staying behind; I would die if—

"It's not Ada," he said. "It's Mother."

Good, I almost blurted, but I forced my face into a semblance of sympathy.

"She's dying for real this time," he said. "Cancer. Isabelle insists she could go any day now, and Mother wants to fly to the Peruvian rain forest. She—"

Xander's shoulders heaved. He emitted a convulsive croak. I'd never seen him cry before.

"She wants to pass on the deck of the ship with a view of the Amazon, if that can be managed, weatherwise." He sniffed. "That's where she met Father. We're already headed over there. And we can't backtrack to pick you up. Too risky. She's very close, so it won't be long."

And then he couldn't speak.

The old woman was dying, and I imagined slapping her so hard that her wig tumbled off her bald head. But Xander was weeping. When I reached out to touch him, my hand passed through his skull.

Three weeks later, the old woman was *still* dying, no doubt enthroned on the deck as Xander and a dozen servants fussed over her. Of course I talked to him and Ada every day, but both of them seemed distracted. Xander kept conversations short and practical, promising that we'd be reunited soon. Bewitched by the troop of robotic monkeys her grandmother had given her, Ada darted in and out of the frame. Shockingly tall, she looked like a coltish little girl. And she hadn't asked for mickimoo in five days.

"Hola madre." She materialized beside my chair. "I'm learning to speak Spanish."

"Impressive," I said.

"Did the boy deliver the food?" asked Xander.

"Yes," I said. "Yesterday."

He'd arrived on an old-fashioned bicycle, a child no older than nine, with jewellike eyes set into pockmarked skin. I'd tried to talk to him, but he shook his head. "No Ingles," he muttered before pedaling away.

"Why don't you fly back to West Virginia?" Xander asked me. "Check on your farm."

"Not yet," I said. "Let's give it another week."

Although I never saw Xander's mother in the background, I could always feel her presence, a dark, burning force just outside the borders of the hologram.

"I love you," whispered Xander, as though he didn't want her to hear him, and I thought I heard a squawk of laughter.

I hung up, watched their images scatter into shining pixels. And then I was alone again on the windy beach.

By the time the old woman died, the pod's tiny freezer was packed with bags of frozen pink fluid, blood-spiked milk, but I still pumped to keep the juices flowing, anxious for the feel of Ada in my arms, the tug of her sweet mouth, her whole body bristling with need and love. Xander had warned me that he wouldn't call on the day of the funeral, but still I felt a bitter ache, a longing for word streams that would revive me like a blood transfusion.

That evening I sat on the cold beach, draped in lab-fur, drinking a decent Malbec from the Maule Valley, something from Ushuaia that the boy had brought. A fox flickered past, turned to stare at me, and then trotted down the beach. A flock of white geese flew over. Out in the black water, some gleaming creature exploded from the surface and dove back into the deep. I got drunk, fell asleep in my chair, and dreamed of Ada floating down from the sky in a ball gown made of clouds.

"Mama," she said, landing on the beach. "I missed you."

Her cloud dress was tinted with pink. I could see her heart, a lump of convulsive purple meat, glistening behind her rib cage. And then Xander floated down, his lips sewn up with coarse black thread. When he tried to speak, blood oozed from the stitches.

*

Xander hadn't called in days and I was sick again—pale, thin, my hair falling out in dry, matted clumps—the same anemia I'd suffered before. My ankle bones creaked when I walked. I couldn't keep warm. My teeth felt loose. I'd had to stop pumping, and my swollen breasts throbbed with a sad ache. Yesterday, a freak snow had fallen, setting the record for the season's earliest. But I had to keep the portal open just in case. Hunkered in the pod, smothered in fur, my whole head inflamed with a sinus infection, I waited. I didn't want to bother Xander while he was grieving for his mother. I ate pomegranate seeds and spoonfuls of raw pâté. I drank *czernina*, canned duck-blood broth from Poland, and stared out at the pale sky.

I was down to three tins of meat and a box of crackers when the boy came squeaking through the thawing snow on his bicycle. He left the bags on the portable porch. For all he knew, I was dead, my corpse ripening, filling the pod with noxious gasses. But I was alive. I'd gotten over the worst of the anemia. Though I'd gained a little weight, my breasts hung like empty wine sacks. The sinus infection had lingered for weeks. I still had a croupy cough. But I got up and opened the portal.

Grieving had given me agoraphobia, and the air stung my skin when I stepped out onto the porch. But the sun felt good. I lingered for a spell before creeping back into the pod.

As soon as I finished breakfast, I began my Internet search for news. So far I'd found only Xander's mother's endless obituary, which spoke of her great family, her love of rain forests, her staggering donations to the cause of deforestation—ironic, given her disdain for actual trees and soil. The article mentioned her funeral, *an intimate family affair*, but neglected to identify a specific location. Of course I'd reported the missing ship to the Intermediate Air Authority, who'd grilled me on my relationship with the family as though I were suspect. But I knew that I'd never hear back from them. So I searched the hinterlands of the Internet until my eyeballs burned.

I searched all morning, gave up around eleven, and called them on the stroke of noon as I always did, hoping that today would be different, that Xander would appear before me, bright with chatter, that Ada would run in from the margins and try to wrap her arms around my ghostly neck.

*

In a dream I floated down the Amazon in a tiny boat, scanning the sky for ships. Gaudy birds swooped and darted, cawed and shrieked. A purple parrot landed on the stern of my canoe, opened its beak, and emitted an electronic bleep. *Bleep, bleep, bleep.* The parrot flapped its wings. Its red eyes bulged. *Bleep, bleep, bleep.*

I woke up. My phone glowed on the nightstand. I snatched it up.

Missed call from an unfamiliar number in Sepahua, Peru.

When I returned the call, Xander appeared on FaceTime, breathless, looking grainy from a bad connection. I placed my hand on my chest. Felt my heart thumping. I took a deep breath.

"Xander, thank God. Where's Ada? Please tell me she's—"

"She's fine, but it's been tough. You must be worried sick."

"God, you can't even imagine. What happened?"

"The ship crashed into the river."

"Ridiculous," I snapped.

"I know it sounds outrageous, but I assure you, it did."

"You expect me to believe—"

"I knew it was flying too low, but Mother had instructed the captain to glide right over the water, sprinkle her ashes near some sacred Incan ruins. I don't even know how many crew members made it or where they—"

"Ada. I want to see Ada right now."

"She's napping in the hotel room. Isabelle's with her. I didn't want to wake her because she didn't sleep much last night and she just ate dinner. We've been camping in an emergency pod with a dead battery for almost a month, separated from the others, hiding from the sun, living on stale provisions. I don't know what happened to my phone. Isabelle lost hers too. We didn't know where we were exactly."

"A fascinating new drama, debuting tonight at nine o'clock." I felt ashamed of the bitterness in my voice.

"I'm telling the truth," he murmured. And I knew that he was.

"We had no way to communicate with the world," Xander said, "but then the rains finally came and we found the town with a compass and an old-fashioned paper map. All it took was an iris scan to get us back into civilization. Sorry about the cheap phone, but it's all I can get in Sepahua. Mother's other ship has to be checked over. It's been in port for nearly a year. But my cousin Andre is picking us up in a week."

"And then?"

"Of course we'll come to you immediately."

He started to tell me about the forest there, but then his connection fizzled right in the middle of an elusive word: *Gush? Gas? Ghost?*

On a cool evening in June, the air misty, I stood on the beach with my bags and watched the sky. Due to the complexities of Xander's mother's estate, due to a malfunctioning shuttle on his cousin's ship, due to freak weather patterns, fluctuating cloud densities, and the mysterious whims of a superstitious aunt, they were coming weeks later than planned. But they were coming.

Every time a bird swooped down from the trees, my heart beat fast. Every time an animal rustled in the woods, I jumped. The lake smelled stronger than usual. The sand glittered with specks of lavender I'd never noticed before. My own hands looked strange, fingertips gnawed, blisters blooming where I'd torn out hangnails with my teeth.

When the shuttle whirred down from the clouds, I clutched my stomach and released the bellow of a sick cow. I'd expected to see a ship appear first. But I wiped my tears on my sleeve and straightened myself.

Xander stepped out first, startlingly thin but still lovely, his skin glazed with a moist sheen. Behind him was a small adolescent girl, a cousin perhaps, who looked a lot like Ada. She wore a 1950s-style frock with a lavish crinoline, her hair swept up into a hot-pink bouffant. When she teetered toward me in ridiculous stilettos, I realized that the child was my own Ada.

My insides felt molten.

"What have you done to my child?"

"Done?" Xander said.

"Hello, Mother," Ada said in an affected British voice that made me wince.

"She's been watching ancient James Bond films," Xander laughed. He hugged me hard.

"She's still the same girl," he whispered. "You'll see."

"I don't understand," I muttered. "How?"

"Premature puberty onset caused by early weaning and synthetic xenoestrogens in the emergency provisions. At least that's what Isabelle said."

"My fault," I moaned, feeling my knees go rubbery.

"Not your fault. And not an unusual phenomenon with sky-children."

But she was not a sky-child. She was half earth, half me. Three months ago, the tiny, eager mammal had drunk milk from my breasts.

"Why didn't you warn me?"

"She was always around when we talked. I didn't want to make her feel self-conscious. She's confused enough as it is. And you know satellite children develop earlier anyway. It was only a matter of time before—"

"She's half earth," I snapped. "Never forget that."

"I haven't forgotten," said Xander, "but she's adapted to our—"

"Mama," Ada said softly, tottering toward me. Her eyes were wet and luminous, beautiful beyond belief. I could still peer into them and see glimmers of my baby.

Shy, awkward, she leaned toward me. She wrapped her arms around my neck.

I squeezed, shocked afresh by the womanly heft of her, the new body humming with secrets. I pictured fruit falling from a bush, taking root, sprouting. I saw bees swarming around a tiny, flowering tree. I saw a self-possessed young woman floating up into the clouds. I felt like a husk, going to dust.

Now Ada was weeping, shaking in my arms. I burrowed my face into her stiff, dyed hair, searching for familiar smells among the alien chemicals. Gone was the silk, the gloss. Gone was the warm, kitten-ish musk.

"Mickimoo, Mama," she whispered as she pulled away, joking, of course. But her smile was sweet, not sneering. And the eyes beneath her contrived hair looked vulnerable.

She slipped her hand in mine, just as she used to do. Xander leaned in on my other side, holding my bag.

"We'll talk when we get a chance," he said, and I felt the full weight of my isolation, the deprivation of communication like the twisting of an empty stomach devouring itself. I imagined us in bed, breath mingling into a warm fog, words merging like a flock and darting into a cloud.

Together, we walked toward the shuttle.

The Million Monkeys of M. Borel
John Crowley

IN THE UNCOMFORTABLY WARM months of December and January in the year 19—, I found myself with little occupation and therefore much time for idle thought. Reading had become difficult for me owing to a progressive deterioration of my eyes, and if there was no one interested in reading to me from that small collection of volumes that I could still count on to give me pleasure, then I did not read, or rather I did not hear the voices of authors. Plato, as is well-known, said that when we read a book we believe that we hear the voice of a person, and yet when we try to put a question to it, it does not answer us.

What occupied my thoughts in those somnolent days was certain metaphysical or logical propositions that had been argued or at least passed around a great deal in the time of my youth. I was considering the million monkeys of Émile Borel, as described in his 1913 essay "Mécanique Statistique et Irréversibilité" (J. Phys. 5e série, vol. 3). As is well-known, Borel posited that a million monkeys randomly hitting a typewriter keyboard for ten hours a day will in time almost surely type all the words in all the books of the Bibliothèque nationale in many combinations, including the order in which they actually occur in those million volumes. In the restatement of the theorem most popular among English speakers, the monkeys eventually type out the collected works of William Shakespeare. The crux of the argument, as enunciated by Borel and those who took up his proposition, was that the term *almost surely* has a precise definition in the language of the mathematics of probability, a definition rather unlike the one we use: *almost surely my mother loves me above her other children; almost surely my ancestor was a hero in the battle in which he died.* These statements differ from Borel's.

In later years the million monkeys of M. Borel were replaced in the theory by an infinite number of monkeys, or by a single monkey typing all the time forever. In the latter formulation, all of Shakespeare *must* eventually be produced; in the former, all of Shakespeare (and every other written work) is produced instantaneously as soon as the typing begins. Neither of these refinements seemed to me to be as

57

worth pondering as M. Borel's million monkeys who could only *almost surely* produce the soliloquies of Hamlet, the madness of Lear, and the love of Antony and Cleopatra—who indeed could almost surely produce them even if Shakespeare had never written them, and likewise all other books both already written and never written before.

At this juncture, a visitor arrived with a piece of machinery he had brought to see if it could assist me in the dilemmas both banal and esoteric that a loss of eyesight entails. He had come to be devoted to certain works of mine, published in obscure journals long ago but apparently ubiquitous now. The machine was a computer of a kind not yet available to the general public, which he could set up in such a way as to cause it to read aloud whatever text it was given, or which it was directed to ask for from its memory. My young friend assured me that the memory of the computer—no bigger than a lady's vanity case—contained the entire works of several of my beloved authors, as well as Shakespeare, the Bible in several languages, and other works of science and philosophy. If manipulated in the right way it could also reach into libraries around the world, where other bodies of miniaturized and encoded texts were kept.

My wonder at this was somewhat dampened when, after working an afternoon, he directed the machine to read a text I had selected (a story of Chesterton's). The voice proceeding from the machine was neither the voice that the story had spoken in when my eyes had used to pass over it, nor the voice of a human reader sitting beside me. It was the voice that the dead gods of Egypt might have spoken in when summoned by Agrippa or Trithemius: a corpse's voice. My shock and grief (for I had greatly anticipated the riches awaiting me) at this inhuman parroting of human words saddened my friend, and not wishing to seem to spurn his good intentions toward me, I began to question him about the machine and its powers.

"There are puzzles in metaphysics," he said, "and thought experiments in physics, that can now be solved or carried out in actual fact. The long-standing problem of how few colors a mapmaker would need to construct a map where no two contiguous countries or regions would be the same color, no matter what the shape of the regions: a computer (more powerful by far than this one) has proven that three colors are in fact enough, which before there was no way to demonstrate. The only drawback is that the proof resides in the computer, and is so complex that only another computer as powerful as the first can certify it.

"And there is the problem of the million monkeys who sit down to type all the works of Shakespeare," he continued, astonishing me with the workings of Coincidence, whose laws might also be known only to computers, and provable only by other computers. He said that computers were easily able to produce random series of letters according to any rule the maker imposed. Suppose, for instance, a rule was set that the computer should generate a text exactly as long as the First Folio of Shakespeare, all letters, punctuation, and spaces being counted. In a matter of seconds the computer could generate a text wherein, as in the Kabbalah of Abulafia, the letters of the Shakespeare text were replaced *en bloc* by others produced at random. It could be shown that if the computer were to produce these false folios at the rate of one per second, it was estimated that the universe would end, the suns burn out, and all would be reduced to aimless atoms and cold, before so much as a single play, perhaps a single entire line, was produced in its proper place.

One rule, however, would hasten the process. (He called it an *algorithm*, a word of the Arab arithmeticians who in their texts had liked to write out their endless equations in words made of letters, and not in the number forms they had themselves invented.) The computer could easily, in its comparisons, determine if so much as a single letter of any false text fell by chance where the same letter fell in the folio text. Preserving that letter in its position, the computer would examine the next, and the next, discarding everything in each one except the letters—it might be two, or ten, or none—that fell where the same letters fell in the text.

"If that little rule is followed," said my young friend—eager and smiling, it was hard not to see him as the herald of a triumphant army, come joyfully to demand the instant surrender of an ancient town—"then the entire works of Shakespeare can be recreated in a very short time. All that's needed is for the computer to save the accumulated coincidences of all the false texts with the real text."

All that was needed then was for the text to exist in advance of the attempt to produce it. It was, as he said, a simple matter. Yet it would never satisfy those who contemplate, in the shadows of ancient libraries, the million monkeys of M. Borel. For the secret longing of those dreamers is not for the books of ours they might reproduce, but for those texts of their own, unknown to us, unknown even to themselves, that they might create. The great computer my young friend contemplated, examining the texts that its blind mechanical monkeys produced at inconceivable speed, retaining only what they shared with an Elizabethan whose works we know by heart—what other works, unknown to us, works we have needed and sought for and dreamed of existing, would it, every day, every instant, discard forever?

When the young engineer had gone—somewhat downcast, it seemed to me, yet promising to return to give me further instruction—I placed my hand upon the box he had brought, as silent now as the statue from which the god has departed. The fact that it—unlike those fatuous and impossible monkeys—actually could generate such things could break the hearts of those who, in another day, were able to smile at the thought of an endless library composed of all possible combinations of all the letters that we know. "We think, when we read, that we hear the voice of a person; but if we question it, it will not reply."

Walking Dead Love Songs
Laura Sims

I was born
and then I died.

I was born and then
I died fighting. I was

born and then I died fighting zombies while the sand
ran out of the holes in my hands back down to the bottom
of the ocean. I was born and then I died fighting zombies like my mother

and her mother before her and her mother's
mother. Women have it so bad, we've got
holes in our hands and in our hearts where the babies
have pierced them

Ouch. I was born and then I died watching TV. I came back

I was born and then I died watching zombies die on TV. I held my
remote like a saber and hoped pushing buttons would make me the
man whose smooth hands are dappled with dust-speckled light from
the redolent land of Arcadia. The smooth-handed man takes up his bow,
knocks the arrow

The arrow goes *thwack*
when it pierces
the eye. That's how they die

I was born and then I died leaning close to you, singing, pouring words
in a river down your small pink ear through the channels to your brain
made of subatomic particles like neutrons, perhaps, though I'm not sure,
because

Laura Sims

I died. Everything in sight smacks of hedonistic lassitude. A box of
soft tissues filled with lotion and a bottle of Chablis. The babe, the
sweet babe, on a blanket, unarmed. He was born and then
eventually
I'll die

*

Three unnamed criminals, first. Then
a zombified child. Two former people
named Leon and Hannah. A family horse.
Wayne (bitten), Ed (eaten), and thirteen
anonymous lives. Amy, sweet Amy, shot once
in the head. "Out of mercy," it says. Jim
died of infection. Two Drs. Jenner, and Jacqui,
who chose to explode. The way the wind
billows a motorbike cover. Stepping over a
tea bag squashed on the street. My husband
says, fondly, *What's left of your brain is decaying*
at breakneck speed. The woman in front
of me's long blonde hair. Almost white. The yellow-
billed loon sounds like someone is laughing—

At me? At me?

*

I want it all: wall clocks
T-shirts

dog tags mugs dolls

The fleece throw
with Michonne

The poster of you
when your hair was too short
with your
crossbow

The bracelet hitching
my heart
to your name

I'm not thinking

of how I'm bewitched
and belittled
by corporate
dominion

or how I've been
yoked
to a man-shaped
ghost

I'm just thinking

At last
the fourth wall
has dissolved

and

My love is
incarnate
forever

*

Inside the dream inside
the car it's dusk your back's

against the window which
the dead. Our talk grows

leaves and stems and
passionless as dust. The light is low

the dead are rumbling like
the thunder in a show your hair

is slicked with great precision
by your ears. You are

my own and someone
forty million else's

how your thigh
lies close to mine and psychically

we meld but we
eternally untouching

look ahead, into the windshield
where the view is of the future

rotting-jawed and so un-
fruitfully unslakable the dead

*

You broke
down the bodies
saying feed me
belabor my soul
in the scraped
bowl of summits

the kings all around

crossing snow
we wore sinews
and hides all the
hellish long haul

Survival
takes time. It takes
place in the mind

Who'll cleanse
& align the charred
morsels of story
we sell

the hacked limbs
the fouled mouth
the hard heart or

the litter of coins
dropped out like a
birth in the stream
running loud down
god's mountain's
improvident thigh

*

Laura Sims

When the train
comes at last
bearing humans

the woman still
eating her husband's face

looks up
flesh burning

the dry white sheet of the past: I can almost

see the new
season from here

Bromley Hall
Valerie Martin

THEY HAD QUARRELED. As she took up the phone receiver and punched in the numbers, that thought came to her. It wasn't an important argument; she didn't care what it had been about. She only knew that they had quarreled—oh, it was unbearable to think of now.

But that morning, when she closed the hotel-room door perhaps too forcefully and flounced down the heavily carpeted steps to the lobby, she knew she was within her rights and he was being obstinate. "I don't want to look at rich people's houses in a crowd," he'd said, which was absurd, he'd drooled all over the paintings at the castle. Was it only that these rich people weren't royalty? Or was it that the most interesting thing about Bromley Hall was the gardens? Gardens bored Frank.

The real reason he'd refused to come with her was to punish her for insisting on changing rooms. But the first room was impossible. The window gave on to the street just over the hotel bar, and the bathtub, a claw-footed steep-sided behemoth from two centuries back, wasn't off by itself as a proper bathtub should be but smack in the middle of the carpet a few steps from the bed. "If it was just for a night or two," Janet protested, "we could put up with it, but we're here for a week."

"I hate this hotel," Frank replied.

So she'd gone down to the desk and asked the sullen young woman with the tattoos of crossed swords on the insides of her wrists if they might possibly have an interior room, as her husband was a light sleeper and the noise from the street would be hard for him.

To her surprise, to her relief, the young woman furrowed her brow with sympathy and turned on her swivel chair to face a computer screen. "Let me just see," she said. "Do you mind a short flight of stairs?"

"Not at all," Janet said hopefully, but she wondered, why stairs? There was an elevator the size of a telephone booth in the hall.

The clerk stood up and took down a heavy key from the old-fashioned board of hooks on the wall. "It's number seventeen," she said. "It's at the top, looks out on the garden. You go to the third floor on the elevator, down the hall, and you'll see a few steps. Have a look and see if it suits you."

Faces the garden, Janet thought, grasping the key in the elevator. How bad could it be?

The hall was short, the carpeted steps, five in all, led to a narrow landing and a white door, like all the other doors, with the number seventeen in polished brass digits screwed in at eye level. Always that little thrill of hesitation, opening the door of yet another hotel room. Janet turned the key in the lock and the door shifted in its frame, then drifted open. She was looking at an open window with a fresh linen curtain fluttering in a soft breeze. The room was twice the size of the impossible room, now clearly the worst room in the hotel, reserved for Americans and probably Germans who had never visited before. There was a writing desk, a tall wardrobe with drawers down one side, and a comfortable chintz-covered reading chair next to the ubiquitous 20-watt standing lamp. She peeked into the bathroom. No scary deep tub, but a roomy, glassed-in shower with one of those round, flat rain showerheads Frank liked. The sink had a wide rim and a cupboard alongside, beneath another long window.

Janet smiled, crossed to the window, and looked down. Idyllic walled garden, late summer blooms, manicured hedges, a brick walk leading to a bench, a trickle of water slithering off the edge of a flat rock into a stone basin. She turned from the window. "This is perfect," she said softly. "Frank will be so relieved."

He wasn't relieved. In fact, when she arrived at the bad room brandishing the key to the new one, he tossed the sweater he was unpacking back into the suitcase and said, "Oh, for God's sake." His view of travel was that you took things as you found them. He particularly disliked wheedling desk staff at a hotel. She knew he felt this way, of course, and for the most part she agreed. But in this case she stood her ground. "I'm not spending a solid week with a bathtub in the bedroom and a window over a bar," she vowed. At this point a trio of arriving bar patrons obligingly burst into uproarious laughter in the street. One shouted at the other, "You loony cunt. You have no fuckin' idea."

Janet pulled the corners of her mouth down, raised her eyebrows, opened her hands, and said "QED."

This only made Frank gloomier and he trudged along the hall, pulling his suitcase behind him with the air of a man consigned to a prison sentence. They had to go up separately in the narrow elevator then reconvene in the hall and drag the cases to the odd half flight that led to room seventeen. Janet watched Frank's face as she pushed open the door; yes, there was a flicker of pleased surprise, quickly reined in. She took her small case and stepped into the bathroom, where she began laying out her cosmetics on a convenient shelf over the radiator. Through the open window she could hear the cheerful chatter of birds, the burbling of water in the fountain. Just let him calm down and unpack, she thought. And then he'll be grateful.

And when she came out his suitcase was open on the bed and he was hanging his jacket in the wardrobe. His shoes were already neatly arranged under the bedside table. "I can't believe this room costs the same as the other one," he said pleasantly.

"Sometimes you just have to ask," she said. She lifted her suitcase onto a luggage rack next to the wardrobe and took out a neat stack of blouses. "Let's unpack and go have dinner at that place the Bangalls recommended."

"Is it far from here?"

"No. We can walk."

"That's good," Frank said. "I'm hungry." He pulled out his light travel raincoat and looked around for a place to hang it. "As usual," he said, "not enough hangers." Then, spotting three iron hooks jutting from a wooden bar just inside the door, he edged past his wife to make use of one.

Janet stowed her underwear in the drawer of the bedside table, her spirits lifting at the success of her effort to improve the arrangements of the trip. When she looked up, Frank was standing very still, clutching his raincoat but making no move to hang it on the hook. Instead he was staring at the plasticized sign affixed to the room door. "Fuck," he said. Janet joined him and read the information card, which listed, among other things, the price of the room. It was half again as much as the first room. Frank draped the coat on the hook and stalked back to his suitcase, radiating fury. "Sometimes," he said, perfectly imitating her chirpy, overconfident tone, "you just have to ask."

These things happen on trips, Janet thought. You have to be flexible when traveling, and really, even at the higher price, the room was a bargain; they would have a quiet, comfortable week to end their vacation. She communicated all this to Frank over the excellent, pricey dinner at the charming restaurant, clearly popular with the locals, and after a few glasses of wine he stopped fuming and opined that it would be nice to sleep with the window open.

And he did sleep; they both did, the deep, companionable sleep of travelers with no particular plan for the next day. They barely made it to the breakfast room before closing time, and the buffet was somewhat picked over. But when the server, an indulgent and amusing young gay man, saw Janet gazing sadly at the two bits of discolored melon left in the serving bowl, he insisted on getting her a bowl of fresh fruit from the kitchen.

"The coffee's good," Frank admitted, still mildly befuddled from the bottomless sleep.

"Let's go to Bromley Hall this afternoon," Janet suggested. "Betsy said they have some very good pictures and there's a luncheon place on the grounds with a terrace."

Frank took a long swallow of coffee, and set the cup down carefully in the saucer. "I don't care what Betsy said," he said.

That was how the argument began. It wasn't a big argument; really, it was just a spat. Frank maintained that he didn't want to reproduce the Bangalls' trip in every detail, that he wasn't interested in looking at rich people's houses, and if he was going to pay a fortune for a big hotel room, he intended to make use of it. His plan was to stay in, catch up on e-mail, and read a novel.

Janet had no counterarguments, just her usual range of defensive maneuvers and her reiterated desire to see Bromley Hall, which was only open on weekends, and this was Sunday. She was torn between her pleasure in the fact that Frank clearly liked the expensive room very much, and her sense that his decision to skip the visit to Bromley Hall was a species of punishment for her insistence on changing rooms.

They returned to room seventeen, where Frank set up his computer on the desk and Janet plopped in the plush chair, consulting her guidebook and the bus schedules. The bus stop, she'd noted on their arrival, was only a block from the hotel. The sky was blue, the air was fresh, warm with a light breeze lifting the curtain on the window overlooking the garden. Bromley Hall was on the outskirts of the city, a longish ride that appealed to her because one could see so much from a bus, especially if it was a double-decker. Actually, she mused, as she turned the page to the history of the house—sixteenth century, wing added eighteenth century, aristocrats rising and falling with the vicissitudes of power at court, internecine rivalries, revolution, and war—it might be a good break for them both to split up for a day. They'd been together for two weeks, never apart for more than a few minutes, and moving around a lot. Frank had slept poorly, and the bulk of the luggage hauling fell to him. Perhaps he was just tired, and a rest in this pleasant room would put him in good spirits. He was muttering at the computer screen, trying to connect to the hotel Wi-Fi, an operation that always aggravated him. Janet fell to thinking about her shoes—the rubber-soled sneakers or the comfortable waterproof loafers? This country was famous for its changeable weather. The travel umbrella definitely; maybe the cotton sweater.

Janet wasn't an adventuresome soul but she tried to make up for that with obsessive planning. She had thrilled to read of the great explorer Richard Burton's perennial charge to his wife: "Pay, pack, and follow." With the right budget, she thought, I could have managed that. She imagined herself arriving at whatever godforsaken outpost he had chosen, comfortably ensconced on the lead camel with a canopy over her head and a thermos of tea at the ready, while behind her for half a mile stretched a caravan of lumbering beasts loaded with chairs and tables, tents and cushions, teapots and saucepans, flatware and table linens, toilet kits, cologne, five hundred bottles of wine, a hundred or so of gin, six cases of orange marmalade, a thousand books. Richard Burton, played by Frank in this scenario, stood on an outcropping of rock, legs apart, peering through his binoculars with a wide grin on his sand-parched lips. "Here she comes," he observes to his keffiyehed companion. "What a woman!"

And then, that night, lounging on the embroidered cushions in the spacious, airy tent, after the dinner of sardines, paté, crusty bread, pudding, two bottles of champagne and another of port, the lamp light flickering, the black night ablaze with glittering stars, what a scene of scintillating passion!

The bus, when it came, was a disappointment, a rattletrap affair with no upper deck, worn hard-plastic benches, and smeary windows. The driver was wearing a white turban. A Sikh, Janet reminded herself as she dropped her fare into the coin slot. Doubtless named Singh. But what did Sikhs believe? "Could you let me know when we come to the stop for Bromley Hall?" she inquired pleasantly.

Without raising his eyes, the man pointed to a sign affixed to the base of the coin machine. PLEASE DO NOT ENGAGE THE DRIVER IN CONVERSATION.

"I beg your pardon," Janet said, turning toward the chilly regard of her fellow passengers. These were few and all appeared to be foreigners, but not, like her, on the bus for touristic purposes. A scattering of dark-eyed men, working men, she thought, slumped on the seats, broody and silent. Two middle-aged women, both overweight, dressed in patterned blouses, long black skirts, and identical caps of curly, dyed-blonde hair, bowed their heads toward each other as they spoke urgently in a language Janet didn't recognize. Slavic, was it? Russian? Polish? The seats across the aisle from them were empty, and she hastened to take the one nearest the window. The engine groaned as the driver changed gears and the bus lumbered out into the road.

It would all be fine once she got to the hall, she counseled herself. A dull sheen of anxiety clouded her vision. Through the smudgy window she could see the long vista of fine stone houses, the carefully tended front gardens that lined the wide central avenue of the town. A Roman road, she knew that from the guidebook. They'd marched through this chilly, windswept country in legions, in their short skirts and sandals, taking orders in Latin, donning togas off duty and building baths, building bridges, civilizing everything in sight. In a few generations Romans would have blond children. What was the Roman name for this city? Unconsciously Janet pulled her travel purse into her lap and unfastened the theft-proof latch. As she did, a clear and startling image flashed across her brain, as sudden and disconcerting as a fox dashing across a road. It was her cell phone gleaming darkly on the bedside table in the comfortable hotel room.

An important oversight, sadly due to bad temper, but how important exactly? She still had the compact guidebook with its comforting section on getting around, including bus and tram maps and the phone numbers of taxis and emergency services. In the old days, not so long ago, they had managed foreign cities perfectly well with nothing but a street map. She pulled out the book: a bright photo of the castle with an inset of a dog working a clutch of sheep emblazoned the cover. As she turned to the map section, the bus brakes groaned and the chassis creaked. It was, she recalled, four stops to Bromley Hall. This would be the first one: Crompton Road.

The bus pulled up to a low stone wall. Janet spotted a metal sign attached to a pole driven into the sidewalk. With a hydraulic thwack the doors folded open. Two more dark-eyed young men, yapping angrily at each other in a language Janet couldn't even get close to— was it Arabic? Hebrew?—took the steps at a leap and tossed their coins contemptuously into the machine. Janet studied the sign on the pole, which read BUS. She looked past it for a street sign but there was nothing. The young men pushed past her without a glance, intent on their escalating quarrel, which, to her relief, they took to the very back of the bus. Again she scanned the street as the doors snapped closed and the bus jolted back into the road. There was only a stop sign at the first corner. Why not put a street sign on a street? she thought testily. The stone wall continued past the corner and at last she spotted a white metal placard affixed to it; this would be the name of the road they were on. Then she could read it: MOREHOUSE CRESCENT.

The driver steered the bus into the center lane and picked up speed. There was more traffic suddenly, the wall ended, the sidewalk disappeared, and a riot of shabby modern shops and rundown row houses crowded the perimeter of the road. Janet fought a swell of panic as she studied the bus-route map, searching vainly for Morehouse Crescent. At a traffic signal the bus took a right turn, launching into a roiling four-lane highway, lined with industrial warehouses, car dealerships, and furniture stores that reminded Janet of suburban New Jersey. She scanned the road for any identifying signage, but there was none. Could this possibly be the road to bucolic Bromley Hall? And when was this rattling torpedo of a bus going to make the second of the four stops?

She glanced at her fellow passengers, the Polish (Russian?) housewives, still talking excitedly, the profile of an older Arabic-looking man dressed in a black T-shirt and black jeans, his long fingers deftly working a cellular device, two seats up and across the aisle. The unmoving back of the Sikh driver. The Arabic man might speak English; he might hate Americans.

Another turn, leaving the highway for a two-lane road that climbed a long hill of gradually thinning urbanization that gave way to agriculture. This was more like it. Ere long they would see sheep or cows, and then, in the distance, rising in the mist, the noble tower of Bromley Hall. She tried to judge the distance they had come, perhaps five kilometers. The hall was about twelve from the hotel. No need to panic. The traffic abated, the road deteriorated, and the bus racketed along; really a new set of shocks was in order. At a slight concrete indentation in a field of what Janet took to be oats, the bus brakes squealed and the quivering beast came to an abrupt halt, its front wheel raised up over the curb. No sign, either of demarcation or of life. In the distance Janet spotted a baling machine suctioning hay into a long bright-green plastic sleeve. *Oh, let's just wrap the entire world in plastic*, she thought bitterly. *That will really help.* As she contemplated the remote possibility that hay bales sealed in plastic might have any ecological advantages, the bus doors wheezed open, and every one of the dark and sullen men rose from their seats and clambered down the steps, filing silently across the road in front of the bus to the field on the other side. Janet watched in amazement: what could they possibly have to do out here in the middle of nowhere? They didn't appear to be agricultural workers; some of them were wearing sandals. She leaned out into the aisle to keep them in her sight as the bus doors closed and the driver wrenched the wheel so that the tires came off the concrete pad with a bump. The men had gathered in a loose gang at the side of the road, a few engaged in rapid-fire conversations, others looking with gloomy expectation down the empty road in the direction the bus was heading. Janet watched them until she could see them no longer, experiencing a combination of bewilderment and relief. Obviously the men were waiting to be picked up, probably by a truck, but as the bus forged along, no vehicle of any kind passed and Janet thought the men were in for a long wait. She would tell Frank about this mystery. It was the sort of inexplicable data they enjoyed puzzling over when they traveled. One of the pleasures of their adventures was encountering unexpected ways, manners, situations. Once, toiling up yet another winding hill-town road in Italy, Frank expertly steering the rental Clio around a vertiginous bend, they had both shouted in terror and wonder at the sight of a wine barrel rolling, leaping, careening, plummeting toward them down the steep incline, followed closely by two handsome, shirtless young men shouting joyfully as they chased the escapee. The barrel missed the car by inches in its crazed descent. Frank jammed on the brakes, casting Janet a look of wild surmise. In a moment the young men and the barrel were gone and the two Americans sat weak-kneed, buckled over the seats with laughter in their still-trembling rental car.

When she got back to the hotel, Janet thought, she would tell Frank about the curious bus stop in the oat field. It made her think of the famous scene in *North by Northwest* when Cary Grant got off the bus at a cornfield to find himself being strafed by a murderous crop duster. Unconsciously she scanned the skies over the fields of grain, noting a threatening buildup of heavy, dark clouds in the west. There was no rain in the forecast.

The road grew worse for another kilometer or so, and the combination of racket and constant jolting began to affect Janet's temper. She continued, as well as she could, consulting the bus map in her guidebook, but this was increasingly a pointless exercise, as she had no idea where they were headed, though it did appear to be roughly west, which was the direction of Bromley Hall. The engine coughed, gave out a series of odd shivers and a loud pop. With a final, fatal gasp the bus coasted to a stop.

The driver, twisting the key in the ignition and jamming his foot down on the gas pedal, cursed in a language Janet didn't understand. The engine made a feeble grinding effort, then fell silent. Dead, Janet thought. A shiver darted the length of her spine and tightened her jaw. The doors flapped open, the driver sprang from his seat and out onto the dusty road. The Russian (Polish?) women stopped their chatter, glancing this way and that, their faces mirror images of mild concern. Janet crossed eyes with one and attempted an inclusive, gregarious, comrade-like smile, but the chilly, searching gaze passed over her as if she were invisible. The driver had lifted the heavy wing of the engine cover and stood gazing forlornly down into the dark interior. As the Russians (Poles?) gathered their bags and packages, Janet opened her purse. Careful of the binding, she nestled the travel guide in its depths.

Though there was clearly no need for haste, she was quick to follow her fellow passengers out of the bus. Surely some arrangement would be made. They would send another bus, or someone—the Russians?—would pull out a cell phone and call a taxi. The two matrons accosted the driver, who had one arm thrust into the maw of the engine. He regarded them hostilely. "Is dead," he said.

English! Janet rejoiced. She wouldn't be left out of the negotiations. The Russians raised their voices, doubtless berating the driver, his vehicle, the country, the government, God, man, and fate, while Janet and the driver looked on, uncomprehending. When at last the women paused for breath, the driver extracted his arm from the machine and brushed his hands together twice in the manner of a teacher dismissing a naughty class. "Is dead," he repeated. "No go."

"Excuse me," Janet said, stepping alongside the women, who had turned their exhortations upon each other. "What are we to do?"

The driver drew himself up, his eyebrows contracting down and together, intent on making himself understood. "No go," he exclaimed. He raised an arm, extending a long finger toward the empty road ahead of the bus. "You walk."

Janet followed the finger. The road stretched away through the oat fields, rustling in the thin, hot breeze; the sun beamed down where they stood, but the bank of storm clouds in the distance was building, darkening, threatening. No cars, barns, houses, side streets, signs, bus stops; nothing relieved the monotony of the scene. The volume of the matrons' voices lowered and they appeared to be in consultation

75

about a plan of action. "This is ridiculous," Janet complained to the driver. "Don't you have a phone you can use to call for help?"

"No phone," he said, patting his shirt to demonstrate the absence of that which Janet now desired above all else in the world. Again he raised his arm, stabbing the warm air between them. "You walk."

The Russians hoisted their capacious bags and, turning in the direction they had come from, set off down the road. Janet watched them closely, waiting for the glint of a cell phone to appear between them, but they weren't even speaking to each other. They strode briskly, as if they had a clear notion of a destination.

But there was nothing that way for a mile at least, and the stop, if it was a stop, was only an intrusion of unmarked concrete into a field of oats. Was their plan to wait there until another bus came along? And if so, might it not be best for Janet to follow them, to have, at least, two other women in sight on this desolate road? She took a few hesitant steps after them. The driver gave a short, exasperated gasp. "No," he said, rushing past her to cut her off. "This is way."

Janet pulled her head back and wrapped her arms across her purse. Was he going to accost her?

Again he pointed the index finger. "You look," he said.

Janet turned and trained her eyes down an imaginary line issuing from the tip of the insistent digit. The clouds glowering over the trees in the distance were not encouraging. She noticed an odd slice of pinkish light pulsing between earth and sky, just above the clump of trees. It was an affecting, magical scene: gently rolling fields, trees, the dark sky, and that slab of pinkish light reflected as if from bright stone. Oddly shaped. Was it crenellated?

"Is that Bromley Hall?" Janet said softly, wonderingly.

"Yes," exclaimed the driver. "You walk."

And so she walked toward what she believed to be Bromley Hall, but after half an hour it occurred to her that the driver had sent her on a fool's errand. The road curved steadily, and though she could keep the stand of trees in sight, the glow she had taken for a tower faded. It could have been a trick of the light, a mirage. She lost track of time but the sun was still high and bright and the air thick and hot. Far ahead she saw a small, dark smudge moving across a field. When it turned into the road, taking on a wedge shape, she heard a droning engine growing louder; it was a truck. Should she attempt to flag it down? As it approached, she studied it for important clues. She was a middle-aged woman alone on a country road, utterly defenseless, without even a cell phone to call for help. The truck was moving toward her at a leisurely pace. It wasn't large or new; it had a cab and a short flatbed. Gradually she made out two men in the front, and the bright-green plastic wrapping of the enormous hay bales in the bed flapped in the wind. Farmers, she thought. Harmless people. Good country people. The truck was very close, and she could see that the man in the passenger seat was wearing a cap. She was uncertain which way to look. She looked down at her scuffed shoes, and then they were alongside her, passing her, and she glanced up in time to see the driver, a large, placid, rosy-faced, redheaded man with pale eyes and deep creases framing colorless lips, raise his palm over the windowsill in a taciturn greeting. Janet felt her own arm bend at the elbow, lifting her hand to return the wave as the truck rumbled past her and she was once more alone on the road to Bromley Hall.

This encounter, or nonencounter, with the farmers in their truck lifted her spirits. First it revealed that there was a crossroads not too far on that went off in the direction of the stand of trees. The casual manner of the farmer suggested it wasn't altogether unusual for a pedestrian to plod along this road; the locals didn't wish her ill, which was sometimes the case in the countryside at home. She squinted ahead, not entirely confident but hopeful that within the hour she would arrive at her destination. It was very warm and she was thirsty, and those clouds were moving toward her and she toward them. In the field, occasional sudden blasts of small birds, rising, dispersing, settling again, served to distract her from the tedium of the empty road. Her bad ankle had begun to throb. When she looked back she could no longer see the broken-down bus and its monosyllabic driver; the road had curved away from them.

At last she stood at the crossroads. Straight ahead the road continued, rising in the distance among misty hills, lined on both sides by rustling fields of oats. To the west—it was west, she felt certain of that—it was a different world. The road itself was different, narrow, paved in a cracked, faded gray tarmac, tufts of weeds gnawing at the edges. A low stone fence that commenced just past the corner surrounded a long, bright-green pasture in which three ponies with heavy manes and fetlocks stood urgently cropping grass, as if, Janet thought, they had a deadline to meet. She gazed past them at the stand of trees among which Bromley Hall might beckon, and she thought the trees at least, if not the pink-hued hall, but surely the same stand of trees, appeared to have leaped a good distance to the south. This puzzled her and she stood for a moment trying to get some sort of bearing. A cloud engulfed the sun, tossing down a shadow that swept across the grain, carrying in its wake a cooling breeze like a wave of water, susurrating and sensuous, a sound so arresting that two of the ponies lifted their shaggy heads and flared their black nostrils to test the freshened air. Just beyond their field, which ended in a rail fence of more recent vintage than the wall, was a dirt drive, widening to a neat white-gravel yard bordered by heather and a strip of grass, and framing an attractive L-shaped gray stone cottage with chimneys on either end of a deeply pitched roof. A neat line of whitewashed windows and two dark-blue doors. A small red car, a Fiat, Janet thought—she knew Fiats were popular in this country—was parked just in front of the door nearest the road.

As she approached the house, that door opened and four people, two men and two women, came out into the drive, talking amiably, exchanging parting remarks, laughing at pleasantries. They didn't notice Janet approaching along the road, but she could see them clearly and she rejoiced in the sight; they looked so civilized and sociable, well-dressed, prosperous, cheerful, at ease in their country hideaway. One of the men was wearing red slacks—that was too bad—but the women both wore practical summer skirts and linen blouses. All four fair haired, light eyed, though Mr. Red Pants had more gray than gold in his neatly trimmed coiffure. Late forties, early fifties, Janet guessed. They milled about the car, then one couple got in while the other drew together on the gravel. It was like an advertisement for the good life, for the car, or whatever insurance company covered the house, or the home security system. Look how safe we are, how secure, how cheerful, plenty of money, away from the hassle of the city, look at our fine stone house, our pristine gravel (how did they keep it so white?), our heather border, our field with ponies, the grass, the oats, and the sky beyond.

The sky. As the car doors slammed and the farewells turned to hand signals, the woman waving from her doorstep looked up past the fence at the sky. Janet followed her eyes. It was blue in that direction with a few thin clouds high up. The house itself blocked the woman's view of the gathering storm in the west. Janet could see it, though, piling up darkly. It didn't appear to be moving and might spend itself over there, over Bromley Hall. When she looked back at the house, the car was inching toward the road. The woman—the home owner—stood on her doorstep with her hands on her hips. She was looking straight at Janet and as their eyes met, she smiled. Her mouth moved; she spoke softly to her husband, who had turned toward the half-open door of the house. She took a step out onto the gravel, dropping her hands to her sides, and as Janet drew nearer, the woman watched her, silent, still smiling. Her husband closed the door and joined his wife, saying something, whispering perhaps, close to her ear, then he too lifted his eyes to Janet and smiled. They were going to wait until she was closer before speaking to her. They would direct her to Bromley Hall. They would know all about the buses out here, and they would have a phone if she decided—and she had begun to think it might be the best idea—to call a taxi, go back to the hotel, and spend the afternoon with Frank in the comfortable, cool room overlooking the garden. How perfect it would be there if it rained. How romantic.

"Hello," the woman said as Janet neared the drive. "You've walked a long way."

"I have," Janet agreed. At the edge of the gravel she paused. The man hung back near the door. He looked friendly, but uncertain, and that diffidence made her reluctant to enter the loose enclosure of the drive. "The bus broke down," she said to the woman. "Way back there." She gestured at the road. "And the driver told me I could walk to Bromley Hall. Am I going the right way?"

"Bromley Hall!" the woman exclaimed. She turned to her husband and said, "She's looking for Bromley Hall." They both laughed.

"I thought it was just there." Janet pointed toward the clump of trees now thoroughly enshrouded in clouds.

"That's Smithfield Church," the woman said. "Bromley Hall is on that road but it's ten, maybe fifteen kilometers further on."

"More like fifteen," said the man. He had stepped off the porch and was striding lightly across the gravel.

"That was unkind of the driver," the woman said. "He should have told you."

"He didn't have much English." Janet defended the driver for no reason but that he had been called unkind. "He just pointed and told me to walk. I think he was a Sikh."

"Oh God," the man said. Janet thought he might complain about the takeover of public services by immigrants and she would be forced to defend Sikhs, who did rather well in the Manhattan taxi line, she thought. Better than the Arabs, who were so volatile.

But the man didn't elaborate and his wife said, "You must be thirsty. Would you like a glass of water?"

"That would be very welcome," said Janet.

"I'll bring it," the man said, turning back to the house.

Valerie Martin

Janet stood still, gazing in at the cool gray stone. An arbor shaded the farther entry, covered by a climbing vine she didn't recognize. No blooms, bright-green berries. "Your house is lovely," she said. "And so secluded."

"Thank you," the woman said. "We live in the city but we're here all summer long. In fact, we're going back tomorrow."

The door under the arbor opened and the man came out carrying a large glass of water. Without thinking, Janet announced, "I left my phone at the hotel. Now I'm thinking I should skip Bromley Hall and go back."

As the man joined them, the woman said to him, "She's left her phone." His eyebrows shot up and he exchanged a look with his wife that Janet couldn't read. As he handed her the glass he said, "It doesn't matter. We don't get much of a signal out here."

"Is there a taxi service nearby?" Janet asked. "I'm a bit discouraged about the bus."

"That dreadful bus," the woman said.

"There is," the man informed Janet. "It comes from Smithfield."

"It's a little expensive," the woman said. "But they take a much more direct route, so it's very fast."

"I know the fellow runs it," the man said. "We use them when we want to go in for an evening event."

"You're welcome to use our landline," the woman offered.

Relief swamped Janet and she understood that she had been through a difficult and exhausting patch, but that now this handsome couple had come to her rescue like pale angels waiting on her path. Already she could see herself in the cab, it would be a Fiat, the driver a local with a charming accent, and in a flash she would be back at the hotel. Frank would fuss about the cab fare, but it was unlikely to be more than the stiff entrance fee to Bromley Hall and she could remind him of that. And look, she had met these agreeable local folks. "I'd appreciate that," Janet said.

Furrowing his brow, the man remarked that the bus service was a disgrace and turned back to the house.

"I'm Nancy," the woman said. "And that's Charles."

"I'm Janet," said Janet.

"We'll have a nice cup of tea while you're waiting for your taxi," Nancy said. The two women went in, side by side, across the drive.

Inside the house was modern and bright, though Nancy explained that it was originally an outbuilding for the farm across the field. The floor was slate, polished to a dull shine, and the original ceiling

80

timbers showed through the plastered ceiling. There was a vestibule with shoe racks and shelves and hooks for shedding wet outerwear and then a large open sitting room, where a stone fireplace occupied most of one wall. Beyond that a half wall created a bar with tall wooden stools drawn up to it, looking into the kitchen. It was to this sunny, cheerful room that Charles preceded the two women. "I'll make the call," he declared without looking back at the women. "What's your hotel?"

"The Moorgate," Janet replied, following him. Now she could see that the entire back wall of the kitchen was a line of tall French doors that opened onto a terrace. The view was westerly, across the oats to the trees she now knew designated the village of Smithfield and beyond that some low hills shrouded in mist among which, she concluded, stood Bromley Hall. The storm clouds were moving rapidly now, dragging a deep shadow across the field, but away from the village and this house. The wind, she observed, was high and must be from the north. "This is lovely," she said as her hostess came up beside her. "What a serene view."

Charles stood at the counter, punching numbers into an old-fashioned wall phone. Nancy and Janet looked out together without speaking while Charles waited for the service to pick up. "I'll make us some tea," Nancy said.

"Right," said Charles. "It's Charles Blake here. Yes. Very well, thank you. I've a guest who needs to get back to Moorgate Hotel. You know it? Yes. Will you come round and collect her then?" There was a pause. "Right," he concluded. "Fifteen minutes. Very good."

He replaced the phone in the receiver. "Fifteen minutes," he said.

"I'm so fortunate you happened to come outside," Janet said to Nancy. "I wouldn't have had the nerve to knock on your door."

"That *was* lucky," Nancy agreed. She was setting cups on the bar counter, napkins, then a plate of dark tea bread. Charles opened the refrigerator and took out a crock of butter. "You're American," he observed. "Where are you from there?"

"We live in New Jersey." Janet approached the bar. The morning papers were spread out on a pretty table near the French doors, with two wicker chairs drawn up on either side. But where had they served the guests she'd seen leaving? There must be a dining room, but they preferred, rightly, to serve an uninvited guest in this cozier space. "It's a small town," she added. "It's called Sleepy Hollow, oddly enough." As she spoke, Charles, having set the butter on the counter, opened a cupboard below the phone and took out something she couldn't see, as his back blocked her view. The electric kettle commenced a rising whistle and Nancy stepped away to silence it. "There we are," she said.

Charles was fiddling with whatever he'd taken from the cupboard; there was the sound of paper tearing. Then, abruptly, he turned upon Janet, she was very near, and she saw that he was holding something shiny between his thumb and forefinger. In a motion so quick, so practiced, she had not a moment to react, he caught her chin with his free hand and dragged her lower lip down with his thumb, bringing the object—it was a thin, flexible needle—to her mouth and lightly pricking the moist, exposed flesh of her gums. Before she could protest, he released her, turning back to the cupboard. Janet covered her mouth with her hand, casting a frantic look at Nancy, who had watched this swift and strange attack from her post at the kettle. She was smiling indulgently at her husband, as a mother might smile at a precocious child.

"What did you just do?" Janet's voice, soft, faintly incredulous, surprised her as it entirely disguised the hard grip of panic that had seized her heart and sent it racing down dark, previously unimagined byways.

Nancy's gaze shifted to her, the smile still in place. "It's nothing," she said. "Just a sample. Charles took it for his database."

"A sample?" Janet repeated. She passed her index finger inside her lip, feeling for the puncture left by the needle, and it was there, a tiny indentation radiating heat.

Charles snapped the cupboard shut, repeating his wife's dismissal. "It's nothing," he said. As he turned to Janet she took a few wary steps backward. "It's a DNA sample," he said. "I'm a clinician at the polytechnic hospital in the city. We're creating a database. We don't get many Americans."

"Tea's ready," said Nancy, cradling the ceramic pot shrouded in a flowered cozy between her hands. She carried it to the counter, where Charles busied himself pulling out stools.

"Why wouldn't you just ask me?" Janet protested. "If that's what you wanted."

"Oh," said Charles, "people are so touchy about such things."

Nancy nodded, taking up a slender knife to slice the tea cake. "And that's rather silly, isn't it, considering that we leave our DNA all over everything all the time? Do come have your tea. This cake is rather good. It's a family recipe."

Janet didn't move. Her brain was in such turmoil it took all her energy to follow it. One strain was about the DNA question. Nancy was right; it was in saliva and hair. Her neighbor had spit into a plastic cup and sent it off to a lab to find out what her ethnic heritage was. You didn't need to prick someone to take a DNA sample. Another part of her brain considered making a dash for the door and running out into the road. If she ran toward Smithfield she'd meet the taxi coming to get her. But had Charles actually called a taxi? He could easily have depressed the call button and pretended to be talking to someone on the other end. And if she ran for the door, could she get out before Charles, who was tall, strong, very quick, stopped her, and then what? Would they struggle? But why would he stop her?

Charles and Nancy watched her candidly, their expressions complicit and faintly amused. Nancy's hand hovered above the teapot, prepared to pour out. Be calm, Janet advised herself. Take a breath. Her mouth had gone mysteriously dry and she was conscious of tightness around her eyes. "It wasn't a sample," she said.

Nancy's hand found the teapot handle and she raised it carefully, pouring a stream of dark tea into a cup. "What makes you think so?" she asked pleasantly.

"It was a drug," Janet said.

Charles, who had never actually taken a seat on the stool he'd drawn out, moved calmly past Janet, careful, she thought, to keep a distance. "There's no need to panic," he said. He went to the door, turned a key in a dead bolt she hadn't noticed there, and slipped the key into his pants pocket. "How are you feeling?" he asked solicitously, facing her, blocking the locked door with his body.

She was feeling distinctly odd. The flesh of her face was hot, tight, dry, but her hands were cold. Her heart had picked up speed, that was natural, that was fear, but there was a hollow aching in her chest she didn't recognize and a lassitude sweeping up her legs, her arms, as if the sinews that strung her together were dissolving. She attempted a step toward the door, the locked door, but her shoe only slid an inch or so across the stone floor.

"She needs to sit down," Nancy observed.

Charles approached, one hand open, extended. What was in his other hand? "Don't touch me," Janet said.

"Let me help you," he said. He grasped her arm gently, just above her elbow, and steered her toward the kitchen. Her steps were halting; she was helpless to resist. Nancy left the bar stool and busied herself at the table, pulling out a wicker chair, plumping the cushion, gathering up the newspapers and stashing them in a bin. "You can

83

have your tea here," she said cheerfully. "You'll be more comfortable and you'll have the view."

Charles eased Janet down into the chair; indeed it was a relief to be off her feet. But what was this absurd pretense, this performance they were putting on for her benefit? Her head cleared and she could speak, she could understand. "What have you done to me?" she asked.

"You'll feel very hot, at first," Charles said. "Then, later, very cold."

Nancy, ferrying a full cup of tea to the table, spoke in a voice as airy and false as a flight attendant in a pitching plane. "You may experience a bit of nausea. The sensation that your skin is crawling. That passes."

"How long before I can go?" Janet said.

At this question the couple standing on either side of her chair exchanged a look of blank surprise. Then Charles smiled broadly, showing all his teeth. "About eight hours?" he said. He'd posed the answer as a question, but directed at whom? Nancy evidently agreed, as she said nothing, gazing complacently at her husband, her eyes bright and avid. They were so amused.

A great despondency settled over Janet; she felt the weight of it bearing down on her neck and shoulders. All she could think of was Frank, and then she could see him, relaxed in the chintz chair in the sunny hotel room, a half-drunk cup of coffee cooling on the side table, turning a page of his novel—it was a new Benjamin Black, he'd picked it up at a bookshop in the airport—while the breeze rustled the curtain and the birds chirped in the garden and the soft plash of water in the fountain murmured, *"Sleep, sleep."* "Frank?" Janet said.

"Yes?" Nancy replied.

Janet pulled herself up as best she could. *These leaden hands,* she thought. "I want to call my husband," she said. "To tell him I'll be late. He's at the hotel. I don't want him to worry." She gathered her strength and struggled to push back the chair. Charles and Nancy made no move to stop her. "I'll just tell him Bromley Hall was further than I thought," she assured them. She was on her feet, unsteady, yes, but focused and determined; she must speak to Frank, they must allow her that. They had nothing to fear from her call. She couldn't tell Frank where she was because she didn't know herself. It was only a few steps to the counter. Did she know the hotel number? Yes, she did, she had memorized it because it was so simple: the city exchange plus the word MOOR. Nancy stepped back as Janet staggered away from the chair. Just a few steps to go. Charles went to the big windows and began drawing a heavy curtain, closing in the dark. But Janet was there, she had reached the counter. She fumbled the phone from the wall set, turned it over in her hand, looking back at Nancy and Charles. Nancy was switching on a lamp near the table. Charles stood at a corner cupboard rummaging through a drawer. They appeared indifferent to her. Painstakingly she punched the numbers into the keypad of the phone. She would get the automatic service, then just put in the room number, seventeen, and Frank would be on the line.

They had quarreled, she thought, as she brought the receiver to her ear. How stupid. What had it been about? He was annoyed by the room change and then had the good sense to stay in the new room while she, in her eagerness to visit Bromley Hall, had closed the door with unnecessary force and hurried down the stairs to catch the bus.

The phone was dead. "Frank?" she said into the receiver. And then, hopelessly, "Frank." She dropped the phone carelessly upon the counter. They had quarreled, she thought.

Sadness welled up in her from its deepest reservoirs, displacing all hope and terror. How long would it be before Frank entered the grueling project that might never end? How long before he put down his mystery novel, got up from the chair, and commenced the methodical, doomed search for his wife?

Tinkerers
Lavie Tidhar

A WHITE FLOWER BLOOMED outside the hospital-room window. The man looked at the sleeping boy and then looked away and he walked out from the sound of machines and into the hush of corridors where slippered feet whispered against smooth floor, and he kept walking until glass doors swooshed open and he stepped outside, into an air polluted by cars. He stood with his hands on his knees, taking deep breaths. When he turned, an old woman was there, wearing a gown, trying to light a cigarette with shaking fingers. She kept muttering all this while, and her bright button eyes glared at the man as her gums masticated, and she told him of great rivers that ran clear and pure, and of wide and wild prairies and of an ancient, never-ending war, and at last of a flower, a rare and precious flower that blooms only beyond the Mountains of the Moon.

He knew her then for what she truly was, but soon she subsided into inarticulate mumblings and at last she staggered away, and then the man too was gone from that other terrible place.

A gaggle of loons called out in tremolo as the Stranger passed their watering hole. He stopped and listened to the eerie calls. Their tremolo was warning, and as he listened he heard the males yodel territorially. Something had spooked the birds.

When he came to the water's edge he saw a pale figure floating facedown in the shallows. Tufts of black hair jutted from either side of the bald pate of the head, and a hole had been blasted with a shotgun in his back. The Stranger turned him over carefully and saw the big red nose and the smiling face of the dead clown and he felt a cold fury. It was a whiteface clown, and whoever had shot him had begun to scalp him, no doubt for bounty money, before being interrupted or scared away.

The sky was darkening and, on the horizon, the Stranger saw that a storm was approaching from the west. Ankhs and daggers flashed briefly, and were replaced with a shower of ichthys sparks that lit up that part of the sky. It was moving fast. The Stranger looked at the ground and saw drops of red blood lead away from the watering hole and he followed them, leaving the loons to their mournful calls.

The Stranger had been riding for a long time and was destined to ride for a long time more, and he had learned patience. He had been riding through the Doinklands for some time but he had not come any closer to his goal. He followed the trail of blood to an outcrop in the rocks on top of a low-lying hill over the little watering hole, and there he found the man who had shot the clown.

The bounty hunter had been a veteran of the Titanomachy. This much was clear from his gimp leg, which had been turned, at some point in the past, into a long and rather graceful string instrument, and from his abdomen, where his gut had become a beautiful if plain clear-glass repository, which had until recently contained several live scorpions.

The glass had been broken rather savagely, and the scorpions had escaped their entrapment and were currently nestled into the crook of the man's neck and two rested over his eyes, but whether it was his injury, or the scorpions themselves, which killed him, the Stranger didn't know, though he took a step back all the same. His feet hit a bottle. When he picked it up, he saw that it was Sticks—the common rotgut that came from mixing substance in water, and that allowed one to revisit that other place. He stared at it for a moment longer, then tossed it away and heard it shatter.

Beyond the little shelter of stones the wind picked up, and overhead the flashes of mandalas and five-pointed stars grew in intensity as the symbol storm approached. In their watering hole, the loons wailed and hooted to each other as they sought shelter from the storm. The Stranger grabbed the bounty hunter's feet and dragged him out of the ring of stones and dumped him unceremoniously down the slope and then he took shelter himself. He hated any and all unkindness to clowns.

In the wake of the storm came a battle, but it was far to the west and unlike the storm did not come closer. All through the night the Stranger lay huddled within the little outcrop of rocks on that nameless hill, listening to the battlefield. Inhuman, high-pitched laughter echoed like thunder across the clouded skies, and interwoven into it like volley fire in riposte were awful bursts of silence as the two sides battled, back and forth, back and forth, Colossi and pupae. He heard the tread of giant stone feet on the ground. He had not realized that the Titanomachy had ranged this far into the clown lands, nor that the Colossi were once more abroad.

Only once was he afraid: when, momentarily, a vast shadow flew overhead, blotting out all sound and light, and the Stranger felt the dread of the chthonic void in his guts. But whether it truly was one of the pupae umbrarum, loose upon the world, or merely a passing cloud, he didn't know for certain, and it was very soon gone.

Bright sunlight bathed the Escapement when the Stranger woke from his fitful sleep. Little caiques chittered excitedly to each other in the trees and the loons hooted in soft, short calls in the watering hole under the hill. The storm was gone and the battle had passed far away to the west. When the Stranger walked down the hill his horse came trotting up to him and in his wake there came three other horses, all riderless. The Stranger stroked his horse's neck and the horse gave him a whinny of greeting.

"Where did you find them?" the Stranger said, but the horse just snorted. The Stranger patted him again and then mounted his horse. As he rode away from the Doinklands the horses followed. Only once did he see a piece of matériel, and it must have been blown over from the battlefield by the storm. It was a swan's long, elongated skull, one hollow eye cavity packed with earth in which grew a solitary worm rose, and it trailed behind it its long and curving neck, like a hangman's rope, in which the multiplicity of vertebrae had been transformed into black metal links. The Stranger did not approach or pick up the piece of matériel, and the horses shied away from it in terrified revulsion. The Stranger spurred his horse on and soon they were away from the Doinklands and into wide-open country.

That was two days earlier, and he never did find out who had killed the bounty hunter, though he was glad the man was dead all the same.

A painter's brush smeared strokes of yellow over the horizon, and the sky gradually turned a light blue. The clouds in the sky resembled clowns' balloons, and the Stranger, on his horse, looked up over the Escapement. The landscape stretched away from him in all directions, with not a town or a hamlet in sight. He was two days' ride away from clown country, and at least another day, he calculated, before he'd reach the small outpost town that was called Kellysburg.

Clumps of heliotrope and fiveneedle pricklyleaf lit up the parched earth with vivid blue and yellow colors. The three horses the Stranger had acquired followed the Stranger and his horse at a sedate pace. Occasionally one would produce a burst of gas and dung, and in that manner they traveled, from one horizon and toward the next, a trail of orderly, still-steaming horse shit in their wake.

The Stranger quite liked the company of the horses. He was used to no one's company but that of his own horse, who was never even given a name. The Stranger did not like naming things, for to do so was to grow attached to them, and to grow attached to things on the Escapement was not an endeavor to be taken lightly. These horses, he reasoned, must have had names once, much as he himself once had. But their owners were dead, and their names were lost, and what private names horses may give themselves the Stranger didn't know.

So they rode, in companionable enough silence, accompanied only by the horses' farts and occasional whinnies, with the horses chomping at the wildflowers or bits of grass whenever they could find them, and the Stranger gnawing, from time to time, on a strip of dried beef. The Escapement here was flat in all directions, the sky serene, and there was no sign of the war.

As the miles passed by, the Stranger rocked in his saddle, lulled by the unchanging landscape. He was brought sharply awake, however, at the sound of a pistol shot. The sound was somewhat muffled, and yet it carried across the open. When the Stranger scanned the horizon he saw, snaking across the plains, what seemed to him the remnants of a white road and, coming in from the west, a plume of slowly rolling dust, which might have been a wagon. The Stranger did not increase his speed, but he directed his horse toward the road, at a point ahead of where the wagon would eventually arrive. The horses followed him obediently enough. They crossed the distance, passing through isolated patches of flowering cacti and fever trees, stopping only for the horses to drink at a shallow pool of muddy groundwater. All this while the small plume of dust continued to roll sedately along the white road, and as it came closer the Stranger could see that it was indeed a wagon, and it was pulled by two dirty, piebald donkeys.

When the Stranger at last came to the road he stopped, and the horses milled around nearby. Such roads could be found, from time to time, in the farther reaches of the Escapement, and who, if anyone, had built them, or for what purpose, the Stranger didn't know.

They led from nowhere to nowhere, seldom in a straight line but rather in a crazy curlicue of a twisting and looping arabesque, like inscribed and secret messages in the landscape. In the Thickening, that part of the Escapement that had been partly subdued, or perhaps suborned, by the relative thickness of human population, there were no ghost roads, and the settlers had constructed new railway lines. And yet even those would often find themselves subject to the external forces of vastation and revel, and often loop upon themselves or terminate abruptly in a place where no terminal was.

The Stranger waited, his hands resting on the butts of his revolvers, and watched the road. The solitary wagon traversed it along its path, never straying, and as it came closer, the Stranger could see that it was a small, wooden wagon, once brightly painted, but the paint had faded and flaked, the wooden wheels creaked, and it was only when it pulled to a halt, at the sight of him, that he saw the legend along the side of the wagon, which read TINKERERS.

Two small figures sat up front in the wagon driver's seat. They were both bundled in rags, as though to defend themselves vigorously against a cold snap, which could, they seemed to silently suggest, strike at any moment. One was male and the other was female, though it was hard to tell them apart. They were both watching the Stranger and neither said anything, nor did they appear to hold weapons, and the Stranger did not draw his own guns.

The male tinkerer at last pulled out a long-stemmed pipe and stuck the bit between his teeth. He next reached for a small cloth bag, from which he extracted tobacco, which he proceeded to stuff into the bowl. Having done that, he struck a match, and a fragrant, cherry-flavored smoke rose into the air and turned it blue.

"How goes it, stranger?" he called. His voice was surprisingly youthful and high, and not unpleasant. "I am, uh, going to assume you are not a highwayman or a horse thief"—his tone suggested that he was far from convinced on that score, but for lack of a better choice, was willing to give the Stranger the benefit of the doubt— "and anyway, as you can see, we are but, uh, poor tinkerers, with nothing worth stealing."

He made a desultory gesture at their wagon.

"I heard gunshot," the Stranger said. "Some distance back."

"Nothing to do with, uh, us, I'm sure," the tinkerer said.

"I can't think where else it could have come from."

The tinkerer shrugged. The woman beside him cupped her hands and whispered into his ear. He nodded. "Ah, yes," he said. "We ran into some problems a while back. That's right. A wild, uh, snake. My, uh, sister had to shoot the creature. A shame, really. We value all life."

The woman measured out a span with her hands.

"A big one," the tinkerer added, unnecessarily.

"A snake."

"It is, uh, so."

"What happened to it?"

The woman whispered again. The man said, "We left it behind. I was, uh, asleep at the time. I sleep heavily, you see."

It was none of the Stranger's business, and he did not press the point.

"Why do you travel on the road?" he asked instead, curiously. "Would it not be quicker to follow a straight route to your destination?"

"Ah," the tinkerer said. "You would, uh, think so, wouldn't you. But the straight route is seldom the quickest, on the Escapement. The roads follow, uh, an *internal* logic, I think. Yes. And, also, there is an old saying, uh, it is the journey that matters, stranger, not the destination."

The Stranger nodded politely. The man puffed on his pipe. In the wagon behind them, something banged sharply, and for a moment the wagon rocked from side to side. The woman ducked under the canvas and disappeared, and the Stranger heard a sharp crack, followed by silence. The woman reemerged and took her seat. She smiled at the Stranger and her teeth were white and even.

"Rats," she said.

"I'm, uh, Fledermaus," the man said. "This is Titania."

"Howdy, stranger," Titania said. "And which way are you traveling, if you don't mind me asking?"

"Kellysburg," the Stranger said. "I have horses to sell."

"You won't get much for them there," she said.

The Stranger shrugged. "I'll take what I can."

"Won't we all," she said, and laughed, a surprisingly coarse sound. "As it happens, we're on our way there ourselves. Not by choice, you understand, but it's the nearest habitation for miles, and bad trade is better than none, in my opinion."

"You're, uh, welcome to travel with us," Fledermaus said. "The road doesn't go to the town but it passes nearby, or, uh, more correctly, it fades as it nears the outpost. Or so it was the last time we traveled this way."

The Stranger considered the two of them. At last he nodded, and the woman, Titania, took the reins and cracked them, and the two piebald donkeys began to pull the wagon without complaining, slow and sedate, as though they had all the time in the world. Fledermaus continued to draw on his pipe, and Titania hummed the same few bars of some wordless tune the Stranger didn't recognize. He spurred his own horse, walking alongside them, and the other horses followed behind—though he noticed they gave the wagon itself a wide berth, and walked some distance from it by the side of the road, on which they seemed reluctant to step at all.

Overhead, the sky's hues deepened by degree, from azure to ultramarine; as the sun traversed the sky, the travelers cast sfumato shadows projected beyond the road, which lengthened as they trailed their originators like furtive ghosts. The road itself changed with the light, growing in turns ivory and snow, ghost white and smoky, until the Stranger found it easier to not look directly at the road at all, but ahead.

"You came from out west?" he said.

"That we did," Titania said.

"I saw signs of a battle there, two days back, on the horizon."

"That is, uh, true," Fledermaus said. "Yes. Yes. We think. We were still some distance away and when we saw the coming storm we sought shelter."

"We reached the place after the battle had moved on," Titania said. "But we are not scavengers, stranger. We didn't dally there."

"You found nothing of value?"

He saw them exchange a glance, though what it meant, if anything, he didn't know.

"What is of value to some is of no value to, uh, others," Fledermaus said.

"We do not trade in substance or matériel."

The sun dipped low in the sky when they caught sight of a dwelling in the distance. As they came closer, they saw it was an abandoned church. The weathered stone was dirty with dust, and the broken windows gaped open like empty eye sockets. Over the steeple only there remained a stylized balloon icon painted a vivid red, and it caught the reflected light of the sun as though it were a miniature sun itself. The travelers, by unspoken consent, halted there, near the old church.

"A strange place for a mission," the Stranger said.

The others did not reply. The woman, Titania, disappeared again under the canvas, and could be heard moving around inside the wagon. The man, Fledermaus, climbed down from the bench and stretched, though it was hard to make him out under his layers of clothing. He looked like a short, fat mushroom.

"It will do, stranger," he said. "It will do."

That night, the travelers built a small fire and sat beside it. The horses grazed in a patch of grass nearby. Earlier, Titania had disappeared into the Escapement, and when she returned there was a bloodied hare held in her hands. The Stranger had heard no gunshots. The woman skinned the creature and her brother set a pot to boil over the fire, the two of them working in wordless unison. From within the wagon they fetched two shriveled onions and several lumpy potatoes, dirt encrusted and hard. They added the vegetables to the pot and Titania flavored the soup with salt and dried herbs, the nature of which the Stranger didn't know. The smell of the soup as it cooked made the Stranger's stomach grumble. It had been weeks since he'd had a hot meal. Fledermaus relit his pipe and sat there content, puffing out clouds of smoke that more often than not resembled ghostly balloon animals. His sister sat warming her hands by the fire, and she hummed the same few bars of that song the Stranger didn't know. Her mostly tuneless humming had a soporific effect on him, so that he found his thoughts kept wandering, trailing off, and returning, and every now and then he'd startle himself awake, and stare around him as though he were seeing the place and his companions for the first time.

No sound came from within the wagon now. If there were indeed rats there, or something else entire, they were silent now, but the horses still did not approach the wagon or come close to it. The swishing of their tails merged with the crackling of the wood in the fire and with the whisper of the soup in the pot and with Titania's humming. The smell of the cooking meat overwhelmed the Stranger's senses.

"It is kind of you," he said, "to share your food."

"You look like you could use it," Fledermaus said, and chortled. "If you don't, uh, mind me saying so, there's less meat on your bones than even on that, uh, hare in the pot."

"You're very resourceful, to have found and trapped such an animal," the Stranger said to Titania. She continued humming, staring into the fire.

"We make do," Fledermaus said. "When we must."

They ate out of wooden bowls, the meat tender and the potatoes soft and full of flavor. The liquid was subtly spiced, and it filled the Stranger's body with warmth. When they had finished eating, the brother and sister both lapsed into silence, staring at the flickering flames. The Stranger found that his own limbs felt loose and heavy, and that a certain light-headedness threatened to overpower him. He excused himself, and rose with some effort from the warmth of the fire.

Standing, he found it hard to balance. All felt peaceful and serene, and in the night sky the constellations shone brightly, moving and changing with a slow majesty. The Stranger felt dwarfed by the stars, which crowded the vast blackness from horizon to distant horizon, and so he sought refuge at last inside the old church.

It was warm and dry there. The air hung undisturbed. Deflated whoopee cushions sat forlorn on the empty pews. The Stranger walked down the aisle. Under the open windows, shards of multicolored glass collected on the floor. The Stranger halted at the altar. It had sustained some damage in earlier time, the wood chipped and bent and the stylized balloon icon violently broken. He walked round the dais and discovered there, hidden in the chancel, a window of stained glass that somehow had remained unbroken, perhaps, he saw, because it didn't look out over anything. The Stranger swayed gently on his feet as he studied the artwork, muted now as no light coursed through it. It was boarded up on the other side, and though the glass was dark the colors had remained vibrant.

The picture portrayed the Harlequin, a creature perhaps male, perhaps female, with a sensuous, almost cruel mouth. It wore a checkered costume made of triangular patches of varying colors, and on its head it wore a three-pointed hat. In its hand it held a bright-red balloon.

The Stranger studied the painting, and the creature bound within the bits of colored glass, or perhaps defined by them, seemed to him to sway and move, as though capering or dancing. The world around him grew fuzzy, then opaque. There was a saccharine taste in his mouth, and he realized what it must have been: the tinkerers had flavored the soup with substance. The Stranger swallowed but his lips and tongue were dry. He touched the glass, from which the harlequin had disappeared, and wiped it, and it was like wiping fog off a glass. Beyond, he now saw, was the other world. It was like looking through a clear glass window onto a hospital parking lot, where a man was standing staring into the night, and the lights of passing cars illuminated his face.

He looked like he'd been crying.

The Stranger violently wiped the glass, and the image, mercifully, faded. He breathed deep and filled his lungs with air and staggered out of the silent church and into the night, where the constellations continued to chase each other across the sky in a sort of fluid dance. The Stranger saw that the fire had burned down to embers, and they glowed faintly in the night. The two tinkerers were ensconced on the ground, covered in their multiple garments. He could not even make out their faces.

Something moved inside the wagon.

The Stranger froze. The sound came again, as though something heavy moved inside and hit the floor. It made metal pots and pans clang within. The two tinkerers hadn't moved from their place by the fire. The Stranger drew his revolver. He edged toward the rear of the wagon.

The broken moon hung in the sky. Under its light the Stranger's shadow lengthened like a blade. The shadow looked furtive there, stealing to the encroaching shadow of the wagon. The Stranger hesitated, his finger on the trigger of his gun. The heavy thump from inside the wagon came again, and the wagon rattled on its wheels. Something fell off the wall and hit the floor with a bang. The Stranger reached for the thick cloth curtain that blocked the inside of the wagon. He parted the curtain and stared inside.

"What do you think you're doing?"

The curtain snapped shut. The woman, Titania, stood in the moonlight, a nasty little sawed-off shotgun in her hands. She was without her heavy coverings, in nothing much more than a slip, and in the moonlight he saw that she was both younger and older than he thought, for she had a young woman's body but an old woman's hands. Her voice, however, and the simple fact of her finger on the trigger of the sawed-off, said she meant business.

"I heard noise," the Stranger said.

"So? And you can put your gun back in the holster. Slowly."

The Stranger did as he was told.

"You put substance in the soup," he said.

"I know," she said. "It flavors the meat. What are you getting at?"

"Nothing," the Stranger said. "This isn't my business."

"You're damn right it's not." She gestured with the sawed-off. The Stranger took a step back from the wagon, and another, and his shadow hastened to match his steps.

He looked at Titania. Her own shadow billowed behind her, a huge undulating mass that swallowed starlight in its wake. The Stranger took another step back and his own shadow hid behind him.

"There was no offense meant," he said.

"Good."

Abruptly, she released her hold on the sawed-off, and with that she was gone. The Stranger took another breath and emptied his lungs slowly. When he returned to the fire he saw that both of the tinkerers were fast asleep, entwined in each other's arms under their heavy coverings. He lay down himself, on his back, and stared at the distant stars. For a moment, as the curtain had twitched in his hand, he got a long, good glimpse into the glum interior of the wagon. He saw the hanging iron pots and pans, old and bent and blackened by countless fires. He saw the bags of nails, the hammered horseshoes, the beaten copper bowls, the kettles and coal irons, the heaps of badges and buckles, and the spurs with their rowels and chap guards.

It was, then, just as described, a tinkerer's traveling emporium, cramped and dark, smelling of rust and the road, filled with the debris of everyday life and its mundane demands. Nothing more, nothing out of the ordinary.

On the floor, in the center of all that cramped space, a vast object lay partially covered in dirty blankets. From time to time it struggled feebly against the bonds that held it down, and its black and gold head would hit the floor with a powerful thump that shook the iron-mongery all about it. It had two glass eyes and a mouth with many jagged teeth. It was about the size of a tuna. Its scales, even in that quick half glimpse of the Stranger's, with the cloth flap only momentarily raised, and but little light coming in, nevertheless shone a bright gold, and its intricate mechanism rattled and whirred as it flopped there on the floor. Behind the glass eyes, a look almost human had stared out at the Stranger in supplication. On the fish's forehead, above the eyes, there was a nasty-looking dent, perhaps from a recent gunshot.

No more sound came now from the wagon. The giant piece of ma-tériel that he had witnessed moved no further within. The Stranger lay on his back and his limbs grew heavy. The embers whispered with dying fire. The stars streaked across the sky, forming sentences in a language he wanted to but couldn't read. He felt himself dropping into sleep.

*

The two impish figures that stood in the moonlight had shed their protective clothes, and in the broken light the Stranger saw them for what they really were, thin and delicate and with wide, clown-like mouths, mischievous eyes, and near-translucent skin under which their skeletons appeared as though composed of fragile fish bones. In the moonlight too, the old abandoned church and the road both seemed to glow a bright ivory white, while the wagon seemed bigger and near palatial.

The Escapement spread outward from them in all directions, and the sky seemed never to end over the lit landscape. The road snaked in loops and curves across the land, and far in the distance, the Stranger felt more than saw, the movement of ghostly yet durable troops, marching. The male who had called himself Fledermaus stood there watching the Stranger with the curve of a smile, and his shadow, like his sister's, grew behind him, immense and cephalopodan. It was as though the shadows were the real bodies, and the tiny human figures were merely the mouthpieces for the darkness beyond.

In her hand, Titania held a small, dandelion-like flower. She blew on it gently and the tiny florets, startled by her breath, detached from their anchorage and took flight, one by one, until they dispersed to all corners and Titania remained holding only the bald stem of the flower.

"Do not seek the Ur-shanabi," she said, in a voice melodious and clear. "For the Plant of Heartbeat brings only heartache when it flowers."

"I need to find it," the Stranger said. "I have to."

"Then find a fucking cartographer," the thing that was Fledermaus said.

The shadows behind them coalesced, and bellowed in an invisible gale . . . somewhere, there was the sound of wind chimes.

When the Stranger woke, he found himself alone by the side of the old white road. The sound of the horses raised him from his stupor, their neighing and farting and the sound of cloven hooves stamping on earth, of tails swishing, of grass being ripped from the ground and chewed. The fire in its circle of stones was dead, and had been so for some time. He stood up groggily. The day was overcast and the sun was wreathed in mist. Of the tinkerers and their wagon there remained no sign. The Stranger relieved himself and washed sparingly. When he went inside the old clown church he saw that only his boot prints were in the thick layer of dust on the floor. And when he reached the place behind the dais he saw that the stained-glass window with the harlequin's visage had been violently broken and the pieces scattered on the floor.

Tucked on the wood board, behind where the window had been, was a small and naked dandelion.

The Stranger rode out that day along the twisting road, the horses following patiently behind him. By midafternoon the road began to grow faint at the edges, and soon it had faded away entirely, and when he looked back he could not see a sign that it had ever been there. He rode on and soon he saw the small outpost town of Kellysburg in the distance, its dismal single-story buildings with their chimneys churning black smoke into the air, and farther away like a series of hash signs was the railway line.

The Stranger spurred on his horse and rode into town.

An Interview with Samuel R. Delany

Conducted by Brian Evenson

BORN ON APRIL FOOL'S DAY 1942, Samuel R. Delany is the author of nearly two dozen novels, a number of highly acclaimed stories, and more than half a dozen collections of critical essays. He is best known as a writer and critic of science fiction, though he has written masterfully in a number of genres—science fiction, science fantasy, fantasy, literary fiction, experimental fiction, pornography. He has been a finalist seven times for a Hugo Award, four times for a Nebula Award, and twice for the Locus Award. He won the Hugo Award for his story "Time Considered as a Helix of Semi-Precious Stones," which also won the Nebula Award. His story "Aye, and Gomorrah" also received a Nebula Award. His novel *Dark Reflections* was a Stonewall Book Award winner in 2008. Another Hugo Award winner (for non-fiction), his autobiography, *The Motion of Light in Water* (1988, revised 2004), is a book that suggests a very different kind of person—racially, sexually, socially—from the usual conception of what, until then, a science fiction writer was thought to be. In 2013, he was named the thirty-first Grand Master of the Science Fiction Writers of America.

I came to Delany's work through his transgressive and often difficult later fiction, books such as *The Mad Man* and *Hogg*, only later circling back to his science fiction. When I did, I found much to admire in the early books, with certain themes and ideas echoing from his earliest books to his most recent, *Through the Valley of the Nest of Spiders* (2012). Throughout his career, Delany has pursued his own path, and the political ramifications and candid sexuality of his science fiction had a big impact on the field as a whole and on the writers who followed him. "Aye, and Gomorrah," which first appeared in Harlan Ellison's *Dangerous Visions* anthology, was a source of controversy due to its frank and disturbing sexual content (depicting a culture of neutered, androgynous astronauts and a sexual subculture that fetishizes them). His novel *Stars in My Pocket like Grains of Sand* (1984) depicts a society with cross-species sex and hook-up zones, and can be read (as some critics have) as mirroring pre-AIDS gay culture in New York.

Samuel R. Delany

Delany's notion of a "General Information" service in two novels (*Trouble on Triton* and *Stars in My Pocket like Grains of Sand*), as Carl Freedman has suggested, "anticipates the World Wide Web with a remarkable prescience comparable to Jules Verne's in anticipating the submarine or Arthur C. Clarke's in anticipating the communications satellite." To my mind, *Trouble on Triton* anticipates the web as it has been, demanding a computer interface, while *Stars in My Pocket like Grains of Sand* suggests where we seem to be heading, with the Internet wired directly into the brain.

There's a great deal I could say about Delany's individual novels and stories, the variety and originality of which is as impressive as those of any genre writer I know, but for considerations of space I'll remain silent. But I'd be remiss not to at least mention *Dhalgren* (1975), which most see as Delany's greatest achievement in the field. It has sold more than a million copies and is Delany's most popular book, though also one of his most controversial (it was disliked by both Philip K. Dick and Harlan Ellison). Ambitious and linguistically complex, *Dhalgren* is the kind of thing that might have been written by James Joyce if he had been a science fiction writer.[1] Set in a ruined city, depicting sexuality of all kinds, often graphically, it has been praised by writers such as Theodore Sturgeon, Elizabeth Hand, and Umberto Eco. It is an expansive, embattled book, one that uses stream of consciousness and other modernist techniques to productively shatter the consciousness of the reader. It is an example of science fiction at its most hallucinatory and most narratively inventive.

Delany is also a serious and significant critic of science fiction, with much of his writing on science fiction gathered in two volumes: *The Jewel-Hinged Jaw* and *Starboard Wine*. In these books he thinks through what it is about science fiction that makes the genre unique, considering the way in which it handles language. He discusses more radical science fiction writers such as Thomas Disch and Joanna Russ, explores more seemingly traditional writers such as Theodore Sturgeon and Robert Heinlein and Roger Zelazny, thinks about sexuality and self in relation to the genre, and (in the later editions of the books in particular) offers the historical context in which he was writing the individual essays gathered here. His book *The American Shore*, first published in 1978, is a critical and largely structuralist

---

[1] "Time Considered as a Helix of Semi-Precious Stones" makes overt reference to Joyce's *Finnegans Wake*.

study of Thomas Disch's short story "Angouleme," and still the most thorough and illuminating reading of a science fiction short story (and perhaps any sort of story) that I know.

After publishing *Stars in My Pocket like Grains of Sand* in 1984, Delany mostly moved away from publishing science fiction,[2] instead publishing literary and transgressive fiction until 2012's *Through the Valley of the Nest of Spiders*, which feels at first like a contemporary novel. In it, Delany blends a literary style with transgressive moments to project forty years into the future. The near-future science-fictional elements here have a different feel and tone than that of his generally far-future early work—they're mentioned offhand, in bits and pieces. The story of two young gay men who meet in 2007, who come to live in a gay utopian community, and who stay together and in love for the rest of their lives, *Through the Valley of the Nest of Spiders* is probably Delany's most total integration of the science fictional, literary, and pornographic elements of his work, and can be read as a meeting place for the various political and generic elements that inform his work as a whole. In other words, when Delany did finally return to writing science fiction in the twenty-first century, he did so in an entirely different way than how he began. Indeed, where most authors would be inclined to rest on their laurels, Delany even into his seventies has continued to take risks and chances, to continue to strike into new territory.

BRIAN EVENSON: Maybe we can start with terms. In *The Jewel-Hinged Jaw* you talk about the terms "s-f," "science fiction," and "speculative fiction" as having connections but dissonances as well. Do you think of your work as being in one of those categories more than another (or perhaps another category)? Does it depend on the work and/or the place in your career? It does strike me that a term like "speculative fiction" might be seen as accounting for all of your work, overtly science fictional or not.

SAMUEL R. DELANY: All texts carry an implicit genre mark; that's because they can be described, quoted, other texts can be conceived as like them or as different from them. This is what allows them to be categorized. At first, the system of categories may rival the complexities of the texts themselves. But that defeats the purpose of categories,

---

[2]The exception is his 1993 novel, *They Fly at Çiron*, though this is an expanded version of an earlier piece written in 1971, and is closer to science fantasy than science fiction.

so that the category system over time tends to simplify and generalize. But in different locales, in different circumstances, different category systems develop different forms. Science fiction has been developing its category system—its genre system and its subgenres—since before the term "science fiction" struggled into existence, first in 1851 (when it was promptly forgotten) and then again in the readers' letters columns of Hugo Gernsback's magazines *Amazing* and *Fantastic* at the end of the 1920s, as the readers attempted to simplify Gernsback's own clumsy term "scientifiction" as a speakable term. The readers are the ones who replaced "scientifiction" with "science fiction" with the agreement that it meant the same thing.

"Speculative fiction" hit in 1947, when Robert Heinlein used it in an essay because he felt it better described what he was doing than any of the attempts he'd encountered to say what "science fiction" itself meant.

And no one paid any real attention to it for a dozen years.

When I began to write science fiction and was fortunate enough to publish, the genre had a very serviceable genre-classification system in place—that didn't include "speculative fiction," but did include the term "science fantasy"—as well as "near future" SF and "far future SF." "Science fantasy" is what I thought my first four published books (*The Jewels of Aptor* and the subsequent trilogy, *The Fall of the Towers*) were. My fifth—*The Ballad of Beta-2*—was science fiction, at least as far as I knew.

Now "speculative fiction" must have had a history between 1947 when Heinlein first used it and when, in England in the middle sixties, some writers who had gathered around Michael Moorcock's English magazine *New Worlds* began to use it and, at the same time, came to prominence both because of Moorcock's program and an arts council grant to the magazine. They drew a certain amount of attention, and to the term they were using. But I have never been able to find out much of that history as it relates to the originator of the term, Heinlein—back at the end of the forties.

"Speculative fiction" was never a term I was very comfortable with and I only used it for four years—between 1968 and 1972. During that time it had a clear meaning, which was not the same meaning Heinlein had given it. It meant science fiction, fantasy, and any experimental fiction that used SF or technological imagery. Soon it entered the conversation of American academics by the trajectory through which so many neologisms enter the critical discourse: where a vague term that slides around all over the place displaces relatively clear and unambiguous terms. It's a process similar to the one through which bad money drives out good. This means that, however radical you may decide I am as a person or as a writer, as a critic and user of critical terminology I am pretty conservative.

I never heard it till after I visited London on my way back from my first trip to Europe in 1966, and returned again over Christmas and New Year's for three weeks in '66–'67. I tried it out for a while (those same four years), but I didn't feel it was necessary for what I was doing. I still don't. It's not a term I really needed to think with. And though I have a sense of what other people probably mean—and when I describe it sometimes I can be a little snide—I don't use it.

You say, rightly, that "speculative fiction" could apply to all my work. Frankly, that's what's wrong with it—the term, I mean. It doesn't make enough distinctions. Up until 1968—and well after Heinlein's fairly careful attempt to describe what he wanted to do (he very specifically excluded fantasy from it)—"speculative fiction" grew to mean the collection of all science fiction, all fantasy, as well as all experimental literature that used technological or scientific imagery. Speculative fiction meant two categories of science fiction and one of literature [that] could be rhetorically identified but were discursively very different—one was literary (a subset of experimental fiction) and two were paraliterary (commercial fantasy and commercial science fiction).

Four years later, by 1972, when those in the academy had taken it over, the critical conversations around commercial SF in this country dropped that already scattered definition (in the sense of what a dictionary of critical terms might say it meant) so that along the path of least resistance, basically the term had come to mean: whatever SF the speaker happened to approve of just then (near future, far future, social, psychological), and more or less informally excludes the rest. I didn't think that was useful and I still don't. When Sheree Thomas put together her two anthologies of black speculative fiction, *Dark Matter* and *Reading the Bones*, she went back to the pre-'68 definition of the term. Terms can be defined. I didn't approve of it. But if you read her introductions, you at least know what she's talking about.

EVENSON: Writing about Joanna Russ in *The Jewel-Hinged Jaw*, you suggest that in Russ's science fiction "the privileges (i.e., the easy sureties) of one mode of discourse are subverted by employing signs from another mode—which causes us to reconstruct the discourse from one mode to the other. . . ." You go on to describe the shifts that causes in the reading experience, how you move from one mode to another and back again, your sense of what it is you're reading going through quite interesting sea changes.

Reading that, I couldn't help but think of your own work. I've always thought of you as a writer who is incredibly capable of crossing genre lines within a work. Reading your work I often think, "Here is someone who is well and widely read, voraciously so, and who has thought a lot about literary form and mode and structure, and is willing to use whatever tools he needs." Just having reread your first novel, *The Jewels of Aptor* (1962), I feel that's something that's been with you from the very beginning. Along with the science fictional elements, there are hints of heroic fantasy, classical literature, supernatural and fairy tales, adventure tales, and other things. I know that novel is quite a ways in your past, but were you actively manipulating those elements at that stage or was it more intuitive? Were you responding to what you felt writers around you were doing, or did it feel like you were entering new territory?

DELANY: Thank you, Brian. If you are a generically sensitive reader, that's what happens when you read Russ's text. If you're not, something else happens. Whatever it is, it is. But I find it very pleasurable, when that happens to me.

I try to respond to what's happening around me. (Look at my Facebook posts.) And every once in a while one seems to get through the Facebook set of algorithms and touch a nerve—such as I think at least one of the last couple have done. (Every once in a while, someone—like my friend Vince Czyz—will make a comment that resonates with me: not only does no one have a piano anymore, everyone has so much stuff they have to rent a storage unit, often one that's never emptied, because no one is really moving into larger quarters. (I thought I was when I came down to Pennsylvania last September. But it turns out I wasn't.) Even I have one, as Vince points out, and he has even helped me carry boxes to it, in what was for him a kind of surprise set of circumstances on his first in-the-flesh visit. As he points out, twenty years ago, no one had one. Today, almost everyone has one. And there are articles—like the one on the destruction of pianos—on how many new storage facilities are being built.) As well, like Charlotte Brontë, in *Jane Eyre*, I tend to respond to my surroundings in an oppositional mode.

At the time, I hadn't figured out that having only single members of an oppressed group in a novel is by definition oppressive because it veers toward presenting such figures in isolation. But I was certainly thinking in oppositional terms. Marilyn Hacker's own description of the typical SF novel she was editing was that the female character was either a wimp whose only function was to cower in the corner and be rescued by the correspondingly over-male hero, or, if she was a woman with any kind of agency at all, she was an evil femme fatale who did nothing but betray and sabotage the hero until, at the last moment, she was exposed for all to understand the evil force she was or for which she was an agent, at which point she was either destroyed or robbed of all power for the rest of her natural life and/or hopelessly humiliated. And the reader and all the other good guys make snide comments about her frigidity and how much she needs a good fuck (to turn her into a proper wimp) and are supposed to be supremely pleased with themselves and with the world.

EVENSON: The other thing I realized in rereading *The Jewels of Aptor* was that much of what I like so much about your more mature work was already there, at least to some degree. Among other things, there's a focus on friendship and community, a questioning of authority, no simple division into good and evil, a lot of gray area. There's also a clear sense of politics, the refusal to let one person dominate as the hero (very nicely depicted in the way the jewels are passed from character to character), and an image of a community that is inclusive and welcoming. Do you see those connections? And, on the other hand, what do you feel separates *Jewels* from your more mature work?

DELANY: The form of an interview such as this lures the interviewee into arrogance and bragging. And that's a bore.

I am much more aware of the continuity of the personal disruptions that plague the point of view that is my absentminded perception of the world around me than the disruptions that fall between the works. That's my way of saying that the world is more coherent than I am, right through here. That's what regularly reminds me of my mortality.

You say *The Jewels of Aptor* is a book about friendship—and male friendship, as well—and it is. But simply from the roughest synopsis you can see the kinds of things it opposes as a commercial genre novel of the early sixties—starting with the fact that the hero is a poet hired on as a common worker rather than as the best/strongest/most heroic . . . (you fill it in), who establishes his alpha status in the first three chapters by besting one of the secondary bad guys in a physical fight.

By the end of the story, the friendship, without having been invalidated, no longer exists: the main character has lost his friend and his arm—they have not ridden off into the sunset together, like Tonto and the Lone Ranger, or Natty Bumppo and Chingachgook. At the time that was also fairly unusual. And there are two female characters who, while not much in light of the women's movement that was to bloom from 1968 on, were nevertheless conceived in opposition to the stereotypes outlined above. Clumsy, immature, with as many awkwardnesses as there are pages, and with almost as many typographical errors—one even survives from an earlier printing into the current reprint that you read: on page 22, paragraph 11, lines 2–3: "metal breasts" should be "metal beasts"—*The Jewels of Aptor* was still the first published novel of a very young genre writer, an original paperback, which, in its year-end royalty report, the following winter, had distributed, before returns, more than ninety-two thousand copies—and garnered a generous review from P. Schuyler Miller in John W. Campbell's *Analog* magazine. This was enough to earn out the advance against royalties.

In the terms you ask the question, *The Jewel-Hinged Jaw* (specifically the revised edition currently in print) collects essays written between 1968 and 1976. And it contains a letter that should have been dated 1974, from London, written in the months after my daughter was born (she is now forty-two) and I was re-writing *Trouble on Triton*, and, just before her birth, my novel *Dhalgren* had been sold to Frederik Pohl of Bantam Books. The current revised edition of *Jaw* ends with a hefty (forty pages) appendix ("Midcentury") written in 2003, in an attempt to do some contextualizing of the 1950s in the United States, a decade [that] all of the essays contained in the book should be understood as some sort of reaction to.

EVENSON: Speaking of *The Jewel-Hinged Jaw*, I've read both the 1977 version and the 2009 revision. It's interesting to me how it's changed, and interesting as well the way in which the later version has numbered chapters, so it seems more like a deliberate progression. In revising it, do you find it's a question of imagining your way back to your younger self? Or of extracting the book from one time and context and giving it a new life in another? Or? There's a great energy in the earlier version (with the inclusion of "Shadows," among other things), but it is much more diffuse. Whereas the later version strikes me as more shaped and integrated.

I'm particularly curious about the movement of "Letter to a Critic" to the appendix. In the first version, it opens the book and seems almost a battle cry. In the revised edition, it's the very last thing we read. Is that because you feel that many of the issues it raises are no longer as crucial? Needed to be understood as a historical moment rather than your current aesthetic?

DELANY: It's more than a matter of "not crucial." It was a call to arms in 1977, followed by a scattershot overview of what was going on in the world of the personal, the political, and the critical in this country, at least as I was aware of it at the time, and what was providing inroads to change. (That's what "Shadows" was for me.) Without the historical context, those issues as talked about in "Letter to a Critic"—based on a real letter to critic Leslie Fiedler, which, along with several others, got me my first real academic job as a visiting professor at SUNY Buffalo, in 1975—don't make sense.

Between the time that the essay was first written, before I even went to London, and the time it was published, the US copyright laws (in 1976) were completely revised. If you didn't live through the change—and live through it as a rational adult in the United States on both sides of it (or spend three months studying the difference in those laws, before and after) you can't even know what the piece is talking about. Literary life in a city with seventy-nine major publishing companies (all multimillion-dollar businesses), with a handful of paperback houses and a few big hardcover houses doing all the original SF is so completely different from literary life in a city with five publishing conglomerates, as New York had by, say, 1986, there are no socioeconomic correspondences that allow you to make the imaginative leap from one to the other. The social context between 1977 and 2009 has changed so radically that most people today, unless they are specialists in the history of American publishing and writing, assuming they are under fifty, which is where most readers still tend to cluster, simply can't bridge it.

Edmund White's collection of essays *Arts and Letters* (2004) opens with an early essay that was among the most radical pieces of nonfiction written on the situation of the gay man in America in the middle sixties. When I gave it to my gay graduate students in 2008, to them it seemed politically troglodytic. That's because they couldn't conceive of a world where, if, in a department meeting in 1965 you had suggested that you teach a class in gay studies, not only would

107

it not have been accepted, but whether you were gay or straight, probably you would have been assumed to be dangerously psychotic and you might be seriously assumed to have been insane—as if you had proposed a class in sexual carryings-on of schizophrenic black women over the age of sixty-two who had been confined to mental hospitals for more than twelve years. (In 1965, both male homosexuality and lesbianism, despite the Kinsey Reports *Sexual Behavior in the Human Male* and *Sexual Behavior in the Human Female*, were still considered diseases and would continue to be for more than another decade.) The response would have been, rather, what sort of person would propose such a tasteless and absurd notion, not whether anyone thought it a good or a bad idea.

That was hard for people under thirty at that time to wrap their heads around.

The universities of most of the 1960s were universities without black studies, without gay studies, without women's studies, film studies, or SF studies of any sort. By the eighties all of those were at least nascent, however—though we still could not pass an equal rights amendment or sustain the repeal of the death penalty, even though that last was for several decades legally set in place.

I've been in four countries in which coins have become practically worthless—Greece and Turkey in the 1960s, England, and now the United States. Only yesterday, I heard that several banks have discontinued counting coins for their customers to change for paper.

I mention this because when, on September 12, I first moved to Pennsylvania, I came with six cartons of metal money, collected from pockets over full with pennies, nickels, dimes, and quarters that I'd hoped to cash in. They are still under a table in the dining room of the house where I had been living, and I expect those will end up in a landfill even faster than many of my books, which somehow I am hoping to preserve intact for awhile. And there's still half a carton of coins in my current Philly apartment. Thinking seriously about what that might mean is what's truly exhausting about analyzing our society.

EVENSON: I want to return to the question of "science fantasy" since, as you rightly point out, several of your works might best be called that. That mode was my entry into the field, through people like Michael Moorcock, M. John Harrison, Gene Wolfe, and Terry Brooks, among others. There's something like a palpable shock when reading, say, Moorcock, you suddenly realize that what you've thought of as a fantasy realm may in fact be a sort of far future. That term, science fantasy, seems to me to have fallen out of critical currency, though it's a very useful one, I think. I wonder if as the term falls away or begins to be used primarily historically, writers will stop seeing it as a viable aesthetic possibility.

In any case, in your criticism you make a distinction between mundane fiction, fantasy, and SF, in terms of their relation to the event. The first concerns events that could have happened; the second, events that could not have happened; the last, events that have not happened. How does science fantasy negotiate this relation to the event? By alternation? Does it have a double-voiced relation to the event? And does it qualify as a sort of SF or as a kind of straddling genre or is it simply specific to individual work?

DELANY: Science fantasy means simply that there are elements of both in the social background of the story, if not in the foreground, and not necessarily clearly distinguished. (Arthur C. Clarke once said, with great insight, that any truly unknown technology will be indistinguishable from magic to the people who don't know it already.) It was the failure of that kind of rhetorical description of genres—events that haven't happened, events that couldn't happen—that led me to the much more detailed examination of the rhetorical surface of the text that I undertook in my book-length essay on Tom Disch's short story "Angouleme" in *The American Shore*, which concerns itself far more with rhetorical similarities between texts—the overwhelming similarities between good SF and good literature—as well as the specifically discursive differences signaled by particular rhetorical figures (e.g., the various catalogs, of objects or of names, the slug, the various voices of the text, e.g., the Voice of History, the Voice of Science Fiction . . . phrases that might be literal in one genre and the same words metaphors—or even dead metaphors—in another) that work differently in one or another genre, SF or literature.

EVENSON: In the revised edition of *Starboard Wine* you suggest that the best SF "conscientiously misrepresents the world." I love that phrase. Can you speak about the importance of writing as misrepresentation? How does one ensure that that misrepresentation is conscientious? Are there writers working today who you feel are particularly good at this?

DELANY: The fact is, I haven't been reading much science fiction—or, to be completely honest, too much of anything. The things I've been writing about in my Facebook posts are a far better index to what I've been thinking about. I oscillate between the cultural significance of objects in my world and what's going on around me. I hope that's why people like them—because they reflect the things that actually concern me.

I know this is supposed to be an interview about science fiction, but—as is so often the case—my mind doesn't necessarily follow the paths that are expected of it.

EVENSON: Thinking about both your Facebook posts and your recontextualizing of older books of essays as you've republished them on Wesleyan, I think one thing you're doing is trying to give context. There was often a context originally (passively?) there for readers, but as we get further away from a particular historical moment, it's lost. How crucial do you feel context is to understanding, say, your early essays, or early novels, or even why certain writers such as Robert Heinlein or Theodore Sturgeon were so important to you?

DELANY: I think I had a great deal of sympathy for the problems of contextualization—because of my own New York life in Harlem, the newly burgeoning new Bohemia in the East Village, the life in my various school situations, Dalton, the Bronx High School of Science, and the trajectory of various universities that I have negotiated since. I don't pretend to understand myself, and the times are too "interesting" for anyone to thoroughly understand them. But we can at least try to keep the focus on one part or the other sharp.

EVENSON: I've noticed as a professor the way in which students sometimes are unaware of the work that was the most influential for me, and don't respond to it the same way as I did when they read it. That's sometimes due to the fact that those writers have been so effective that they've genuinely changed the discourse of a genre. I'd argue that Heinlein is like that, and probably Sturgeon as well—later writers have climbed on their shoulders. Can these writers be appreciated now to the same degree they were when they were first published? Does giving a context for them help? I remember my parents—who were not really SF readers—reading *Stranger in a Strange Land* when I was a kid. I think today it's hard to imagine what a huge (and broad) impact someone like Heinlein had.

DELANY: Neither of my parents were SF readers at all. In fact, my sense of them was that they weren't big readers at all. But they had a family respect for education. My father had been born on the

110

campus of a black Episcopal college, St. Augustine's, where most of his older sisters and brothers at one time taught. But among all the doctors, dentists, teachers, and lawyers, he only barely got away with a high-school degree. My mother had two years of college that had been interrupted by the pressures of the Great Depression of the 1930s. And she'd gone to work for the WPA. My academic yearnings leaped over my parents, as it were, to the rest of my family. I needed Heinlein and Sturgeon, and was lucky enough to find them in one genre. I needed Disch and Russ—and Roger Zelazny, for that matter. I needed Katherine MacLean and Alfred Bester, and was able to find them there in the same magazines and paperbacks, sold from the same racks in the same bookstores. I needed Guy Davenport and Susan Sontag and was surprised when they answered my basic fan letters civilly, once I got up the gumption to write them. I was surprised when I found a neighborhood where there were writers socially close enough for me to find things like the Theater for the New City and the Judson Poets' Theater and the St. Mark's Church in the Bowery Poetry Project for my nourishment. I had an education in prose and poetry, that seemed exciting enough at the time—which still seems, now and again, to be going on, however eccentric, however idiosyncratic. I worry about my tenacity. I used to write hoping I would be making texts I might want to read later. And I don't know whether that's what I've actually done, in anything. It all sounds and feels like the uncertainties of age—which is probably what it is. But I still find people who are interesting, even when, for a day or a month, writers don't seem so. Then I find ideas that can command my attention. And I talk to more people. . . .

My next two books to see print will be the first volume of my collected journals, in five volumes at least; at least I hope so. After that Dover will return a 2007 novel to print, *Dark Reflections*, which won an award—the Stonewall Book Award, back in 2008, which still means something to me. And Wesleyan has contracted to bring out an until now unpublished 1989 collection of letters—*Letters from Amherst: Five Narrative Letters*. I am humbled that, after all this time, they felt it still was interesting enough to publish.

I don't need "speculative fiction" to talk about any of these, in the same way that I don't need "creative nonfiction," just as I myself don't really need literature to talk about them either—though I certainly have learned most of what I know (and probably all of what I intuit about writing) from it and the genres of poetry, film, art, and music in so many forms over the years, not to mention the novel and the drama, through what my own notions of the best art for this one reader vouches safe. But the larger and grander terms are for others to assign to these texts, not me. I can do with "letters," "science fiction," "comics," "nonfiction," "pornography," "sword and sorcery," "memoir," "fiction," "movies." Precisely the terms that carry value, and carry it most nakedly, I feel I have to earn—and, indeed, earn again and again, with each new printing, with each new reader, with each person who looks at a comic-book page or turns on a DVD. As time passes, artists get fewer and fewer readers, most of them. (MacArthur winner Guy Davenport is my favorite contemporary writer. At his death, in January 2005, probably I could name twenty-five people who felt the same. Today, eleven years later, while I think a number of these people might probably still agree, how many people can I name who have actually read a story by him in the last year? None, for certain. And that includes myself. If someone told me that not a single Davenport collection of stories had sold since I last taught *A Table of Green Fields* three years ago, I would be un-happy and think the universe blatantly unfair, not only to Davenport but more so to the readers who might get so much out of reading him. But I couldn't be surprised. Thus it would be naive of me—or any writer—to assume that anything better will happen to anyone else.)

Here are a few short works that I think can function as turn-ons to flog you toward writing again if somehow you've slipped away:

Ann Lauterbach, *The Given & the Chosen* (2011)

Hugo von Hofmannsthal, *The Lord Chandos Letter* (1902)

Laura Bohannan, *Shakespeare in the Bush* (1961)

They are among the most pleasurable brief works on writing that I have read.

EVENSON: For those readers who are coming to your large body of work for the first time, where would you suggest they start, what books do you see as a good entrée into the world of Delany? And what books do you feel really represent your deepest vision the most?

DELANY: Well, I am two writers: one is a critic who writes about creative writing and science fiction and some specific writers as examples of some of those notions. As far as my SF criticism is con-cerned, a small galaxy of texts that you might look at consists of my initial academic offering, "About 5,750 Words." It's a popular place to begin—if (and only if) you immediately go on to look at some critical pieces I've written that think against it, as it were, that take you further on: "Three Letters to Science Fiction Studies," at the end of my collection *Starboard Wine* and "Reflections on Historical Models," which follows in that same book. Without those two, however, I don't think the earlier piece is anything other than a not-very-interesting five-finger exercise.

Another galaxy of longer critical texts that I hope work well together are the essays "Alyx: Joanna Russ," followed by "Letter to the Symposium on 'Women in Science Fiction,' " and "To Read *The Dispossessed.*" This last is, in effect, my unnecessarily tentative coming-out letter to a number of science fiction writers, all of whom, with one exception (James Tiptree, Jr.) had known I was a gay man for years.

Finally, the essays "Sturgeon," "Russ" (both in *Starboard Wine*), and "Racism in Science Fiction," which you can find online, leave you pretty much ready to attack what, for better or for worse, are my two major critical endeavors, *The American Shore*, a book-length reading of an SF short story by Thomas M. Disch, and "Atlantis Rose . . ." (in a revised edition that will likely see print in a year or so; till then the unrevised version in *Longer Views* will have to do), which is a biocritical study of Hart Crane.

From my book *About Writing*, I like "Thickening the Plot." Some readers have found it helpful. Others have found "Some Notes for the Intermediate and Advanced Creative Writing Student," a consideration of the structure of novels, of particular use.

After that, there are my two major nonfiction pieces—*Times Square Red, Times Square Blue* and *The Motion of Light in Water.*

My fantasy series of eleven stories, novellas, and novels, *Return to Nevèrÿon* is one fictive project that was about a decade's work. *Dhalgren, Triton, The Mad Man, Nova*, and the short stories in *Aye, and Gomorrah*, probably in that order, are the fiction works I'd recommend if a page or three of any of them interested you. For separate reasons I like both *Phallos* and *Dark Reflections*. As well there are a handful of short works, the three long stories in *Atlantis: Three Tales*, along with other short works: *Empire Star, Equinox, The Einstein Intersection, They Fly at Çiron*, and the aforementioned *Phallos*, which really belongs with them.

There are also the highly challenging works such as *Hogg* and *Through the Valley of the Nest of Spiders.*

That's one way through the maze of Delany—but there is no right one. Indeed, if you read one and find something in it you recognize or smile over or frown at, I will be humbly delighted.

But for any writer even to take on such a question seriously seems to me the height of arrogance. What is called for by such a request is a silence that assumes anyone seizing on any thread that dangles from any door of the maze as privileged over any other is, in itself, absurd. To read or not to read is always the reader's choice. It's never the writer's to recommend. Likewise the reader starts where chance and propinquity places her or him. And it goes on or ceases as long as she or he likes—and no longer.

The Transition
Matthew Baker

OF COURSE, HIS FAMILY HAD HEARD of the operation, knew not only
that such a thing was possible but that there were actually people
doing it, and although his family was conservative, his family wasn't
radical by any means, in fact his family was really quite moderate, so
much so that during elections in which the conservative candidate
seemed especially intolerant or corrupt or feebleminded his family
was occasionally even known to vote for the liberal alternative, and
although his family was religious, his family certainly wasn't the
type to speak of issues in terms of good and evil, and for instance
had no qualms about nudity in the media, and sometimes drank to
excess, and wasn't opposed to gambling, and believed in evolution,
and although his family was poor, not destitute exactly, but decidedly
working class, and possessed no college degrees, his family held no
prejudice against people who elected to have vanity surgeries like
liposuction and rhinoplasty, and were always heartened to meet
people benefiting from bionic modifications such as pacemakers and
prostheses, and enjoyed watching programs of an educational nature,
and took naturally to new technologies—and yet there was something that set the operation apart from other issues, something that
repulsed his family almost instinctually, something that filled his
family with contempt, a fact his family had made no effort to hide,
like back when the news had been flooded with stories about a
famous architect who had transitioned and his family had spent an
evening sitting around out on the stoop ridiculing the architect, or
back when the news had been flooded with stories about a former
model who had transitioned and his family had spent an evening
sitting around out on the stoop bashing the model, and so the fact
that his family found the concept utterly loathsome certainly would
have been clear to Mason.

Then there was also his personality. He was profoundly reserved.
He rarely smiled. He seldom laughed. He spoke clearly, without
any animation. Although he often complained, he never became
angry. He never seemed gloomy. He never appeared excited. He must

have cried occasionally as a child, but no incidents came to mind specifically, and regardless he certainly hadn't cried in the presence of his family since. He never showed signs of feeling powerful emotions.

So, considering that he was showing signs as he sat there at the table, that his hands were trembling, that his voice was shaking, that he was so nervous that the feeling was actually affecting him physically, and that he really wasn't in the habit of joking about this type of thing—or, quite honestly, joking about anything—there seemed to be no doubt that he was serious when he interrupted a moment of silence to announce, or rather confess, that he was planning to have his mind converted to digital data and transferred from his body to a computer server.

Mason's father, who was wearing his favorite apron, with the cartoon pelican across the chest and the maroon stain just beneath the pockets, gaped at him from the counter in the kitchen, frozen there in the midst of dipping a silicone spatula into a container of the latest batch of his secret sauce. Mason's brothers, who planned to drive the motorboat down to parkland at dusk to go shrimping on the gulf, were reclined around the table in athletic jerseys and camouflage cutoffs, squinting at him with expressions of confusion. Mason's mother had come in from the backyard when she had heard him arrive, wearing the straw hat and baggy caftan that she'd been sunning in, and she felt such a jolt of panic when he said what he said that she had to set her iced tea down onto the nearest surface, the stove, or else she surely would have dropped the bottle onto the floor.

Mason stared at the table, and then, as if suddenly daring to hope that the idea might be met with no resistance, looked up and blurted, "We'll still be able to talk or whatever."

His mother crossed the kitchen toward the table, feeling past the counter with her hands, her eyes never leaving him. He must have come from a shift at the supermarket. His uniform was rumpled. His name tag was askew. He'd always been scrawny, but recently he seemed especially frail. His eyebrows were so light in color that he didn't seem to have eyebrows at all, which had caused him untold trouble on the playground as a child. He had watery eyes, a delicate nose, thin lips, and a weak chin. He looked like the type of person who'd probably have a milk allergy. She couldn't explain what that was supposed to mean exactly. A neighbor had said it about him once, though, and as soon as she'd heard it, she'd known it was true. She loved his face. As she slid into a chair at the table, she had to resist an urge to reach over and cup his jaw in her palms. The thought of losing him was terrifying.

"I mean, I'll be able to chat whenever you want, I'll be online literally all of the time," Mason said, gaze falling back to the table.

His mother turned toward the counter, searching for some indication of how his father was reacting to the announcement. The heat from the sun was already leaving her skin, and the sensation seemed almost like a manifestation of her fear, as if the emotion were sapping the warmth from her skin as the feeling spread. She had been relaxing in a canvas lawn chair all morning, sipping from that bottle of iced tea, watching with amusement as sparrows hopped along the branches of the tree, basking in the occasional gust of wind that rushed across the backyard, letting loose tremendous yawns, stretching her limbs out, rubbing her eyes with the heels of her hands, scratching her belly periodically when the urge struck, savoring the tart aroma of the charcoal burning in the grill, enjoyably aware of being dressed in a bright caftan and floppy hat. Coming in from that realm of bodily pleasure to be confronted with somebody who wanted to leave all of it behind was intensely jarring. She didn't understand what he could be thinking.

Over by the counter his father set down the spatula.

"You do realize that not having a body would mean not having a body?" his father said.

"Yes."

"As in never again?" his father said.

"Yes."

"What the hell is wrong with your head?" his father said.

His father swore only when he was deeply afraid, which told his mother that she wasn't the only one taking the announcement seriously. Despite how grave the situation was, however, his father apparently really did need to check on the grill before the ribs burned. Scowling, with the hem of his apron flapping at his shins with every step, his father marched out the door into the backyard.

Mason, who had been staring intently at his knuckles during that brief exchange with his father, glanced back up again. His cheeks were flushed; sweat pitted his shirt. His mother suddenly felt sure that this discussion, albeit awkward, would be easily resolved. Years from now, his family was going to look back on this moment and laugh about his mistake, like how the family still joked about the time that one of his brothers had considered quitting his job in order to sell dietary supplements for a company from door-to-door until the family had explained to him that the operation was obviously a scam, or how the family still joked about the time that one of his brothers had considered starting a jazz group until the family had explained to him that yes he might love the drums but honestly he had no rhythm and he didn't belong anywhere near a stage. Certainty spread through her, and a bit of pride that she had been the one to realize that this was all a misunderstanding. She felt so relieved that she had to suppress a grin.

"You're just not thinking," she announced.

"About what," Mason said.

"I don't know what put the idea in your head, but you're not like those other people doing it, there's too much you'd miss about having a body," she said.

She could tell from his stare that she hadn't yet convinced him, and she folded her hands together, searching for an example.

"Like dancing," she exclaimed.

"I hate dancing," Mason said.

"Oh you do not," she said, and then she fell silent, because she knew of course that he did.

Until now his brothers had been sitting back observing the scene, picking their teeth, biting their nails, but his brothers finally exploded.

"What the heck, bro?"

"Where did this even come from?"

"How could you actually want something that messed up done?"

"Our own flesh and blood?"

His oldest brother leaned in.

"You'd even give up sex?" his oldest brother said.

Mason didn't reply, just gazed at the centerpiece, a vase of wildflowers.

"What about sex?" his oldest brother demanded.

Mason gave a faint shrug.

"More trouble than it's worth," Mason said.

His mother had never seen his brothers look so offended.

His oldest brother sat back, knitting his fingers behind his head with his elbows thrown wide in a posture of dismissal, and sneered, "Well, who cares if you want it done, you'll never have enough money to pay for it."

"I already do," Mason said.

Mason apparently had been setting aside a substantial portion of each paycheck for years now. His mother fiddled with the bangles around her wrists in distress. Back when his family had sat around mocking the celebrity chef who'd transitioned, back when his family had sat around trashing the piano prodigy who'd transitioned, he must have been saving up money for the operation even then. He had sat there and had listened to his family call people like that monsters and had secretly believed that he was a person like that all along. The thought stunned her.

Mason stared at the table, then glanced back up with a desperate look, exclaiming, "I hate having to deal with clothing. I hate having to go shopping and trying to find things that fit and having to put together an outfit every single day and worrying about what matches and having to drag everything down to the laundry. I hate getting sick. I hate getting headaches and getting backaches and getting earaches and getting toothaches and puking especially. I hate having to get checkups at the doctor and the dentist and the optometrist every single year. I hate always having to make meals and eat the food and wash dishes afterward. I hate having to shower. I hate having to sleep. I'm tired of wasting so much of my life on taking care of a body. I just want to be able to read stuff and talk to people all the time."

"Sweetie," his mother said. She leaned across the table, her heart beating wildly, and laid her hands over his hands. "I know you might feel like that right now, but if you'd just stop and think about it for a couple days, you're going to change your mind."

"I've been thinking about it for over twenty years," Mason said.

He eased his hands out from under her hands, pulling away, as if ashamed.

"I don't belong in a body," Mason said.

He lowered his head.

"I've always known," Mason said.

He left before the meal was served, slipping out the door with his shoulders slumped, then sputtering off down the road in his rusty hatchback. While his brothers sat around the table bitterly rehashing that comment about sex, his mother drifted in a daze out into the backyard, where his father was squatting next to the grill. Looking up from the ribs with an expression of fury, his father confessed that he had come out to the backyard not so much out of concern for the ribs as out of fear that he had been about to cry, which he had never done in the presence of the children before and didn't want to.

Mason had scheduled the operation for later that month, taking the earliest available appointment the local clinic could offer. As his mother brushed her teeth that night, an activity in which she usually found much enjoyment—the tingle of foam on her tongue, the prick of bristles against her gums—she couldn't focus on the experience at all, but instead was gripped by a feeling of dread. She had driven past the local clinic before, a nondescript facility with screened windows and tinted doors, and the place always seemed to have a sinister aura. Although he had asked his family to be there for the operation, there was no way that she could go. She found the concept disturbing enough when the procedure was done to a stranger, let alone her youngest son. What frightened her most was imagining the actual transition. The exact moment when his body would be empty. The exact moment when his mind would be gone.

She had never suspected he might want something like that, but now that she knew he did, she couldn't help feeling like she should have suspected all along. He had always been different from his brothers. He had been a puny, feeble, pallid child. Even back then he had whined about everything. He hadn't liked doing puzzles. He hadn't liked making crafts. As an eater he had been picky, declining to eat fruits, refusing to eat vegetables, not even liking candy, subsisting mainly on cereal and macaroni. He'd sipped reluctantly at colas. He'd nibbled grudgingly at cookies. His brothers in contrast had eaten with gusto, devouring multiple helpings apiece of whatever she'd cooked, praising the flavors in exultation, licking salt from lips and grease from fingers. His brothers had been playful too, wrestling each other and racing each other and spinning each other dizzy and taking great joy in both resisting and surrendering to gravity, climbing trees and leaping from roofs and soaring and plunging back and forth on swings, but he'd had an aversion to physical activity. He hadn't even liked walking. He'd had a listless gait, walking about with his arms limp and his feet dragging, as if having to walk was an arduous task, simply onerous. Getting him to make the walk from the front door of the house to the bus stop at the corner on weekday mornings had been nothing short of a miracle. He hadn't liked going outdoors at all. If she had tried to take him bicycling, he would crank at the pedals a few times, then grumble, gradually coast to a stop, slide off the seat, let the bicycle fall onto the pavement, and flop down on the curb, refusing to go any farther, complaining that pedaling made his legs hurt. If she had tried to take him canoeing, he would heave on the paddle a few times, then mutter, slump over on the seat, and stare at the bottom of the canoe, complaining that paddling made his arms hurt. If she had tried to take him swimming at the ocean, the water had always been too hot or too cold or too salty or too wet. While his family had tossed a foam ball around in the shallows, he had sat on the beach with his arms wrapped around his shins and his chin propped on his knees, either in the sun, complaining that the light was too bright, or under the umbrella, complaining that the shade was too dark. Sitting on the sand had made his butt hurt.

He was remarkably annoying. Yet despite how finicky he was—or maybe even because—he had always been her favorite. She adored him. As a child the only time he had ever seemed content was when he had been left to his own devices. He had preferred to stay indoors, hunched over a screen on his beanbag in his bedroom, poring over online encyclopedias. Compared to how reserved he had been in person, he had seemed to come alive when exchanging messages with people over the Internet. Occasionally she had even heard him chuckle or snicker in there at something he had read. She had taken pains to keep him from being disturbed.

Now she couldn't help blaming herself for what was happening. She had only wanted him to be happy, but in the process she had ruined him. She should have forced him to play with other children. She should have forced him to eat whatever she had cooked instead of letting him prepare meals of bland grains. She should have forced him to bike and she should have forced him to canoe and she should have forced him to swim until he had learned how to love the world. It was her fault that he had ended up like this. She had failed him as a mother.

She spat toothpaste into the sink, rinsed the toothbrush under the faucet, shut off the lamp in the kitchen, set an alarm for work the next day, and then climbed into bed. His father was lying there on his back with the blanket thrown off. Moonlight coming through the window illuminated the strip of gut exposed between the band of his briefs and the hem of his tee. She stared at the silhouette of the fan on the ceiling for a while.

"I reject the notion that somebody can be born that way," his father grumbled.

She felt the mattress dip as he shifted to look at her.

"If you're born in a body, then you belong in a body, and that's that," his father said.

When she didn't respond he swiveled back toward the ceiling.

"He's just lazy. Doesn't want to work anymore. Just wants to live for free. God knows we've got enough of those types in this country. Well, OK, he's paying for it himself. So maybe he'll be more like somebody who's retired than like some freeloader on welfare. Fine. But you can't turn somebody into data. They can turn his memories to data, they can turn his beliefs to data, they can turn his knowledge to data, and his particular mannerisms, and his thought patterns, and his exact vocabulary, but even if they put all of that stuff into the computer, there's still going to be something missing. I'll tell you this much, those things in the computers don't have souls. Because you can't turn that to numbers. You just can't. And for the record, he could have at least stayed for supper," his father exclaimed.

And she knew he needed to rant, so she let him rant. And later, she stuck her face into her pillow and wept so violently that the bed shook, and he knew she needed to weep, so he let her weep. And then for the rest of the night she alternated between fidgeting and lying as still as possible, too upset to sleep.

From then on, that became her norm, both at night and during the day, just constant worrying. Even when she wasn't thinking about it she was thinking about it. No matter where she was at, no matter what she was doing, whether she was searching through the envelope of coupons in her purse to pay for tampons at the pharmacy or she was concentrating on the descriptions of the various deductions that her accountant recommended making before filing taxes, an awareness of the situation was always there in the background of her other thoughts, interrupting. I am losing my son.

Since graduating, Mason had been renting a house with some roommates, who no doubt would claim his belongings after the operation. But there wouldn't be much to claim. His furnishings were spare, just a bed with a sheet, stacked crates with folded clothes, a battered plastic hamper, dirty bowls on the windowsill containing flecks of dried milk and crusted cheese, a framed photo of his family on the wall, the tangled cords of his chargers on the floor, and his beanbag. She had been over there a number of times, once to bring him chicken broth when he had the flu, once to bring him emergency funds after he had been mugged. The roommates who he'd found were strange—women with glazed looks who played video games excessively, shifty men who were always busy mailing and receiving mysterious packages and constantly reeked of curry and patchouli, aggressively chatty people who believed that the moon landings had been a complete hoax and that astrological systems were indisputably factual—and she had worried about him living there. That his roommates might pressure him into doing something risky, like heroin, or orgies. Activities so pleasurable that the activities were addicting. And there had in fact appeared to be cause for concern. He

122

had seemed unwell in recent years. Not just because of how frail he had become, but the bags that had formed in the skin beneath his eyes, and the furrow that had formed in the skin between his eyebrows. She had wondered if he was depressed.

After confessing his plan to his family, however, Mason immediately seemed to improve. In the following weeks he occasionally drove over in the evening to hang out on the stoop with his family, sitting there in his regular chair with his usual slouch as if everything were normal. Sipping from a bottle of iced tea, his mother would study the changes in his appearance from across the stoop. The bags beneath his eyes had faded. The furrow between his eyebrows had disappeared. Some of the color had actually returned to his skin. In fact, the nearer the day of the procedure came, the healthier he seemed, and that alarmed her more than the symptoms of depression ever had, because his growing excitement seemed like proof that he genuinely believed he needed the operation.

She set her bottle of iced tea down onto the stoop, then shifted in her chair to turn toward the street, returning a wave to a neighbor in a passing car. She had always assumed that once hormones hit he would finally become interested in the lively social network at school, but even as a teenager he had preferred digital interactions to relationships in person. His brothers had been daredevils in those years, exploring abandoned factories with friends, egging the vehicles of enemies, roaming around heckling tourists for fun, constantly coming and going from the house with every departure and arrival announced by the thwack of the screen door and stomps on the front steps, but he had been as much of a homebody as ever. He had dated a few people—the longest had been a timid mathlete with a strand of hair dyed aquamarine—and the romances had at the very least been earnest sexually. Sorting through his dirty laundry, his mother had occasionally discovered a sock stiff with dried semen; dumping the contents of his trash can into the garbage container in the garage, his mother had sometimes spotted a condom wrapper in with the mix. Yet he had never seemed truly enamored with anybody, speaking of the girls he dated with the same reluctant preference he showed for cereal and macaroni, as if sex were merely another appetite to be sated. And otherwise he hadn't shown much interest in his schoolmates at all. For the sake of convention she had wished that he would join some extracurriculars, maybe try out for a musical or run for student council, but for selfish reasons she also had been glad that he had spent most weekends hunched over a screen in his bedroom.

She had loved having him nearby, just getting to glance at him as she walked past the room to fetch a sponge from the kitchen, or getting to dust the mirror in the bathroom knowing that he occupied a room just down the hall. Stopping to visit him between chores, she would see apps flashing across his screen at an almost blurry rate as he switched between chats and forums and the comments beneath articles. She had marveled at how many conversations he could engage in simultaneously.

"What are you talking about on there?" she had asked him once, standing over his beanbag with a vacuum cradled in her arms.

"Everything," Mason had said, drawing out the syllables of the word for emphasis.

And he had in fact seemed to be interested in everything, occasionally sharing at supper what he had learned throughout the day, the topics ranging from subjects like oceanography and astrophysics to bits of gossip about mods and other friends online. Puberty had added a lump to his throat that dipped when he spoke. His scalp had shed dandruff that his mother was forever having to brush from the back of his shirt, and though she had insisted that he and his brothers be asleep by midnight during the school week, on the occasions when she had risen in the wee hours to use the bathroom and while padding down the hall had spotted the faint glow of a screen shining through the crack below his door, she had never asked him to go to bed. She had taken any chance to accommodate him, even when that had required breaking her own rules.

Thinking of that, she actually could remember a time he had cried. A particularly catastrophic hurricane had blown through when he was a teenager, and though the house had been spared any significant damage, the power had been out for weeks afterward, with no way to get online. His brothers had always thrived during outages, enjoying the novelty of eating canned goods by the light of a gas lantern and flushing the toilet with water stored in plastic milk cartons, and had treated those weeks like an extended camping trip, lounging around the living room spooking each other with urban legends and playing board games that hadn't been pulled from the closet in years. Mason, however, had struggled. The longest the power had ever been out before was a few days at a time, and he must have assumed that would be the case again, because he had spent the first few days after the storm sitting on the windowsill in the living room with his arms folded across his chest, watching the street with an intent expression, as if utility trucks from the electric company were due to arrive at any moment. As the outage had dragged on, his bearing had changed from impatient to agitated, with a set clench to his jaw and his lips pursed tight, and he had become increasingly anxious, replying to questions with distracted grunts, ignoring requests to join activities, just pacing around the window in the living room, kicking at the carpet, or for hours sometimes simply slumping on his beanbag with a blank screen clutched in his hands, until finally one morning after waking up to discover that the power still hadn't been restored, he had broken down weeping at breakfast, burying his face in his arms, with the descending knobs of his spine protruding through the stretched fabric of his shirt as he sobbed. His brothers had stared at him with mild shock.

"The power has to come back on eventually," his mother had said, trying to reason with him from across the table.

But he had been inconsolable, his body trembling in frustration.

"This is the worst thing that's ever happened to me," Mason had cried.

At the time she had dismissed the statement as a bout of melodrama, just another complaint from a child prone to complaining, but now she realized that he might have meant what he had said: that the worst he had ever felt was being cut off that long from the Internet.

Her name was Emily, but she was a mother—even before giving birth to the boys, she had always felt that was what she was meant to do, her identity—and his mother especially. She loved his father, she loved his brothers, yet the family hadn't felt complete to her until he had arrived. When she had first held him, a bleary newborn with a wisp of pale hair, she had been struck by that exact thought. This is everybody. And she still felt that way, sitting around on the stoop, like the family wasn't complete without him. He balanced out everybody else, that gawky figure over by the railing. She loved how he would set his ball cap in his lap to fuss with the snaps on the plastic adjuster for a while absentmindedly. She loved how he would tuck his hands into the webbed cup holders attached to his chair as if the holes had been included for that exact purpose. She loved how when she accidentally bumped the bottle of iced tea by her feet while laughing at his brothers, he lunged to catch the wobbling bottle before the iced tea could spill. When she slipped indoors to blow her nose, the gentle lilt of his voice drifting in through the screen door gave her a sense of well-being. When she returned outdoors with a file for her nails, the sharp odor of the sneakers he had kicked off by

Matthew Baker

the front steps made her swell with contentment. He had a presence she could feel even when she wasn't looking. And now all of that was tinged with dread. She knew what the stoop was like when he wasn't there, from days he was at work, or days he was home sick. On those days there was an empty space. An absence over by the railing that she was constantly aware of, no matter how hard she tried to be happy with what she had. And after the operation, that empty space would be there forever, the rest of her life.

His family avoided talking about the operation around him without exception. His father, who had never understood him but had always made an effort to understand him anyway, had given up, maintaining a polite yet firm silence on the matter, as if acknowledging the choice might count as consent. His brothers, who had defended him from any accusations of weirdness when he was younger with a ferocity that had sent critics running, now just sat back looking embarrassed if the issue was mentioned, as if too humiliated to speak. His mother, who in truth usually couldn't resist a topic that promised a bit of drama, was struck dumb with fear when given the opportunity to join a discussion about the decision. Even Mason himself avoided the subject. Although he may have been relieved to have confessed his plan, he was obviously still ashamed of his plan too. Whenever anybody brought up the operation, his hands would tremble and his voice would shake, the same as when he had made the initial announcement. And the operation came up often when he was on the stoop. By now word of his plan had spread through the neighborhood. He was a spectacle, like somebody out on bail for a crime that would mean life in prison, a local landmark about to vanish from the neighborhood forever in a sensational fashion. Neighbors would wander over to the stoop under the pretense of talking with his family, chatting about basketball or landscaping or potholes or the weather until enough time had passed to be able to turn to him casually to ask about the operation, as if the subject had only just then come to mind.

In general the neighbors seemed less interested in hearing his perspective than in reporting what they personally felt was so worthwhile about having a body and then explaining that he actually liked having a body just as much as they did. He would tug uncomfortably at the collar of his tee while a neighbor expounded on the wonders of bubble baths; he would fidget uneasily with the rips in his jeans while a neighbor testified to the greatness of scented lotion. And his mother thought that he did seem to give serious consideration to what the neighbors said. Yet whatever the neighbors insisted would be worth keeping a body for, he always responded that he would still prefer to live as data. He wouldn't miss driving with the windows down. He wouldn't miss wearing slippers, dressing up for weddings, or changing out of wet clothing into dry pajamas. He wouldn't miss jambalaya, peanut butter, mustard on pretzels, burritos bursting with cheese and beans and salsa bundled up in wrappers, pepperoni pizza with the crust flavored subtly like cardboard from the box, lobster so tender that the meat flaked apart, the maraschino cherry off the crest of a banana split, the extra portion of milk shake in the steel cup that always felt like a surprise bonus after you had finished the serving in the glass, pancakes drenched in maple syrup and waffles dolloped with whipped cream, bacon dripping with so much grease that the oil had soaked the paper towel underneath, popcorn coated with so much salt that a layer of crystal had formed at the bottom of the bucket, chili dogs heaped with onions and seasoned with the smell of cut grass at a ballpark, buffalo wings slathered with cayenne and seasoned with the smell of lit candles at a pub, toasted marshmallows oozing out from between slabs of chocolate and graham cracker with the scent of campfire on your fingers, toffee so buttery you had to wipe your lips afterward, fudge so rich you would feel your toes curl involuntarily, the tang of a bite of pickle with the peppery aftertaste of a pastrami sandwich still fresh on your tongue, hot fries with cold ketchup, chocolate-chip cookie dough, fried green tomatoes, pecan pie, grits, or beignets. He wouldn't miss getting buzzed on coffee, wine, or cigarettes. He wouldn't miss the shiver of ecstasy after scratching a mosquito bite. He wouldn't miss roller coasters. He wouldn't miss wave pools. He wouldn't miss turnstile gates. He wouldn't miss funnel cakes. He wouldn't miss souvenir hats. He wouldn't miss anything about amusement parks whatsoever. He wouldn't miss the rush of adrenaline after running a stoplight, the almost giddy relief following a bout of hiccups, sucking drinks through straws, having caricatures drawn, feeling drowsy, collapsing into a mound of blankets and pillows, naps so intense you woke up drooling, the sound of rain, the smell of rain, or wind chimes.

"It's unnatural," a neighbor grimaced, speaking of the operation, which was the closest that any of the neighbors ever came to condemning him in person. When he wasn't around, his mother knew, the neighbors gossiped about him constantly. When he was around, the children on the street weren't allowed on the property, as if the neighbors were afraid his thinking might be infectious.

"The Internet is a beautiful place," Mason murmured. He had never left Louisiana. He had lived in the same neighborhood in the same district in the same city his entire life. He had always had his family nearby to protect him. The Internet wasn't a beautiful place. The Internet was a dangerous place. His mother stayed up late into the night, sitting alone in the kitchen with the lamp lit, searching the news for stories about postcorporeals. Earlier that month a postcorporeal from Winnetka had been infected with a virus that had damaged her programming so severely that she had crashed and hadn't been able to be revived, effectively killing her. And only the week prior, a postcorporeal from Baltimore had been attacked by hackers, had her memory looted for credit card information and her social security number, had random sections of her data vandalized apparently just out of spite, and been left in the digital equivalent of a coma. While the year before in a highly publicized case a company in Phoenix that hosted postcorporeals from across the country had failed to maintain its facilities properly, not out of negligence but rather in a deliberate attempt to increase profits, regularly skipping the safety inspections standard to the industry, which had come to the attention of the public only after the servers at the data center had been fried by a power surge from a lightning strike, resulting in hundreds of postcorporeals vanishing from the world in a flash, in a disaster the magnitude of a collapsed hotel or a crashed plane, an event that never would have happened had the place been up to code.

She wouldn't have any way to watch over him anymore.

How long would he survive out there?

For Mardi Gras his family had a tradition of spending the day together, which was an important event every year but this year had taken on particular significance, because the operation was scheduled to take place the following morning. She tried to suppress her sense of grief to focus on making the day as perfect as possible. That was all she wanted, a perfect day, so that after losing him she could at least always remember that her last day with him had been special. She shook her head at his father and sent him back into the bedroom to change into something nicer than the tank top and cargo shorts he had picked out. She made his brothers promise not to pick any fights with tourists. She loaded her purse with spray-on sunscreen and bottled waters.

And the day was perfect. His family looked beautiful, proud parents and polite children dressed in fine clothing made by respected brands, and in the morning his family snagged prime spots for viewing the parades and saw floats so spectacular as to be truly among the best in living memory, and in the afternoon his family got ice-cream cones piled high with generous scoops of butter pecan and rocky road and vanilla bean and blue moon and then strolled along the river-front cracking jokes, and in the evening his family stumbled onto a live performance put on in the park by an unassuming band and heard a zydeco concert that wowed the crowd to such an extent that afterward members of the audience formed a line to shake hands with the musicians. And then after dusk his family set up on the patio of a café, splitting a platter of nachos and sipping from pints of ale, people watching over the fence, and that was perfect too. The temperature was mild, the breeze was pleasant, and dazzling stars filled the sky above the street. The road was strewn with colorful debris. Metallic noisemakers, cracked to-go cups, a trampled bouquet, tangled strings of beads, fluorescent dildos, an acrylic bong. Revelers streamed past the patio, people grinning behind feathered masks and people primping rainbow wigs and people whose skin was painted with mesmerizing swirls and people in sequined outfits twirling bejeweled canes that glittered under the streetlights and people breathing fire to the cheers of people riding by on unicycles and people embracing strangers and people chanting nonsense with friends and people in billowing capes skipping with each other down the street, and even in the midst of all of that pleasure and joy and happiness, Mason still seemed faintly bored. Eventually he took his phone out of his jacket, hunching over the screen, responding to messages, sending new messages, ignoring the carnival completely. He had only nibbled at the nachos. He had merely nipped at the ale. And at the concert he hadn't clapped between songs and instead of watching the performance had just fiddled with his phone, and along the river-front he hadn't even wanted an ice-cream cone and instead of watch-ing the steamboats had just fiddled with his phone, and during the parades he hadn't bothered to catch any of the throws and instead of watching the floats had just fiddled with his phone. The day had been perfect, and the day had been ruined anyway, because he had been too distracted to experience any of it. His mother leaned back in her chair with a frown. She had worried that she might get so sad tonight that she would cry, but all that worrying had been for nothing, be-cause she wasn't sad. She was furious. He might as well have already been gone. He couldn't look away from that fucking screen.

   She stood from the table so suddenly that her chair toppled over backward with a smack.

"You disgust me," she spat.

Mason glanced up with a startled look.

"I want no part of whatever type of life you plan to have after tomorrow," she said, walked out of the café, and drove home alone.

Back at the house she changed into baggy sweatpants and a shirt that had been washed and dried so many times that the fabric was soft and wispy, an outfit that generally gave her great pleasure to wear, but which of course now she was too angry to enjoy. She had meant what she had said. She hadn't planned to say it, but she didn't regret saying it either. She was done with him. She was livid. She grabbed a bag of caramels, popped the cap from a stout, and sat down at the table in the kitchen with the lamp on to eat and drink and enjoy it, not just out of spite for him, but out of spite for all postcorporeality. She was still sitting there when headlights swung into the driveway and a key rattled in the door and in walked his father, who could see that she was in no mood to talk, so kissed her head, patted her shoulders, and then went into the bathroom to get ready for bed. Snoring soon filled the house, but she was too restless to lie down, too wired on beer and sugar, so she cleaned instead. She scrubbed the toilet, she scrubbed the tub, and she scrubbed the grime that had formed around the faucet of the sink, trying to avoid thinking about him, which she couldn't, so eventually she gave up. She thought about him. She wandered the house in the glow of the streetlights coming through the windows, inspecting the contents of cabinet drawers and closet shelves, examining different mementos from his life. Here were the stuffed animals that he had tolerated sleeping with. Here were the action figures that he had endured playing with. Here were the hand casts that he had complained about posing for even after having finished posing. And, oh, here, this was the container full of messages he had written to her at school during lunch. She peeled the lid from the container with a sense of awe. When packing lunches, she had always slipped a note into each lunch box. And at a certain age he had begun writing her back, shutting a reply into his lunch box for her to find when she opened his lunch box to empty out the used bags later that afternoon. His messages had been written on scraps torn from the corners of notebook paper, using whatever type of utensil he had favored at the time. Crayons, then colored pencils, eventually markers, and gel pens as a teenager. The messages had never said anything memorable, just remarks about his classes, or comments about his schoolmates, but she had loved those notes. None of his brothers had ever written her back.

She remembered now, that was the last thing he had said to her at the café before becoming engrossed in his screen. He had been explaining the logistics of the operation. He had smiled, "I'll message you after it's finished."

She dozed off on the couch at some point during the night and ended up with an arm and a leg dangling over the side and her face pressed into the crack between a pair of cushions. His father woke her just before leaving for work. Rain was drizzling. She brushed her teeth, tied her hair back, threw on some eyeliner, put on some lipstick, and got dressed in her uniform for the motel. By then the rain was a downpour. The wipers on her car needed to be replaced, and her breath was fogging the windows, so she could hardly see as she drove. She felt terrible. Mason would be at the clinic by now. Nobody had gone with him. She should have kept her mouth shut the night before. She had just been so angry, but even if his choice was abominable, he was still her son. The guilt was awful. The wipers thocked back and forth. She swiped at the fog with the cuff of a sleeve. Her pulse sped up as she made the decision. She had to go. She was terrified by the thought of being there for the transition, the moment when his body would be suddenly empty, the moment when his mind would be suddenly gone, but she needed to hold him one last time before she lost him. She drove past the motel and merged onto the highway.

The clinic was locked. After buzzing her in, the receptionist asked for her identification and checked a list for her name and then led her down an empty hall into the operating room, where he had already been sedated. Tears welled in her eyes. The procedure was under way. She wouldn't have a chance to say goodbye. A machine enclosed his head completely, with the rest of his body extending out of the machine onto a gurney. His palms were crossed over his chest. A neon-pink plastic wristband identified him for the operators. Aside from a pair of plain white boxers, he was naked. Seeing him in there like that was so upsetting that she almost turned to leave, but instead she wiped the tears from her eyes and forced herself to take a seat on the stool next to the gurney. She leaned her umbrella against the wall, she set her purse on the floor, and then she held his hands in her hands. The operators nodded at her, and then went back to work, adjusting dials and skimming scans. There was nothing to do but wait, and the wait was terrible. The constant feeling of dread that she had been living with since his announcement was so much worse than ever before. Rain pelted the roof. Indicator lights blinked.

The operators murmured to each other. She kept wondering whether the moment had passed, waiting for some sign that the transition had occurred, but there was no way of telling. Her muscles were tensed. Her teeth were clenched. And her dread just kept building.

She was bracing for the moment of the transition, squeezing his hands with a tight grip, breathing so fast that she was slightly dizzy, staring at his body, when she became aware of a faint beeping coming from a monitor on the machine. The sound made her think of her phone, tucked into the breast pocket of her uniform with the volume on high. She actually would know when the transition had occurred, she realized. When he messaged her, her phone would chime. She glanced down at her uniform, looking at the bulge her phone made in the pocket, and when she did, the strangest thing happened. She felt a burst of joy. Excitement so intense that a shiver passed through her. This sense that she wasn't about to lose him forever, but instead was finally about to meet him, truly meet him, for the first time. The feeling confused her, but the longer she stared at the pocket expecting her phone to chime at any moment, the stronger the feeling grew, until she was nearly overcome with anticipation. His hands were still warm, but whether the life had left his body yet didn't matter. She felt certain of that suddenly. It wasn't him. It never had been.

Blind Spot
Paul Park

"The thing is, you can't tell the difference. At least not from the outside. Because of interbreeding and genetic manipulation."

"What are you saying now?"

"It's a moral difference. That and perception. They have sharp ears, for one thing. Hear things from far away. Walk past a house from the outside, just along the garden walk, hear what people are saying around the corners. Hear people in their bedrooms."

"That's quite funny, the thing you do."

"What?"

"Using the same word in different ways so close together. 'From the outside.' 'Difference.' 'Walk.'"

"That's what I meant," he said. "They're very sensitive."

By "garden walk" he meant the crazy paving next to the stone wall, chest-high. There were hollyhocks. By "around the corners," he meant because the bedroom faced the street. The stone wall was in the back. You got to it across the meadow through the butter and eggs.

"Please go on."

"Because they are reptilian originally, they have a nictitating membrane. Some of them do. It's very quick. It slides across. Yellowish, I suppose."

Or else he meant because the bedroom was on the first floor, the windowsill high above the ground. The house itself was yellow stucco with a tile roof.

"No."

"I'm telling you. It was in the book. Long tongues. They smell through their tongues."

Roses among the hollyhocks around a corner of the wall.

"And you can't figure out by looking?"

"What do you mean? They can see through walls."

"I mean by looking at them."

"Not anymore. It's been too long. They could be you or I. Thirty-six hundred years is their planet's orbit, and now the first ones have assimilated. But guess what?" he said. "They're coming back."

An older man, he stood by the window, looking out onto the street. Gauze curtains. The other one lay on his back across the saffron bedspread. Tufted chenille. He smiled. "Go on," he said, "pull it again. Pull it harder."

"I'm telling you, they started everything. This was in Mesopotamia. Before that we were just living in caves. I'm speaking of the wheel, written languages, agriculture. They were technologically advanced. They'd have to be, coming from outer space. But not just that. They could see the whole past, the whole future, the whole world laid out. Worlds beyond worlds. Like it was written in a book."

The older man's name was Roland Styce. He had been born in Wales. He was a big man, unshaven. For seven years his psychiatrist had been prescribing him a combination of serotonin inhibitors—most recently fluoxetine—to treat his symptoms, with an antipsychotic (Zyprexa) to stabilize his moods. Sometimes, though, he tried to do without. As now, for example. Since his midtwenties he had worked as a teller in a bank. He was forty-seven.

The younger man lay propped up on his elbows. He had less time behind him. And even barring any sort of cataclysmic interruption, he had less in front of him as well. Soon, he would work another tattoo into the pattern on the inside of his left arm, an image taken from a tarot deck. He would spend six years in jail. Soon after, he'd be dead.

Even excepting some sort of violent interruption, he would be dead in nine years' time. He would die in the hospital, in the city of Leeds, not a hundred kilometers from the stucco house. Leeds is in the center of the United Kingdom. Above it, in the night sky, there is no trace of the twelfth planet as it approaches perihelion. You can scarcely see the stars.

"What's the problem then? Maybe they can help us sort out some of this mess."

"I wouldn't be so sure," said Roland Styce. "They don't care anything about us. They're very cruel."

Despite his years of service to the Midland Trust, he had never once been promoted, because of his low intellect. His flesh had a pasty look to it. His hands were large and fat, with fingers like moist rolls of uncooked dough, painted with egg white, dusted with red spots of pepper, and then sprinkled unaccountably with hair, according to the recipe of some deranged pastry chef. They were a masturbator's hands. No one touched them voluntarily to say hello: his

superiors in the bank (he had no inferiors) avoided greeting him, preferring instead to touch him vaguely on the shoulder, which, though
disgusting in its own right, a wobbly pudding of tufted flesh, at least
had the advantage of being clothed. No one had liked him in a long
time.

He was the kind of man who said most things twice. "We're like
nothing to them. Every single one of us could die."

"I don't get that," said the younger man. "You said we were all
mixed in now. Interbred for two hundred generations. . . ."

"They don't care about themselves!" Styce interrupted. "They're
cannibals on Niburu. That's their home planet. We were nothing but
slaves to them, slaves to mine gold, which they used to make heat
and light. Most of them were eight feet tall. We worshipped them as
gods. You can see in those Sumerian bas-reliefs in the British
Museum.

"I read about it in a book called *The Twelfth Planet*," he continued after a pause.

The younger man grimaced, then stretched out his jaw and snapped
his teeth together. Yellow and discolored, they made a satisfying
snap. In nine years, barring any sort of incomprehensible calamity,
he would die of an intracranial neoplasm in the city of Leeds. "So
we'll have to fight them then," he said. "We're not as helpless this
time around."

"Perhaps not. They do have an advantage, though."

"What's that?"

"They can read minds."

All day he'd been afraid. That morning he had woken as if under a
dim, inchoate nebula of doubt, riven with anxiety as if by spears of
light. "The Twelfth Planet," he had muttered to himself as he had
blundered out of bed into his slippers: this mania of his, gathering
now, was a way of struggling against these feelings by a process of de-
flection, the way you might squeeze your thumb with a nutcracker
as a cure for seasickness.

The younger man saw nothing of this. He saw an older fellow,
overweight, standing by the window, just beginning to unbutton his
shirt. He scarcely listened when the fellow spoke: "The light is dim
where they are. Most of the time, except for the foci of the ellipse,
you see, they don't have a setting or a rising sun. They seed their
atmosphere with molecules of gold, which reflect light from the rifts
in their own oceans, the volcanic activity there. The light is always
dim, so they don't sleep."

"What are you, an astronomer then?"

"No, I work at the Royal Bank of Scotland. I'm the chief teller there in town," which was a lie.

"That's all right," said the younger man.

Roland Styce turned toward him. "There is one advantage, though. A blind spot, if you will."

"What's that?"

"It's because of the way they reproduce in an abnormal way. Because of their reptilian nature, and the way they go into a stasis without sleeping. They don't understand anything about love. You know, what we call love. It's like a blind spot. It enrages them."

"Well, that's all right then."

The garden wall was low, about five feet, and faced with yellow stone. Beyond it, and beyond the raised beds, the grass spread flat and featureless to the back steps, like a lava field abraded into greenness under the acid rain.

The door was locked and barred. Solid oak, imported from Poland. On the other side, a tufted Oriental carpet ran the length of the hall, various living rooms on either side. Mr. Styce had inherited the house from his mother in 2016. She had died of an aneurysm that same summer.

Along the way down the corridor, you smelled a number of competing fragrances, more intense at intervals if you licked your lips. Sawdust. Lemon furniture polish. Then you went past the kitchen's open door, the sealed cabinets full of sealed jars of Indian chutneys and pickles. A bowl of onions. Some wilted flowers. The stair rose up and turned a corner to the first floor. A skylight shone west above the landing, and the air was pricked with motes of gold.

These people, these creatures, sealed up like jars or cans, struggling to see or know or understand even a little bit, how could you not open them and spill them out? Caught in a spacial moment, how could you not twist them, stretch them out beyond their capabilities? Some broke open and rose up higher and higher until you could see the world and time and space spread away.

Yet up there, behind that closed door, two men embraced on a yellow bed.

Favored by Strange Gods:
A Selection of Letters from
James Tiptree, Jr. to Joanna Russ

With an introductory note by Nicole Nyhan

JAMES TIPTREE, JR. WAS BORN on a typewriter. He was the secret invention of Dr. Alice Bradley Sheldon, a behavioral psychologist who lifted "Tiptree" from a jar of marmalade and covertly wrote under the name for nearly a decade. Tiptree debuted with *Birth of a Salesman* in the March 1968 issue of *Analog* and rapidly gained a reputation for his bold, original voice and fast-paced interstellar adventures. A coruscating experimental talent, Tiptree rose to the upper echelons of SF at a time when a new generation of transgressive writers was beginning to claim the genre as serious literature, including J. G. Ballard, Ursula K. Le Guin, Robert Silverberg, Harlan Ellison, Samuel R. Delany, and Joanna Russ. Tiptree's name was recognizable to most SF enthusiasts within a couple of years, but his "real" identity remained a mystery. Until 1977, Tiptree refused to attend live events or answer personal questions, and could only be contacted through P.O. Box 315 in McLean, Virginia.

As Tiptree, Alice Sheldon exchanged lively and intimate correspondence with some of the most important writers of speculative fiction. Over time, James Tiptree, Jr. took on a life of his own, developing long-standing relationships. While as a story writer Tiptree was known for deploying short bursts of robust prose, in his letters Tiptree was effusive and gregarious, a comic performing with preternatural bravado. An ingratiating and charmingly self-deprecating correspondent, Tiptree was alternately a compassionate listener, educator, contrarian, and avid advice giver, often picturing himself as a wizened old sage and referring to himself as "Uncle Tip." With women, he was also an audacious flirt.

That "Tiptree" was a pseudonym was initially obvious to some, but few questioned the authenticity of Tiptree's "masculine" voice. Beyond exhibiting deep technical knowledge of military tactics, weaponry, and biological science in his stories, Tiptree revealed in his letters a conventionally masculine CV, including references to positions he had held in the government and military. Tiptree also displayed surprising compassion for women during an era when SF was still widely viewed as a "boys club." Some of his friends wondered if he was homosexual. In Robert Silverberg's introduction to Tiptree's story collection *Warm Worlds and Otherwise*, he lambasted the theory that Tiptree might be a woman, comparing the author to Hemingway for the "prevailing masculinity" and "veiled complexity" of his writing. (Silverberg later wrote Sheldon, "You've given my head a great needed wrenching.")

Igniting what would become a lifelong epistolary friendship, Tiptree wrote a fan letter to Joanna Russ in April 1972. At the time, Russ was a young writer and academic who was emerging as the premier voice of radical feminism in SF, and had recently completed writing her magnum opus, *The Female Man*. Under the guise of Tiptree, Sheldon wanted to discuss feminism with Russ, but the gender balancing act of maintaining a male persona created regular turbulence in their relationship. Russ was extremely skeptical of Tiptree's motives. Moreover, Sheldon's own views on feminism were complicated; at the height of Women's Lib, Sheldon identified as a feminist of an "older school," and, pessimistic about women's potential to achieve meaningful collective power, she worried that women of Russ's generation were too vocal, too militant.

The rockiest period in Tiptree and Russ's relationship occurred around 1974, when the two were invited to participate in a written symposium that addressed the growing and heated debates about women's roles in the genre. The symposium was organized by Jeffrey D. Smith (later published in his fanzine *Khatru*), and included contributions from Vonda N. McIntyre, Suzy McKee Charnas, and Samuel R. Delany, among others. Tiptree submitted an essay positing two major behavioral patterns to be found in human beings: "the male pattern," characterized by aggression, and "Mothering," characterized by the instinct to nurture. As a research psychologist, Sheldon looked to evolutionary biology as a means of overcoming sexist cultural conditioning, and as an apocalyptic thinker, she believed that motherhood—as a psychological state—was key to humanity's salvation. But Sheldon's personal concerns were wrapped inside the man who represented them, and when Tiptree argued, "Men have the power," Delany simply countered, "Who are you threatening?" The essay was widely dismissed, and for years Russ attacked Tiptree in private, in part for attempting to resurrect an old dualism between the sexes.

By this time Sheldon had begun submitting stories under a new persona, Raccoona Sheldon, a former schoolteacher from the Midwest. Tiptree informed Jeffrey Smith that his friend Raccoona used the pen name—taken, obviously, from a masked animal—because her own name had been "used up by a high-voltage media star so it no longer belongs to her." In reality, Raccoona was a kind of repository for Sheldon's overtly feminist tales, which she believed wouldn't pass under a man's name. Raccoona enjoyed modest success, earning a Nebula for her novelette *The Screwfly Solution*, but her name would be largely forgotten.

Russ and Tiptree eventually reconciled. They continued to spar, but Tiptree made Russ feel understood in a way that no man ever had. Russ, openly lesbian, later told Sheldon, "I was madly in love with [Tiptree] . . . and sensed uneasily that this was odd." Still, Sheldon wasn't fully comfortable embracing Tiptree's role as SF's token male feminist, and when "The Women Men Don't See" was nominated for a Nebula Award in 1975, Tiptree withdrew it from the ballot, believing the story to have earned a nomination, not on its own merit, but because it was written by a man.

When Sheldon was finally "outed" by Tiptree's fans, she was terrified of losing her literary friendships, which included perhaps the only feminist comrades she'd made in her lifetime. Insecure about her position within the women's movement, she feared that Russ would not forgive the deception; among second-wave feminists, the mask of Tiptree risked being perceived as a cowardly escape route. To Le Guin, Tiptree confided, "entre nous & sub specie aeternitatis, I am one of those that always get accidentally guillotined when the Great Day of liberation comes, because . . . I guess . . . I am full of parentheses. Revolutions can't abide parenthesis." Upon hearing that her secret was out, Sheldon picked up the phone. "Oh, you're going to hate me," she told Russ. "This is James Tiptree, Jr."

Russ took the news graciously. Their correspondence grew open and frank, and homed in on the subject of Sheldon's sexuality. Despite the fact that she had married two men in her lifetime, in her youth Sheldon kept falling for "beautiful, unscrewable, hideously rich and very ill-fated girls," although she never had a physical relationship with another woman. Sheldon told Russ about her mother's attempt to seduce her as a teenager, and identified herself as a "frustrated gay." In reply, Russ sent Sheldon a love letter. She proposed to meet in person: "Consider yourself well and truly propositioned. . . . Are you ready to have mad adventures in your waning years?" Sheldon, petrified, replied with only a postcard, apologizing for sending on "such dreary gloop."

By January 1977, Sheldon was depressed. Tiptree, she felt, was dead. "'I' am not a writer," she wrote in her journal, "'I' haven't a story in my head—all that went to J.T. Jr. and became, or was born, somewhat deformed or deracinated, by being his."

Following the unveiling, Sheldon lamented the change of tone she perceived among her correspondents, and, as a woman, Sheldon felt she had lost the implicit narrative authority upon which Tiptree thrived: "As Tiptree, I had an unspoken classificatory bond to the world of male action; Tiptree's existence opened to unknown possibilities of power. And, let us pry deeper—to the potential of evil. Evil is the voltage of good; the urge to goodness, without the potential of evil, is trivial. A great bore. Part of the appeal of Tiptree was that he ranged himself on the side of good by *choice*. Alli Sheldon has no such choice."

Sheldon continued to write under Tiptree's name, authoring numerous stories and two full-length novels, but for her, the "magic" of his persona was gone. Russ and Sheldon continued to exchange letters and phone calls for the remainder of Sheldon's life, but, as with the majority of Tiptree's correspondents, they never met in person. Russ and Sheldon shared hundreds of letters over the years, and although the letters here are only a sample of their correspondence, this is the most comprehensive selection of Tiptree's letters to Russ published to date.

NOTE. Alice B. Sheldon's preferred spelling of the name "James Tiptree, Jr." included the comma after the surname "Tiptree," although the author often neglected to include the comma in correspondence. We have maintained the comma in our title, running heads, and introduction, but we have left the name as Sheldon wrote it in her letters. In some instances throughout this selection (typos, punctuation, underlining, etc.), we have standardized the letters to fit editorial style; in others (neologisms, atypical capitalization, numerals, British-inflected spelling), we have maintained the original style.

We are grateful to Sheldon's biographer Julie Phillips; to Sheldon's literary executor, Jeffrey D. Smith; to Linda Long at the University of Oregon Libraries; and to the Lesbian Herstory Archives for their generous assistance in the compilation and publication of these letters.

James Tiptree Jr.
Box 315
McLean, VA
22101   [c. April 1972]

Dear Joanna Russ:

Liked your GENRE piece in the Bulletin so much it finally nudged
me out of my shell, I've long been a crypto-admirer of your work but
have denied myself the pleasure of saying so. Consider this a simple
fan-ism requiring *no* response: I have a bad habit of writing mash
notes when writing moves me and the last thing I want is to take up
the recipient's writing time!

Funny thing—when a work is so universally (& justly) admired as
your [AND] CHAOS DIED, one feels, Oh, X doesn't need any more ego-
boo, my god, everybody's genuflecting. And then you later discover
that X is getting lots of brickbats and jealous darts along with the
acclaim, and has many bad days when the mail-box yields nothing
but woe and abrasion, and often wonders why the hell keep on struggling drearily to make something right . . . and maybe an extra cheer
from the back benches isn't out of order after all.

When one is young one cruelly measures oneself against the landmarks of the great, delighted to pounce on flaws, and accepting as a
right the fact that their work has furnished a great part of the inside
of one's own head . . . And then one day the great X dies and it's
revealed he or she led a life of great bleakness and almost zero feed-
back . . . and the tiny grain of support one could have furnished is
forever withheld . . . This verges on bathos and the illusion of uni-
versal omnipotence, but it happened to me a couple of times . . . and
probably accounts for the mash-notes.

So—just to let you know there's one more highly appreciative and
eager-for-more admirer out here . . .

All best,
James Tiptree Jr.

* * *

141

James Tiptree, Jr.
Temporarily
c/o Bradley Lodge
Florence,
WISC 54121   [c. Aug./Sept. 1973]

Dear Joanna:

Your letter was more appreciated than I can tell you.

But holy peanutbutter, dear writer—do you imagine that anyone with half a functional neurone can read your work and not have his fingers smoked by the bitter, multi-layered anger in it?

It *smells* revolutionary—no, wait, not "revolutionary." Not the usual. It smells and smoulders like a volcano buried so long and deadly it is just beginning to wonder if it can explode. Fantastic anger. Like the writer is watching every word, saying, Cool it, cool it, don't say it.

I don't have a sample of your work in my duffle in this broken-down forest, if I had maybe I could show you some of the pages where the sentences feel actually *bitten off.*

What the hell do you think sends some readers like me so? The scent of a new just anger, the sound of someone saying the new true word. I mean, we already have Jane Austen, all the decorous ones. We even have Sylvia Plath. I personally am watching you . . . Hostile? Sweet feathered Quetzalcoatl, it has not escaped even my tiny dimming brain that you belong to the oldest and worst-squashed race on Earth. What more appropriate emotion than anger? What task more urgent than freeing & finding yourselves now and the hell with any other minor claimants?

I dig it, Joanna. I am fascinated by it intellectually and emotionally. I am an old type with no near woman to oppress or free, but I am glad to be alive while it is happening, or beginning to happen. I read and learn as much as I can, starting with de Beauvoir—yes I have read Korda—I guess I have spent most of my recent writing income on books from the feminist presses. I'm trying to evaluate my own work very critically—let me mention that later if you're still with me.

The point I want to make here is that I don't expect strokes or friendship for my sentiments.

You see, I had a crazy upbringing in which I got early acquainted with some of the bads in life. (Crucifixion, anyone?) And for some reason, maybe because I caught a little of it myself, I knew immediately which side I was on. The bottom side. When the jackboots kick

142

in the door, it's *me* they're coming for. My fantasies are of escape, not of wearing the jackboots.

So, of course, like a good little Midwestern liberal (with a brain formed in the Congo) I used to sidle up to the local oppressed with my heart offered on my little outstretched hand. Dear Socialist brother, dear Black brother, dear American Indian brother (I said), this is a terrible wrong; here is Tiptree come to help you all I can.

And of course—as per historical process—the scowling Socialist-Black-Amerind-Etcetera brother promptly took one look and instantly shat all over me, as the handiest representative of the oppressor.

Now oddly enough I wasn't alienated. Because in the intervals of beshitting me the oppressed or some of their representatives took time to teach me a little about the mechanics of time and power and political movements, which greatly edified me and struck me as perhaps the facts of sex strike others. One of the things I learned was to keep my ears open when I heard any group of people described as:

Childish
Emotional
Incapable of reason
Happy when labouring unpaid
Given to artistic expression rather than thought
Excessively compassionate *and* vicious
Excessively loyal *and* treacherous
Excessively cowardly *and* murderous
Requiring leadership for their own good

and
Supremely content with their lot *unless stirred up by outside agitators.*

Plus, of course, an amplitude of reasons from theology, physiology and common sense why all these things should be true.

Ring any bells?

Anyway, the point I'm trying to make is that as I sidle up to the scowling Female brother with eyes alight with sympathy, experience has taught me to wear my catcher's mask and offer my little heart neatly enclosed in washable plastic. I recognise history at work. But the heart is beating all the same. I am no masochist; I merely refuse to have my enthusiasms dashed by the purely incidental behavior of the dramatis personae.

James Tiptree, Jr.

Not because I'm a sweet type, Joanna. I'm not. I'm not even un-prejudiced. I do loathe most people without much regard to race, sex, creed, or national origin, but I have also deep reservoirs of bigotry on the subject of Arabs, prelates of the Roman church, and particularly for Germans and other Upper Paleolithic survivals. If you happen to fall into one of those brackets, though, don't worry. (Not that you would.) I don't try for consistency in my *dis*likes; it's hard enough to keep up with one's admirations.

But look—the usual guilt about writing to a working writer is getting to me. If I go on a bit, do I have your agreement that you won't read or answer unless you actually happen to feel like it *and have time?*

You see, your letter sent me mumbling to myself all the way out to Mother's hospital and back. (I'm here standing by a catastrophically aging parent with a heart attack.) It was the best thing that's happened around here in—well, I guess it's only two weeks but it seems years. I yearn to go on about specific points, but scout's honor: dump this if the time is wrong, right?

Have I said enough to make clear that your hostility is not only no surprise to me but is part of what I admire? I'm the amiable one. You can do the eviscerating.

Specific points:

That term "abortion." Joanna, I have always taken that to refer to a defect in the fetus, not the mother. Am I wrong? Should I associate it with the fetus-bearer?

But how, when the vast majority of spontaneous abortions are in fact due to fetal defect? And when it is notorious that maternal physiology tends to support and favor the fetus even to the cost of the mother's health? Should I regard involuntary abortion as something a woman does, for which she is in some way blameworthy so that the term reflects on her?

(I'm not of course talking about voluntary abortion, of which I am heartily in favor; I cannot see what business men have telling women what to do with their own bodies.)

I wish I had your MLA [Modern Language Association] speech, I'm genuinely puzzled. But I will certainly stop using the term.

And of course my saying the book is an abortion does cast ACE in the role of mother, which is pretty silly to contemplate.

But I do resist calling my book a premature ejaculation—although several of the stories deserve no more—because to me an ejaculation is a non-viable half of something looking for completion. It is my

144

hope that a couple of the stories, maybe the book as a whole, have at least a *tenuous* zygosity.

Will you settle for "a semi-addled blastomere"?

Next point: Dammit, where did you find a story in which there are "chicken-people who did in the Earth ambassador by having him seduced by the maid"? Jealousy twinges my old bones; I think you spent the afternoon writing letters to six people who sent you their books—there, *that's* done!—and got mine mixed. There is not, I swear, a chicken, an ambassador or a maid in mine.

What there is, Joanna, is a batch of very early Tiptree-with-Meccano-set first stories, mixed with a couple from later on. (I started all at once bang in '67, and stunned myself because everything sold. I do NOT know how to write.) That "alien giantess" one was '68, I'd just been reading Koestler's THIEVES IN THE NIGHT, remember—if I have the title right—the psychically scarred girl? Probably a male fantasy, although I swear I've met something close. Similar to people of any sex who've been stomped by gangs.

Anyway, I was running through a lot of stereotypes. I blush. I've counted up, intending to mention it to Vonda McIntyre, who occasionally educates me. Of those 15 tales, only one has a female hero, and she's dependent on a male mutant dog. (But she is only 15 and is armless.) There's also an aged female explorer who is now crazy (Mother), one race-track steward, two assistant girl revolutionaries and a nurse. The rest of them range from flat-out sex-objects, "kittens," spear-carriers and off-stage noises to total absence. (Oh, I forgot the raped polyglot who learns to love.)

Joanna, when I realised this it struck me quite serious. I then looked at my other, later stuff. Not much better, Joanna. Not much better. Oh, there's a giant arthropod mother who is forgetting intelligent speech, and a girl who tries to have sexual congress with the Earth, etc. etc. I do have one coming out in MFSF [*The Magazine of Fantasy & Science Fiction*] where two women are so fed up that they manage to leave with aliens, told from the point of view of a semi-macho male who misunderstands the whole thing, maybe that's better—or maybe it'll just be embarrassing, like whites writing about blacks. We all know how *that* works.

What to do, Joanna? This is serious, you know. It obviously can't be solved by just changing all the hes into shes. Vonda or Quinn gave me a blast on Heinlein's female jocks, who are just men writing in skirts.

I suspect what you'd say is, look about you. That's the trouble, I do. The women—most of them—aren't born yet, I think. I have just finished hours of conferences with the phalanx of women caring for Mother. Most of them strike me as aging little girls, locked in farm wives' bodies. (Most men are the same, I hasten to say; the trouble is, I'm *in* my body and I can't get the same understanding of theirs.) (No; what I really mean is *I'm in my experience.*)

I don't know Golda Meir. I don't know Indira Gandhi. I guess I don't know any self-actualised women, although I've met and worked with some damn competent ones. I know they weren't adequately recognised. And I sensed the thing Quinn or was it Vonda told me, the terrible scars in their self confidence. A man with their abilities would have had the world by the ears.

But the inner voice asks, is it my bias that makes me see them as their *abilities*, that is, their competence in male-type jobs? This is male-type people-seeing. And the view of an old, old male person at that. I know there's something out there, something that will tip the landscape into a whole other dimension if it gets born—if it gets seen.

But what the hell IS IT?

Do you wonder I read your stories?

Well. This has been unconscionable.

Excuse me while I go write a story about a male grizzly bear who is trapped all alone in a space capsule headed out of the galaxy . . .

> Reverently as ever,
> Truly best.
> Tip

P.S. I'm usually called Tip. Are you ever called Jo?

* * *

Still in Extremis, I mean Florence
WISC 54121
c/o Bradley Lodge   25 Sep 73

Dear Joanna:

This is being writ after reading your letter only 3 times which is an error because your paragraphs are incandescent and crowded and only by repeated instant replay will I really find everything in them.

And they evoke the urge to communicate back—irresistible—I yield to it without even token defense, but please, once and for all, Be It Understood this is *not* to be a burden on you. Is that really understood? I have always had friendships in which the ground-rules were that one could wander off unexpectedly for 5 or 10 years and walk back in the door and resume—"As I was saying—"

Two things sort of wrote themselves in neon letters over your pages as I was reading, one big, one small.

Small first: It is obvious since you write on both sides of the page that YOU DO NOT KEEP CARBONS. This is *very wrong*. This is a sin. Sin. Why? Because you are tossing off stuff like a fire-wheel, gems— like the line about what feminism means to some men (Big Mama Will Fix), about the faculty wives and colleagues, the creepy adolescents, etjesuschristcetera which are too good to be sown on the wind, they are notebook stuff. You think they will stay there, in your mind— please, human, take it from me they will NOT. They will change and evolve and shed themselves—or just ignominiously be forgotten. Letters in which you SAY anything should be part of your notebook. Then they will be there when you need them fresh and beating, not even because you're a writer but because one of the most useful things a thinking person can have is his own past. I mean *useful*, not just elegiac.

I mean this so strongly that if you get a gross of Letterex for Xmas you will know who sent it.

That's the small thing. But don't toss your head and paw, it's not so damn small.

The bigger thing is that I kept thinking all the way through, Oh god, but I wonder if she realises it is double trouble. Joanna, I know you realise abstractly that in addition to being female in a male-dominated and fucked-up world (uh, male orientation there? Forgive it, let's get on). And being human in a world being quite probably ruined, and extinguished—you have the nearly unbearable state of being a writer, a bright, sensitive one, a fast head, the pointy-asymptote of the distribution curve—in a world of relatively *dumb* people. This situation serves as an amplifier to everything else, it's Woolf and Plath's problem too, of course, it's Crane and Dylan and the high IQ kids who end up mutely running elevators and reading Sanskrit between stops. It's very nearly insoluble, because if you join with people to right the wrongs of women, or the wrongs of the world, the difference in your head will make them nearly intolerable to you and vice versa.

Some of the impossibility of living is quite simply due to this, not to the being woman problem (sorry about that "problem," consider it shorthand).

I did a lot of reading once about bright kids, the really brights, and the thing that stands out a mile is one common problem—shattered ego. They speak—and no one hears, no one understands.

A marvellous example of this, Norbert Wiener, you know, certified genius infant prodigy who went on to continue prodigising. At about 55 he was speaking at Brandeis with an old friend of mine, a journalist-pundit type. Wiener goes out and makes his usual brilliant speech, leaves them on their backs in the aisles adoring him, totters back to my friend, who is about 3 feet tall, and grabs his hand and gasps, "*Was I all right‽‽*" Shattered, the self-confidence never regrows.

So you must, I think, try to separate the shit-storm into the part you're getting because of anti-female stuff and the part you're getting because you are that barely viable thing, a bright creator.

This is, of course, no solution—who has solutions?—but I am a great believer in dividing one's enemies into boxes.

Let's see, I should say something about me, I guess. "Old" means coming up sixty . . . and means also 15 years of increasingly feeling the discrimination against age. When they look at you and see only the oncoming claims on their pension plan. You start becoming invisible, you're going, you DO NOT COUNT . . . It does not bug me much because internally I'm in better shape than previous decades, youth I recall as a series of suicide attempts.

No, I'm not gay so far as I know. Although the young of any sex are starting to have a wonderful irrational glamor for me, I don't think it's actually sex. I'm more or less non-sex, it was a disaster area for me too. Mixed up with hopeless adorations for people who not only didn't but couldn't conceivably love back, who had no such needs. Also discovering I had not the easy capacity to take, to enjoy myself—that I was only weakly macho, that there was in fact Something Wrong With Me Inside.

I think you can take it as proved that the people who have some kind of ear for other people's harrowings always have Something Wrong Too. Whether it's a tour in the booby-hatch, a terrible parent, a crippled leg or gonad, a struggle with alcohol—somehow they too have been on the outside. Even if only in their heads . . . I'm not really sure exactly what was or is Wrong with me, but it's there. I am not one of THEM . . . A good bit can be put down to an insane upbringing—did you ever know any missionaries' sons? I'm not one but some of the circumstances were similar. By 10 I was already a solitary not by choice, and have continued so . . . Over the years I have built odd relations with other solitaries and with a species I think I have discovered, the crypto-solitary.

As I mentioned, political movements came to obsess me for a time, the fascination of the psychic castrate for actually doing something, and it was then that I realised that people who said, "Women are a mystery, I can't understand them" had never tried the reference-frame of quite simply an *oppressed minority*. I proposed this to a friend who ran much of the ILGWU [International Ladies' Garment Workers' Union] political side and received guffaws. (Interesting especially in that the ILGWU is mostly women.)

I remember also what a shock it was to discover that the oppressed are not all burning angels awaiting the striking-off of chains, that oppression does things to the victim, makes them into [Stepin] Fetchits, or they twist shockingly to survive, or become talking brains, anesthetised—all the gallery of cripples we have learned to know when the Black lid came off . . . Bettelheim's imitation of the oppressor being not the least chilling.

I was thinking for awhile that it is covert recognition of the anger in your work which accounts for the peculiar pall of silence among some readers anyway . . . books let go out of print, strange mutedness. Each one pulls back their pseudopods, puts it out of mind. Dangerous, irregular. Don't look, maybe it'll go away . . . I think that *is* operative. Giving you the impression of being invisible, inaudible, unrecognised.

But also it's what happens to good stuff, to things above Conan level. Almost everything I like gets treated thus. The double problem of being bright plus being a social force for change and protest.

By the way, something of this death-by-oblivion seems to have happened to Kit Reed's ARMED CAMPS. An imperfect story with some amazing stuff in it. Screams rather than roars.

(I wonder if you reviewed it? Don't have any books here, can't look it up.)

Every writer I like with whom I correspond seems to have mentioned that they live in a pall of silence, get no feed-back.

Maybe I should confess about my writing letters to writers. You see, in my early solitude, books meant a great deal—they were my only conversation. I was among other things a great Yeats fan. (His bleakness suits me like familiar underwear.) (And of course his wings fly.) So . . . suddenly I noticed Yeats—the actual person—had *died*. And I had never in any way sent back one iota of the life he had sent out. Never pipped. Not because it was a great thing that Tiptree "appreciated" him, but just that there was *a reader* out there. A person whose head he had in part furnished. And then somebody else died . . . Orozco. He had meant [something] to me too, I actually knew him tangentially. And it came to me that maybe living creators lived in considerable solitude and anguish and the mail-box might contain not a daily stream of Nobel prizes but complaints, soap samples and tax bills. And it wouldn't hurt to drop a card, to put my money where my head was. So I sort of started writing, you know, little cards saying That was Great. Well, you do know. You got one.

Probably stupid as hell, call me a frustrated mother with delusions of fixing up everybody.

What the hell, it's what I do.

And it's easy for me with writers because I came to my own mediocre efforts so late that my ego isn't invested—which means the writing won't ever be much more than mediocre unless I'm favored by strange gods. It does mean that I look at the thing itself, not prizes, and haven't that deadly competitiveness. Which is a great relief; I've HAD that, in other fields.

I don't know if this is a proper answer to yours, Joanna, obviously it isn't, yours was full of real stuff, mine is more a Bear of Very Little Brain, and at 3 AM too. (The scene here is so threatening I do my living from midnight to dawn.) But I mean more than the gummy brain can say.

That Artaud quote is fine. I used to cling to a Cocteau phrase— "The people who live with a perpetual nausea, *people whose passports are not in order*" . . . In the Nazi times that meant more resonance than now.

Now I'll go back & read your letter again . . . and find out what the ugh day has in store.

May I use "ovular"?

Deepest regards
Tip

P.S. I meant to ask you about the senses in which you use "femininity" and "female." I have been taking "feminine" as the Betty Friedan type of thing, Oooh, that horrid mouse! And "female" as the Real Thing. Whatever it (a) is and (b) will turn out to be.

N.B. Hey, mind if I make you mad by saying, damn it, face it, however painful & nearly lethal—I envy you. Why? Because oh jesus, you have MATERIAL. The last aliens to report in. New Stuff . . . even if it's killing you. Can you imagine how *dull* the world would be if suddenly you woke up as a male? Talk about castrated, you'd feel robbed. They've taken my STUFF away! . . . For comparison, look at Tiptree, think of the marvellous new insights to be forged out of, what, getting old? Timor mortis conturbat me? 2000 years of brighter minds working that vein . . . whereas every ten minutes you can say something that's never been said before, your letter had five I never heard. The writer may laugh where the person weeps, no?

P.P.S. Can't resist—I too have had deep friendships with rats, I dig bats—one is hanging up in the corner of my cabin; I like snakes a lot and have the illusion that spiders like me. Large ones espec. (Just to revert to normalcy, being myopic I do *not* like fast armored flying things that go SSSRRRR and sting.)

* * *

James Tiptree Jr.
P. O. Box 315
McLean VA. 22151
S.F.W.A. [Science Fiction Writers of America]   23-4 Apr 74

Dear Joanna:

Well, this was going to start Here I am in calm of mind & midnight about to enjoy a really high-class dialog with a really h-cl. mind—and I made the mistake of first opening some suspicious-looking mail in this pile. So now I find that some dear sweet stupid maniacs have nailed me for some official award and loused up my self-image and I am all shook up—never mind about that Calme-toi jazz, I am a shook-up type. So I am vibrating like an unstrung racquet and vomiting inconspicuously and wondering, does my aversion to awards mean I am really an avidly ambitious creep with a sterling reaction-formation—version A of Tiptree, you're no good? No: What I really feel is that I don't like real life getting so much like fake life; I don't like divisions, labels, phoney crapology no matter how well meant. Above all, I don't like medals and prizes. All the medals I ever got somebody else should have gotten only for political-chauvinistic reasons they weren't "acceptable." All the art prizes—no, *most* of the art & lit prizes I've ever seen awarded had a purely random connection with merit. And look unfailingly insane to later eyes. I was brought up on the motto:

Life is fair. Some people have talent and other people win prizes.

Excuse me while I take some more Bentyl.

All right, that's enough of the inner-convulsion dept, let's go back to the calm of midnight.

Listen, would it kill you to drop a line about the tenure madness?

Glad you liked nutsy grandpa. Steal anything, it's an honour. And listen, I stole from you, you'll see if Vonda takes HOUSTON: your line about "the night side of Tiptree." I now feel obligated to collect tags you might like in return—but it'll have to start next letter; no felicity right now.

You're right of course about the miserable plight of the young Maya girl(s); *if* they could combine with other women they could break out. The tragedy is that their mothers—*and the man's mother*—would be the first to lynch them. Man, Uncle Tom is no word for the problem of the indoctrinated slave women. The fear, the fear. The bone-deep acquiescence.

The age disparity, by the way, is common in primitive societies and constitutes one of the basic power-mechanisms whereby men rule. Little girls are pitted, individually, against full-grown men . . . This same system has been evolved by certain spiders, by the way, I found it in John Crompton's book and used it in that LOVE IS THE PLAN thing. The mature female is larger and more ferocious than the male; so they have solved the problem by programming males to capture and tie up and feed immature females, with whom they mate. When the female becomes strong enough to break loose she is fertilised and the impregnator has escaped. If you're interested, I'll look up the species; it's a striking bit of biology.

What I meant by fearing that women cannot free themselves with the present large proportion of men alive is that men act in concert and in an adversary way; they are power-oriented. They also act on & against the youngest women. Women are isolated from each other by the reward structure of the male world; they can rarely act in concert without jeopardising themselves or their children short-range. And I tend to think, on the basis of say, Goodall's chimp observations, that much of the female primate's "bonding" ability is taken up by her bond with her offspring. She forms small groups with her daughters rather than lateral female peer-groups. This is great for the race but weakening for women.

No, Joanna, it is not that men are individually all-powerful ogres. (God knows I would quail before any small female gymnast.) It is that they have a *margin*, which they amplify by unequal age-ratios (25 to 12) and they drive for power. I became enormously impressed with the pervasiveness of men's power-orientations as I worked up an imaginary world for Vonda's antho. In every interaction, I was confronted again and again by the unneccasriness—sorry, *unnecessariness* of our standard way of reacting. The insanity of it. The depth of it. Of course, writing from a tense work-ethic Western competitive base it is seen in exaggeration, but I've seen it in the Congo. The insistence on confrontation, on dominance-submission structure . . . I tried peeling it away, and what came out was a world that so charmed me that I have another tale started in it.

And I'm going out on the limb of saying it is a predominantly, biologically male behavioral orientation. I do not go the whole killer-ape route and I deplore Ardrey (not to mention Lorenz) but in every other major primate with two exceptions you see the same thing, and you see it in most of the old-world simians: The males authority-structuring themselves, the females utilising a fluid, informal, unserious power-structure or no power-structure at all. (The exceptions are the gibbon, a fairly remote relative about whom nobody is too sure except that they live in pairs, and the orang, about whom no one is sure of much of anything . . . Gorilla males are also far more peaceable & permissive to others than most apes; that may give us hope, close as we are. On the other hand, gorillas are extremely lethargic about nearly everything.) . . . I guess my cover is fraying a little here, Joanna; yes, I was sort of mixed up in what are known as the "soft" sciences. But I am not anybody anyone ever heard of, Tiptree's vast original research had about one (Polish) reader. I am deeply interested in applying some of our new, eleventh-hour information about our cousins to our own behavioral predicaments; if possible more carefully than has been done. Fascinations.

Well, this is more monolog than dialog, but the dialog empathy is there. Let a well wisher hear if you can? . . . Eager to see that novel bit.

LOVE BACK,
Tip

Oh—about that "writing from POV of woman" bit. Call off your artillery, all I meant was merely having the female characters do & say realistically. That *has* to be done, for crissake.

James Tiptree, Jr.

* * *

James Tiptree Jr.
P. O. Box 315
McLean VA. 22151
S.F.W.A.   9 May 74

Dear Joanna,

Very glad to get your letter. I can imagine what a hellish, sickening, lonely, hunted-animal, stinking situation this university mess must be for you, and I admire your being able to attain private composure and mastery over it. By coincidence I just picked up Gertrude Ezorsky's "The Fight over University Women" in the NY *Review of Books*; evidently yours is one instance in a totally shameful scene. If you haven't seen the piece you might look at it for hints on helpful organisations and lines of action. From your comments on the two other women professors I would judge that your university is in drastic non-compliance. If you don't win your particular guerilla skirmish you may have to bring war to Buffalo . . . But my comments are all so long-range and out-of-it; doubtless you have been over and over all this.

What is clear, though, is that war has got to come to the universities; I had no idea they were so appallingly on the wrong side . . . Okay, call it a militant social movement, or enlightenment, or what; symbolic war. But real goals.

One item in the Ezorsky piece I had not known of was her reference to experiments by Goldberg and the Bems in which an article was rated for excellence with (a) a female and (b) a male author's name, and apparently rated lower by both male and female subjects under the (a) condition. The Bems' experiment is described as "informal"; perhaps the data isn't too solid. But somebody should replicate this fast, with an adequate paradigm. I'm subjectively sure they'd catch some good smelly fish . . . Wish I was still in a position to do it, it would be quick and cheap.

(By the way, is there any chance of your doing it? Probably not.)

This new Slater sounds good; would you believe I am still waiting for the original Slater you recommended, [THE] PURSUIT OF LONELINESS. My bookseller deserves a grenade up his computer, I keep on with him because he has an elderly-European-Intellectual telephone voice, and also lets me run up bills, but his attitude of doomed collapse toward anything that has to be "ordered from the publisher" is getting thick.

Listen thanks for the good words on the Nebula and the "Love Is the Plan" story, there is no one dead or alive from whom I could more value such kindness. But there is something wrong, incurably, with me and awards. That you liked the story is more than enough. My attitude is that someday maybe I can learn to use part of this Meccano set . . . someday . . . maybe. But whatever I'm working on is always the one before the one that's going to be better . . . Fflthh.

Listen, THE FEMALE MAN—dear jesus, what a title, the end-all. I hadn't connected with that before. What? What? . . . Okay, I'll wait to find out. But with difficulty . . . THE FEMALE MAN, my, my, Oh christ . . .

Yeah, as you say, men are as unknown as women, I'm just realising.

And I'm not a "new man," whatever else . . . But your radar is uncanny, "middle-size, slight, sandy-hair" would be just right before the grey came in. Also to be known by a scar on the (unmustached) upper lip where a house fell on me, giving me a vaguely cynical right profile. (The left one just looks like a homeless CPA.) . . . I don't know what Barry Malzberg looks like, outside of a smudgy image of something in hairy motion in an SFWA communiqué, but it would be hard for me to fit an imaginary body to his writing, unless it was some kind of eerie junkyard sculpture. But writers have accidental physiognomies. None of them look right, except for the same kind of crooked, anxious peering-out from behind the facade. I know what you look like, though: a black swan with some red feathers or flames or aura, whatever. I was glad to see this confirmed, again smudgily, by SFWA.

Yes, it was fine for Vonda. I relish that dauntless little gang out there, Quinn too. Now Quinn should win something, this mystery thing, I gather, is possible. I have to lie down after one of her letters, she has this cast of hundreds, and more activities than the Mafia, and an inescapable aroma of courage against odds rises up. A world I never knew. I have since heard that part of the courage concerns dreadful infirmities of the legs . . . So unfair when the young are assailed. So unfair.

I am trying to determine from your letter whether some kind of dignified letter from a fellow writer, presumably to . . . to what? Not the Dept., certainly?—would be of any service. Could you be less gallant and more specific?

(I doubt it.)

155

If it would be of even marginal help, though, do. Sort of "congratulations on having obtained such a towering & dedicated talent to teach this significant field, now turned to dismay at news that she is not to be kept on, wondering if you perceive how important this type of teaching ability is for an important group of students, etc." type of thing?

Maybe she thinks I have to make up my own mind? And me with my out-of-date university directory . . .

All strength to you in adversity. Don't laugh when I say I know a little of what you're going through. In 1943 I was court-martialled by the U.S. Army, on grounds (unfortunately justified) of insubordination. Restricted to quarters in a strange city, awaiting trial, I recall one very, very bleak night. It CAN'T happen to me! Maybe it doesn't sound so much, but in those days of, you know, fighting Hitler, eleven million people in it, the Army was the world. Which was declaring me surplus . . . Luckily they were hard up for junior officers, in the end I was just sent to a kind of Siberia, from which I weaseled back. Slowly . . . Never underestimate the power of a company commander, or a department chairman, even if he has the soul of a poisoned woodlouse, he has the buttons . . . So I picture you in similar plight. But at least you have a cause, a war, where I had only the results of personal folly.

May the power & calm at your centre increase amid the fray,

Love,
Tip

* * *

James Tiptree Jr.
P. O. Box 315
McLean VA. 22151
S.F.W.A.   17 July 74

Dear Joanna:

Happiness is having a free hour, a good sandwich and a glass of tea, and sitting down with a Russ essay on science fiction. Dammit, you make sense. You are about the only writer on science fiction whose nouns and verbs I understand. I hope this does not dismay you—

nothing greater than being appreciated by imbeciles—but I personally of course believe that it means that you think with precision and great range and express it all with divine succinctness.

I refer to your Subjunctivity piece in EXTRAPOLATION 15/1, which I have at last subscribed to.

That's an elegant bit of definition by Delany, isn't it? (I should send for that back issue.) You've probably forgotten your own thing entirely by now but it gave me such pleasure. I had about resigned myself to grunting and pointing after reading some of the Panshins' efforts—hope I'm not offensive here, just put it down to terminal aphasia on my part. Then I came on a thing of Delany's some time back, forget what, but it was like chopping open the cloud layer. He has a clear, clear head. He knows the tools, he knows what the hell he's doing and [where] we're all at, he has the feel of the open-endedness. And he has the learning. Rare in sf, he has a trained mind. And he has the delicacy of the true thinker, you never catch him clumping in heavy definitional boots past the sign that Angels Stop Here . . . I don't mean that he fails in definition or that there are mysteries we cannot name, that rot. I mean he keeps the subject alive on the operating table. He does not insist on putting in that last brick that includes infinity *out*.

All the above applies to you, too. That is what I mean by sense. Epistemological tact.

One of the beauties of his "has not happened" is that it places naturalistic fiction, the ugh mainstream, as a sub-division of sf. (Has not happened but could have.) I've felt for long that the so-called larger field of literature was in fact a restricted phase of the genre sf, not vice versa. That it was writing under constraints (could happen) that are in fact crutches for the reader whose thinking is limited to "could happen." And not only "could" but "is very probable in my little world and doesn't upset me."

The sf reader is one whose mind naturally races to the limit when a category comes up, who when told the boat is leaking immediately realises it may fill and sink, to put it in the narrowest possible case. I have been increasingly, slowly appalled as I go thru the years to discover that one is surrounded by a solid phalanx of people who when told "the boat is leaking" simply register—if that much—the item: "the boat is leaking." Period. *Period* . . . One in a hundred may even remember it next day.

The one in a thousand who asks, How fast? Or, Where are the lifeboats? or Should I help bail? . . . that one is a potential sf reader.

"EXTRAPOLATION" is really a very acute name for the journal, isn't it? Not in the sense that sf is extrapolation, but in the sense of a mental activity which can go along any dimension.

Well this is all in a very didactic vein which is not my natural way (I hope). Comes from the fact that your piece gave me a kind of grimly satisfied empathic glow, sort of Well, I guess THAT fixes 'em. Not that it was aggressive or controversy-seeking, just that it was a delighting demonstration of How to do it right. Like seeing a mama osprey demonstrating flying, a pretty scene I had the chance to watch in Yucatán. The great silver creature soared and did aerial arabesques, ending up with an extraordinary dance-in-place in the sunrise air, hooting what may have been encouragement to the large chick awkwardly flapping from palm to palm below.

Your observation that the reader carries his own actuality frame with him into the work has an interesting corollary. It might mean that the readership of at least some sf is bound to be extra-limited. Since there is a tacit dependence on the reader's *having* an adequate frame. Thus if the frame changes too much between cultures or times the work will be left inadequately anchored, more so than a could-happen work where the frame is explicit.

Even in my limited experience of writing, I've noticed a problem which I now understand since reading you: Being old, I've accumulated a heap of miscellaneous actuality data, rather a large heap. And I've been aware that effects I was trying to get were dependent on the reader's sharing that heap, or parts of it. And yet I could not bring the actuality itself in, it was as you said the effort to keep alive a *fluctuating* relationship between unnamed elements of actuality and the whatever-it-was I was trying to make. So I had simply to cut out parts that depended on the reader's sharing an improbably large part of my actuality . . . A totally different sort of problem than non-sf fiction faces, isn't it?

To take an absurd example, one can depend on the reader's frame for "the pastoral peacefulness of the twentieth century." But you can't do so for "the eleventh century."

Thank you, Joanna. Now I understand.

I love that description of a shifting, many-stranded relation in the work. I love your understanding of complexity. The description of the play of disbelief in satire. When something new is really well caught in words it gives me actual tangible joy. Like having an itchy brain scratched right? No; more like eating a perfect peach on a scorching hot day.

158

I have moments of wishing acutely that I could attend a good sf workshop or seminar, say one of yours. Or could at least listen to you and your few peers discuss or argue out some point. And then I have reality awakenings in which I know that if I had that luck I should doubtless never write again, that the kernel of my output is the lonesome exploration, powered by ignorant & infatuated curiosity. What I would learn is that I can't do it.

Now this was supposed to be a short snappy farewell note (I'm going on my travels for a couple of months) and a renewed hope that your fight is going well. Would it be a strain to drop a card saying what the status is? The bystanders do fret, you know.

And I was going to ask what you thought about Anna Kavan's ICE. (I don't know what I think yet, the jolt of European real craziness that comes off it first blurs vision.) And I was going to rejoice that you too rejoice in PALE FIRE. That Nabokov. And I was going to inquire if you enjoyed Calvino. And I was going to mention—apropos of your comment on the frame of actuality around a work of fantasy—how Tolkien seems to me to have built a doubleframe, using the Hobbits as a half-actual anchor to go into wilder fantasy and tying back again through a Hobbit-ending to the world of men . . . and then the strange effect of the Appendices.

Ah yes—this was to have been a very short letter. Are you well? Are you okay?

Mother Hen

* * *

22 Sep 74

Dearest Joanna:

[. . .] [Y]ou must not dump on Ursula Le Guin. For this reason: Whether you know it or not she does good to your movement. There is a place on the front for those gentle souls who only say it indirectly. (I have told her she hasn't really found her voice yet—I happen to like—maybe love—her personally very much.) In any movement the out-front radicals are always peeing on the moderate wing, but you forget what a terribly broad spectrum of opposition you confront.

159

The moderates—Uncle Toms if you will—convert their own sector of the opposition very effectively; they speak to people who would run screaming from you. You are a Malcolm X; she is a sort of Martin King. Her LEFT HAND OF DARKNESS—also even her (to me better) LATHE OF HEAVEN—quietly and unforgettably undercuts sexual stereotypes for certain readers you can't reach. Now maybe they *should* read you & more radical things, but they won't. They are only susceptible to seeping radicalism, to the slow percolation of low-voiced ideas. And the ideas ARE there, you know. Her style is the very quiet statement. When and if she tries to make a more direct one she may well fumble and lose effectiveness. I wish I could convince you to be glad of any elements of alliance and stop insisting that there is only one way to skin the chauvinist pig. Some pigs you have to reassure as you do it. You and your outspoken like are *indispensable*. But you are not alone. As Lenin or was it Marx said, from each according to his powers. She uses her powers. Quietly, persistently, she inserts the impression that there is something very wrong and absurd between the sexes. (Maybe you don't realise how clearly that idea comes through? It does.) That is a very useful function. Whether she lives up to what you think a WOMAN should be & say is, ultimately, irrelevant. Be content to lead and to be out there where the cold winds blow and save your imprecations for Phyllis Schlafly.

My life-gained impression of revolutionaries—from early labor-unions to you—is that they have a tendency not to remember who their real enemies are. They pour their hottest bile on deviationists whom the world sees as part of their movement.

Well, this is all much too avuncular. But I really have seen a fair amount of people working to Turn Things Around and liberate themselves in various ways and this phenomenon is one you see every goddam time. Of course it's so understandable. The one *almost* doing it right is the one you feel acutely about.

U. K. Le Guin is, besides, an odd human animal. She would, I think, die doing what only annoys you. Maybe you could call her a bourgeois liberal; she is comfortable in some of the life-roles she's found. (After all, who really knows how to be a mother???)

I repeat, you really do not know how strong you are. You suffer, god do you suffer. Like Cocteau, you will live always gripped by an inexplicable nausea, you are one of those, in his piercing phrase, "whose passports are not in order." You should try to disentangle those elements of your pain which arise from your non-sexual superb intelligence—a guaranteed ticket to anguish—from those which arise from your being a member of an oppressed class. Many of your predicaments and "outsideness" would happen if you were a man, you know. Christ the brilliant colleagues I have seen crucified for brilliance. (And some thorniness of personality.) Brilliance plus a refusal to compromise or close your eyes is the supreme crown of thorns in man or woman.

This is cold comfort, Joanna, but one of the few not wholly ineffectual remedies I have found for life is to find out what is doing which to you. And if part of your suffering is caused by a more general human fate at least it relieves you of the sick bottomless rage you have to feel about an injustice.

It is not of course "justice" that the brilliant be persecuted but it is hard to know how that will ever be avoided given the normal distribution curve. If the curve shifts so that everybody is as smart as you are there will still be another miserable half percentile out there under the asymptote suffering from people like you. There is no way to cure that loneliness given inequality. You have the choice: be born on Mt. Everest and shiver in the view or be born in the warm valley and live no farther than your sheep can see . . . Well, maybe "choice" isn't quite the word . . .

But I do see intelligence as a boon, though entailing eternal pain. Remember that tremendous passage in *Peer Gynt*, when Peer, who has gone along with all the Troll Kingdom's demands that he wear a tail, etc., etc., finally balks when they want to *put out his eyes.*

By the way, this Jeff Smith enterprise on "women" . . . Thank you for his relayed invitation to be an Honorary Man or an Honorary Man being an Honorary Woman. I shall try. But as I wrote him, I have visions of Joanna Russ making off with my left tibia in consequence. Remember, I labour under difficulties.

Phil Dick . . . I'm afraid he may have addled himself, like Gerald Ford, he might have left his helmet off too long. (His Vancouver speech.) Or perhaps he always was that way. And his "women" are a strange breed, probably figures he drapes his fantasies around. But there remain his books; the only thing a writer is, after all, required to do is to produce good books. My slender 6 inches of Phil's paperbacks contain some of the best sf—some of the most mind-nourishing sf—on all my shelves, and it matters nothing that he may be wandering around like [cummings's] uncle. (Who was "led all over [Brattle] Street by a castrated pup.") . . . I believe him to be totally impermeable by voices from the outside.

James Tiptree, Jr.

(We have corresponded extensively and he still doesn't know my name.)

Speaking of people & correspondence, you know Chip Delany is one of my real Upper Pantheon, and I wish someday when you have an empty line in a letter you would tell him there is a character called Tiptree who keeps writing him fan letters in my head. His works are so goddam well-made. So full. So—oh shit, you may ask, why don't I write my own fan letters. The answer is, I did . . . I'm delighted to find he is also a great decent soul. He could so easily have been a blazing brilliant kook . . . Funny the deep impulse one has to make the admiree *know* of your admiration . . . It really bubbles up inside. That was why I first wrote you.

I'd send you my Anna Kavan except I sent it to this Indian (Craig Strete) who is starving for books and stealing the Celina library blind. She's Popular Library pbk. It's pretty strange.

Have marked on a card GET Carol Emshwiller's JOY IN OUR CAUSE. Thanks. [. . .]

(All much better here, British Columbia & not hearing the name of Richard Milhous Nixon did me infinite good.)

> Love from your advice-prone
> Tip

* * *

22 Oct 74

Dear Joanna:

Back again after another emergency trip to Ghastly Scene of Interminably Perishing Aged Ma, of which we will say no more. I'm afraid you'll find that my friendship is something like being friends with somebody sinking for the 34th time in the entropic flood, I flounder up, throw flowers & kisses wildly—only to submerge again with only bubbles to mark the site of dismal private dramas.

That sentence needs editing. Oh well, perhaps you get what I mean. The problem of being full of enthusiastic philosophical agreements whilst stuck in the dentist's chair with no novocaine.

[. . . .] I hope I get time to write Chip Delany before the Silence strikes. If not, then on revival. But must do it right, I feel my old timidity about him. So goddamned good. And so unmistakably self-possessed. A been-through-fire type.

It's odd, at my nearly-60 age—I feel everybody else, I mean everybody who counts—has Been Through Experience, has *lived*, while I have only, what, fumbled through unsuccessful apprenticeship, got ready to begin to start, and stand eagerly upon the brink of figuring out How to Live—just as hook from shadows is snaking out to yank me off scene.

(I also have moments of believing I am transparent, something that did not jell. Everyone else seems to have so much density, self-organisation. Personality. If asked who they are, they *know*. I asked myself that the other day—could I write an autobiography just for my own amusement, OK, who you? And all that formed in my throat was, uh, uh, well, I guess just the something peering out from this totally random manifestation. Something *small* peering out. And incurably young, not perhaps in the best sense.)

And then I find *I* intimidate the occasional fool. Wonders never cease. Who, *me?*

Thanks about the Bowling Green U. idea. Having *your* goddam letters now puts a responsibility on me. Do you realise that, you maniac?

About Phil Dick's books. UBIK and OUR FRIENDS FROM FROLIX 8 are pretty damn good. There's another with some weird philosophy which I can't recall now, will look up . . . I'm afraid the Great Chipmunk has gotten to him, too, Joanna, I really am afraid.

About his house being ransacked, while everything is possible, I would apply Occam's razor here and suspect a more casual ransacker rather than gov't. In this case. You saw what dreadful problems those clowns had getting a CIA reject to ransack Ellsberg's psychiatrist; the incompetence of government should never be underestimated.

About the either-or roles for women. Jesus, I read that with aching heart. Prescription for self-mutilation . . . the life of the very intelligent is in any case a drunkard's walk, but that's cold comfort. I hate to say this, but one of the most sexually sane woman friends I have had was—is—an almost complete homo. (Some disastrous early marriage attempt, soon over.) I begin to wonder if female sexuality isn't a biological accident, a nightmarish side-product of your inherent masculinity. (All women's, I mean.) Maybe there are only 2 sexes, men and mothers. (Oh, and two asexual sexes, children and the old.)

163

Oh—I note that Jeff Smith is trying to get his Women in sf thing off the ground. A worthy commotion, I guess. My contrib, due to the hand business, is going to have to consist of a solo input from left field, I'll just scribble down some thoughts that'll probably offend everybody. And then sit back trying to figure out how to blow my nose & reading what you all say.

Would like to see the George story very much. But time brings all things.

So you are a desert type. My, my. The one experience I had of being drastically short of water traumatised me. I am a vapor type. The misty plains of Stonehenge and plenty of moisture in the woad please.

Yeah, about Ursula. It is my theory that the "contentment" masks something not yet born. She has been at a "contented" stage. There *is* something about mothers, you know. One of the faces of Eve. There are so many ways of being female. And it is something about how to deal with pain; she puts it "inside the song," as Tolkien does. Is this admirable or a cop-out? I don't know. I know that something in THE LATHE jumped out clear at me . . . I worry about the load of sociology she carries, too. It may take some time before the real U.K.L.G. stands up. But in LATHE it signalled.

I confess she affects me deeply. She radiates something. Maybe not an ultimate solution, but . . . something . . . maybe it appeals to my Victorian background, in which crises were handled in the third person. Some kind of invincible non-immediacy—no, I'm babbling. But here's a thought. You know, it can take a sort of courage to admit one is happy, I mean, it's an ignoble situation in the world today. That "contentedness" is a kind of confession, maybe. I think she *is* happy at times, not even "determinedly" happy . . . Do I make any sense? Happy even in face of knowing that the grey sea will roll over all.

There are so many ways of being human.

I was fascinated by your comments on Justine & porno and taboos and will go lavishly into it all at length except that life has come ringing & knocking & been thrown out twice but will not stay thrown. (Mostly doctors' offices scheduling pre-operation exams of unbelievable complexity. Christ I wish they'd just take the damn hand and start chopping, who cares what my EKG is.) But general tone is agreement. Nobody seems to share my taboos, which are mainly I suppose ethical and aesthetic. I'm really a fearfully conventional Bertrand Russell–type old liberal ethical atheist, with an odd eye out for fact. Let's not be beastly.

And you should guess what I look at on TV, really, where's your writer's smeller. What does a character like me watch? Why, Public TV, of course. Masterpiece thee-ayter. THE GREAT AMERICAN DREAM MACHINE. BBC products. Occasional glances at old Mission Impossible reruns. A little—very little—Archie Bunker, mainly because I once went to school in Bunker territory & they have some of the syndrome very sharp. HEIMSKRINGLA—did you catch that? Electronic compositions, a bit muddled. Sometimes a Jap. monster sf show. And—beat me, spit on me—I *wuvved* STAR TREK.

OK, I go, I go—

Love,
Tip

P.S. Novella—oh, hell, my left hand CANNOT! New murderous novella sounds good. What title?

* * *

James Tiptree Jr.
P. O. Box 315
McLean VA. 22101
S.F.W.A.   5 Mar 75

Dearest Joanna,

[. . .] This is jerky, because I just got back, delayed en route by a tooth blow-up (damn thing was under a lot of bridge-work). And found the usual body-bag full of mail, really frightening. But I wanted to write you quick just apologies and appreciation. You have such a beautiful mind, Joanna. The effect of a kind of calmly towering lucidity, sounds rather like an unearthly light-house, but maybe you know what I mean. The dervish phenomenon is real, too, I think you get gripped by a kind of frenzy. It makes your output almost unintelligible to the non-genius reader—in fact for a bit I was actually worried that you were on speed. (I've been hooked on Dex a couple of times since the Army dumped it on me in 1944, and it's the sweet trap of all traps for writers. Wow.) The thing about your mind is that you are so quick. So almost intolerably quick. There is this multi-faceted torrent effect, which must be what your inner life is like to yourself.

165

You must spend an awful lot of time editing yourself and reducing the flow for purposes of linear communication with the clods outside.

But the effect, as in your letter of 16 Dec, is worth it. I have sadly learned in my gabbling life that it is worth taking the time to get the poor oaf reader firmly by the hand before hustling him off in all directions . . . Not that you would know it by my letters to you, I fear you evoke a kind of answering frenzy too, a wistful one up to now. You have no idea how helpless I felt being unable to write a word, and unable to tug at your arm!

Anyway, signing off with a real question. In your letter you advised me to look at the sexes "as an existentialist—that is, as human choices to be made in specific situations."

Now here is where I am intimidated. The word "existential" is still, despite all effort, an empty word to me. Can you explain more? Can you tell me what to read—I know you are busy, it is unfair to ask this. But as it stands, it does not clarify for me. Your example is to look at it as Success vs. Babies. How does that apply to raccoons? How does it apply to Mme Curie? I simply don't know . . . Am I being very stupid? Do you mean simply that there are two patterns, success and babies—or that looking at them as *choices* is better than patterns? How does that explain, say, the Canadian commandoes who in the midst of their raid on Dieppe found themselves so horny they dashed into a whorehouse—with the Germans about to exterminate them? (It may be this anecdote is euphuised, it may have been rape or a casual encounter, but fuck they did.) This is to me a type of behavior which is very physical, having to do with congruent neural pathways, adrenaline, etc. It *could* have been done by a woman, but it is no part of Mother . . . Is it?

Next I want to look at the differences between Mother and Male in terms of speech. Verbal ability. I persist that Mother lies at the origin of our most prized possession & ability, you know: speech itself. The "male" attitude toward speech in every society I've seen is constipated, difficult, sacred—actually *frightened*. Whereas Mother is a verbal virtuoso. (And accordingly hated by "males.") And it is interesting that male-type "art" speech has become known as the "majesty of language" or some such nonsense.

Wonderful about the sex of god, the Lewis bit. I have all your letters very carefully in a notebook, you know. Someday maybe you would like me to Xerox them for you, because in your effort to educate me you may have written several essays you could use?

One thing you and Sam Delany have in common is that both of

you have in some sense nearly migrated into literature, transmogrified yourselves into art forms. A degree of that sense one has about people like Borges, that he is totally transmuted into another continuum, so that every event is handled in the terms of his Riemannian literary space. I admire this, though cannot do it. (Perhaps, will not.) But it is beautiful.

And the other thing you and D. have in common is that neither of you know your own strengths. You are both still like Alice before she realized everybody else was only playing cards. Remember? She took them all seriously and strove with all her strength. And then suddenly stood up and turned the jury-box over. "Why you're only a pack of cards!" So you both hit hard enough to stun brontosaurs. And we all fall dead!

Now adieu + love
Tip

How are the eyes?? *Really*: worry, worry. ♡

* * *

James Tiptree Jr.
P. O. Box 315
McLean VA. 22101
S.F.W.A.   15 Mar 75

Dear Joanna—

You are a brave and gallant and friendly person; I had not expected letters, and most especially not such a careful and good explanatory one. I do, abashedly, realise what a distraction this has been for you. Please recall that in my very first letter I asked you NOT to reply at the cost of your writing time and energy. This, I hope, still goes. ~~I am not one of those who are easily offended by serious things~~ (pompous). You can walk back in after a ten-year silence and start out, "As I was saying—"

And I hope you do.

However, I'll take the occasion to go on a bit, because both you and Delany—who comes across very nice in his letter, no problem—you have both mistaken me very profoundly. Maybe I can explain a bit of it, but I rather despair. As we learned during the McCarthy period, it takes one sentence to accuse and a page or a book to get the accusation off your back.

First, let's tidy up a couple of loose ends. I have read nearly everything you recommend, in some cases long ago. My de Beauvoir is 1953 and dog-eared. It was not, to me, a revelation; I preferred Woolf, better Mary Wollstonecraft, whom I came to by way of Mills. Not that de Beauvoir is not very good, but SS was to me tainted with that peculiar slavishness of spirit so deeply stamped into French women. She got rid of most of it in THE COMING OF AGE.

Slater I have enjoyed, although the revelatory quality tends a little toward the pompous. There is a bad thing about being nearly sixty; so many bright young voices seem to be earnestly rediscovering the wheel. But that is, too, unfair.

I have most of the feminist works on your list, but not THE GLORY OF HERA. (I wonder if Robert Graves will substitute, at least temporarily.) It makes me very happy to hear some sense and good, sound revolution being talked at last, after the decades of Lundberg's MODERN WOMAN: THE LOST SEX, Babette Deutsch, and the rest of the dreary crowd devoted to making women comfy with someone's foot on their necks.

I have always bought novels and poetry by women, too; I bet you never heard of an extraordinary person, a steel-worker, called Elma K. Lobaugh who in 1946 wrote a thing called THE DEVIL IS LONELINESS to a reception of resounding silence.

Now of course it is perfectly possible to read all these things, and say all the things I do, and still be totally wrong-headed. We've all met that. If that is the case, I'll never know it—idiots don't know they're idiots—oops, there I go eliding and you will come back at me to say yes, idiots do, which is true. I meant "fools." Nor do the senile know they're senile, which is the only bright aspect I have discerned in my future.

And it may be, as Delany said, that age has got into my computer and all is lost. Age does that. If so, all we can say is I love you, Goodbye. I do resist the implication a bit—one tends to—because what I see age as having done to or for me is a little different.

You see, I grew up believing very much what I think you believe in an age when it was very unfashionable to believe it. For fifty years I plugged along at the Biology is NOT Destiny line; the total difference between humanity and animals, the reality of human free choice, was deep in my soul. Is, in fact. The mutability of humanity by its culture, the tricks you so well describe in your letter that training and expectations play. You and I would have got on perfectly even ten years ago, when I was finishing a doctorate in one of the softer sciences. I mention this because (a) yes, I have read all the basic stuff you have, e.g., I know the fallacies of cultural evolutionism as you do. And (b) you may have taken for granted that my education took place when Yerkes was writing his twaddle about chimpanzees. (That was a marvellous and much-needed send-up of Yerkes by Herschberger. It is a pity few researchers of the currently active generation will read it. Let us hope there are some apes left when people with better educations come to look at them.) So I mention, diffidently, that my transition from sophomore to the kind of doctorship which does no one any good took place in the midsixties. (As to my research, no one has ever heard of it, although for some reason I seem to have a small following behind the, uh, Iron Curtain. It dealt with perception.)

So maybe by being such a late-comer to so much I have staved off the ravages of age in one or two directions for a little while. But what I want to get at here is that the suggestions I put out in the symposium are in a sense foreign, tentative steps for me. This is a secondary level; I am going against my own deepest dogma. Maybe if I had explained that, you might have understood the extreme trepidation with which I put it forth. But I don't think you would have, on second thought, especially if you read it as carelessly as you seem to have.

I don't blame you one bit for this—my god, you are a writer and terribly overworked, and if someone puts out an odd and peculiar-smelling document which can be dismissed with a casual swipe at a stereotype, why not?

But you have stereotyped me unjustly, you know. You are as rigid in your ways as I in mine, and scant blame to us. One of the hard necessities of life is knowing What Not To Pay Attention To.

But it confuses me to have one item treated as you did—you with your subtle, sarcastic fire of thought. Of course that offer of the dreadful bracelet was symbolic. (Among other things, it has been given to a museum which financed my folks' early work in Africa.) What I wanted to convey by that was a reminder of the power-distribution in the great expanse of the world and time.

Now here we come: You (and Delany) took that as a "threat." Well, again I can't blame you. You were more acute, you saw me as simply paranoid, which I probably am. There are a lot of motives

169

from which people yell, "Look out!" Some are simply nutty, like Chicken Little. Some are from self-aggrandisement, like the boy who cries, "Wolf! Wolf!" Some are because they've seen it happen again and again until they are stuck in the groove. Perhaps that is me. I did have a rather brutish early experience; the first dead people I ever saw had been crucified—not on large impressive posts but on nasty little saplings. And they had been tortured first. Their crime was witchcraft—it was an orderly process of that society, but it struck me rough. I also spent an evening as a child about a hundred feet from where a man was being prolongedly killed and then cooked and eaten. That was all right too, he was accused of thievery. But it wasn't restful. He made dreadful noises. And then I got to see the *real* bad stuff—the death-camps the Belgians ran. Life expectancy, two months. Crime, non-payment of arbitrary taxes. In short, I was early impressed with the idea that "orderly" societies can wreak considerable ravage on the deviant individual.

And then of course came Hitler and all the rest.

But this odd upbringing really, Joanna, did insulate me against any simple idea of inevitably programmed human nature. When I saw a man on the steps of the Ganges reverently—and quite inadequately— burning his mother's body, and then leaping into the water to fish up the still recognisable skull and pry out the gold teeth, I was young enough to recognise that these were the exact, equally pious analogues to the equally ludicrous rites with which my mother had buried her mother in Woodlawn Cemetery near Chicago. (I can still recall the dressing-down I got for suggesting this.) But I really am prepared for nearly any behaviour to come out of anybody, given the conditions.

But do not fear that I will "snivel in the bunker," Joanna. What I am trying to do is to suggest that it would be wise to *build* the god-dam bunker. I don't do too much snivelling in life; everyone has their quota. My weakness is more on the line of collecting ammunition. (During the McCarthy hearings I actually took a .38 down to the hearing-rooms just to see if one could still get close enough, in case the worst came to the worst. Yes, I'm paranoid. It delighted my heart to find another who had done this. That was what Germany lacked in 1931, before he [Hitler] could have been a martyr myth.) I am, I know, no fit citizen for Utopia. Let us hope that I am as obsolete and ridiculous as possible. (Please read that sentence.)

By building the bunker, I mean quite simple things which could prevent women from being plunged back into powerlessness in the event of panic. (And panic can be quiet.) Like, I would be happier if a female-run and -staffed company made, or could make, the pill. I would like to see women-run financial institutions (yes, I am watching that First Women's Bank). I approve all the self-help stuff starting. (Yes, I did get that Our Bodies, Our Selves handbook, and gave it to a woman friend who needed it.) In other words, I would like to see women's rights defended by more than the vote, more than the laws. Because I distrust the vulnerability of unimplemented laws. By implemented I mean reflective of existing power. In even simpler words I think the Black Muslims are right. Without an independent power base one is permanently vulnerable.

So much for paranoia. I put this forward simply as thoughts; perhaps I will believe quite differently next year.

I have said all this so you can judge whether my warnings are as Delany says a covert threat—or whether they simply spring from what you sense, fear. My experience has led me to believe that the civility on which all our rights depend is unusual and vulnerable. I see myself as potential victim—among other things because I am an atheist.

Will you guarantee me three safe decades?

I used to work (volunteer, natch) for an old liberal organisation which infiltrated the lunatic right. (Friends of Democracy, run by Kenny Birkhead—they left their files to the B'nai B'rith.) The activity, the sheer tireless activity of those types was amazing. They were not, of course, numerous; say about 10 to 15 percent hard-core authoritarian paranoids in the country. And our future, of course, is to be determined by the vast uncommitted middle. I am not in the least afraid of them—unless we get the kind of panic that killed Weimar. That's when those ghastly old inner qualms of guilt—we have sinned, we better get Back to Poppa—spread out into the center. The sort of thing the Right To Lifers are trying to get going. That, in concrete terms, is all I really fear, I mean, barring one of the fifty-seven delicious oncoming Dooms.

Well, really, Tiptree; Enough.

Let's see. I enjoyed your primate examples. I'm familiar with all of them except the gorillas separated by the small door, which I suspect I can find. And of course I agree about the limited applicability of animal observations. But I am an animal. How free am I? Really? (An *unknown* animal, though. Thus we meet.)

And still and all, in a somewhat different sense—maybe having nothing to do with women intrinsically—I do think we have treated child-rearing badly and blindly. BUT I AM SHUTTING UP ABOUT THIS HERE.

James Tiptree, Jr.

What I am doing is writing a story in which an alien culture has large, strong males who are also biologically equipped for child-caring. (Rather like sea-horses.) Let's see what that would look like, if I can.

Well, child of the fifties, farewell and love. I haven't answered much except to enter a general plea of Not Guilty, Misunderstood. My desire to tiptoe back to the taboo territory of sex differences will have to be gratified in some other arena. But I do tiptoe, ready to recoil back to my previous position. Only I am not going to die believing that the emperor is naked, if he really is wearing a smidgen of g-string. When you're old, taboos lose their teeth. Even one's friends' best, shiniest taboos.

Thank you about existentialism. You have got through to me where Sartre himself did not.

From your friendly child of the thirties, love.

And for Christsake *don't* answer this—we'll get it all sorted out one day. Or we won't.

> But always,
> Hold the warm—
> Tip

P.S. Any resemblance between my views + P. K. Dick + I throw up.

* * *

James Tiptree Jr.
P. O. Box 315
McLean VA. 22101
S.F.W.A.   31 May 75

Dear Jo:

[. . .] Mother did scare lions. She used to have to escort me to the can with a 30-30 at night, on the Serengeti. (That was before they had autos, dear.) She also spoke seven languages, including Malay, and was a teensy little woman with big blue eyes people used to open everything for. I could go on and on . . .

Anyway you can see why I went for girls who couldn't hit a running cheetah at fifty yards plus learn Malay. Your remark that they

172

(the doomed delicate etc. girls) sound like me, plus your icy Wasps is netting perilously close to animae, animusses, animalculae—the Jungian zoo we both love so much. But you may be right, righter than we know. I trust your hunches.

And you are right about it turning out deadly dull, if you get close enough. Someday under more favorable conditions for the libido-to-libido chat we can recount our mutual disasters.

Haven't read Dhalgren yet, nor the F. Man, nor in fact anything since my Stapledon orgy, except the dreary drafts of this exquisitely awful first novel I am trying to perpetrate. If only they would let me fall on my face *quietly* . . .

I'm sorry, as you must realise, about the can of norms known to "man." Damn the rhythm and beat of the language which is built into so many things we have to extirpate.

But you know, I am increasingly coming to resist *being* my body—this apropos of your good par. on de Beauvoir—although I know perfectly well that I am it and it is me, as age comes on and I feel it start to fail under me like a tiring horse I have to disassociate myself from more and more of it, and the "detached p.o.v. offered by Western Culture" becomes, well, not such a bad thing, personally. I do have this stupid belief that the mind can sometimes ride herd on its fading synapses for awhile.

But that is of course no reason for making people pretend they have some other body with wholly different experiences and political problems.

I blather, incipiently.

But, again by the way, you may recall long ago I said that the movement is women-to-women, that we are at the stage where men are as out as white liberals in the black movement. *That* I do understand.

Did you ever know anyone who took so long to say goodbye?

Love, may Boulder be good. (*Boulder* . . . ?
Embouldened . . . well, it is bould enough getting you.
[signature ("TIP," with a drawing of a door)]

P.S. Were you ever raucous enough to enjoy Tom Lehrer? I played some tapes over the other night . . . "good old American know-how, as embodied in good old Americans like Wernher von Braun . . ." I love the bastard.

And did you see Edith Efron's piece in of all things TV Guide about the new American media tilt toward the Arabs, the total fallacy of

James Tiptree, Jr.

Arab moderation? . . . I give you the oncoming nightmare of the late 70s—if we're lucky.

Tip

* * *

James Tiptree Jr.
P. O. Box 315
McLean, Va. 22151
S.F.W.A.   17 Aug 75

Dearest Joanna,

At last I have read THE FEMALE MAN, I have to write you: This is great. I read it wincing, grinning like a skull, saying Ooops—and then O My at the miraculous saves, finally simply reading in swinish inhalations, gulp, Yes, yes, *yes*, O Jesus, *Now* I understand, go on— whoops, wait—yes, it's okay, and finally over all, sheer swooning wonder that she puts out this book as what, *science fiction*? a cuckoo's egg like a bomb in our little ghetto.

Seriously, Joanna, the thing is a progression, it starts out as (possible) sf and then progresses, migrates into a roar that has to be in the mainstream, or in its own stream. It ends with the words pouring out of Author as hippogriff, as supernatural whirling dervish, a kind of Letter from the Cosmos which happens to be a person . . . I am certainly not going to say this to anyone else, I mean, anyone alien, because yes let us keep up the fiction that it is an "sf" novel, anything so the book can get read. So I can do that paltry thing, voting for it for some plastic award. Anything so it gets read.

I haven't read DHALGREN but I'm afraid I already have a closed mind. D. will have to be writ in blood to sway me. (I do not, I never have confided in anybody before what I intend in the voting matter, this is a break with my own small tradition, just from me to you.) (It is not of course important but it is the only importance immediately available.)

The strength, Joanna. That's the thing. I've read some other perceptive, poignant, wince-making reports, veracious, revelatory . . . but not with the strength.

One quibble. Does Janet really cry, p. 182–3, and also later? Now I understand, Joanna. All that you were trying to get through. I see where I was irrelevant. I won't say, "wrong," because nothing I meant wronged this truth, but it was extremely irrelevant. But it takes a book to get it said. Go, little book.

Love,
Tip

Don't answer if busy I mean this.

* * *

James Tiptree, Jr., SFWA,
Box 315, McLean, Virginia 22101   12 Sep 75

Dear Joanna,

(You'll never know the unnatural exertion it takes to keep me from calling you Dear Jo, or Dear J or Dear Cygnus Negra or whatever, I am an inveterate nicknamer and hate my own full name. But I will not do as you don't wish!) This is simply to exclaim, have to unload on someone—just read Doris Lessing's THE GOLDEN NOTEBOOK and am stunned. Always thought she was too weepy; this one is weepy all right and features Woman as Kudzu Vine—but Oh my, the form. Most sophisticated *formal* work by a woman, barring Woolf's ORLANDO. And so new, so different . . . Oh yeah, barring Stein too. What do you think?

And Oh yeah, I'm real handsome. Like Duke (Gov. of Samoa) in Doonesbury. But I have peachy, blue grey eyes . . . Are there any physically beautiful writers? You know we're all lumpy. Too earnest in the face. Eyes give it away too.

LOVE
TRAPTROOP
Tip

* * *

James Tiptree, Jr.

James Tiptree, Jr., SFWA,
Box 315, McLean, Virginia 22101   29 Sep 76

Dear Jo,

After writing you I sat down with WE WHO ARE ABOUT TO [. . .]—
in the old Galaxies. Jesus, what a story, Both good and bad. I wish I
knew what you thought about it. I finally concluded you had *two*
stories fused in there; the long, apparently self-indulgent dying
monolog being most of one of them. Of course it no more belongs in
GALAXY than a—well, you name an utter incongruence. But then
there *is* no appropriate home for people trying real new things. Very
troubling story. The usual unbearably real flashes, the usual flapping
loose ends and unknown implications; the usual fierce impact. But
Jo, don't *be* life; write . . . Is that comprehensible? Probably not . . .
I'm a shade worried. Tell me how it really goes with the writing, if
you care to . . . Is real writing really possible?

> Love,
> shook.
> Tip

* * *

James Tiptree Jr.
P. O. Box 315
McLean VA. 22101
S.F.W.A.   14 Oct 76

Hello Jo dear,

It's 4 AM, and I'm up early to try to get some (writing) thinking
done . . . but all that comes is an imaginary dialog with you. I chuck-
led, puzzled, laughed, sighed, over your last letter—which you have
doubtless forgotten in the passing maelstrom of your mind. (I don't
mean your mind is chaotic, although it is, a bit—just that so much
goes on, and also, you're writing.)

You mention the break-up of your c.r. group, which is what caused
the chuckling. You see, I visualise you and them from the outside,

176

while you only experience it from their intimidated and furtive escape from you.

Listen, love, you'll get a lot fewer mysterious tiptoeings-around in life if you face a couple of things:

You *are* egotistical. I am [as] certain that you talk too much as I am that the earth turns. I imagine that when you are consciously *not* "talking too much" you sit there like a smoldering basilisk with ever-larger gouts of smoke coming out of your ears until your "silence" dominates all the talk in the room . . . Or like when the ocean suddenly recedes for miles, leaving the bottom of the bay bare, and people venture forward into the strange, unaware that the odd line on the horizon is a five-mile-high wall of pent-up words rushing down on them with the speed of light. I can just see it.

And of course you intimidate people. You intimidate the hell out of people. When you're being carefully gentle and non-intimidating I imagine it's like being gently dandled from paw to paw by a Kodiak bear. Your natural way is to intimidate everything and everybody in the environment, simply by being in there faster and more complexly and volubly and positively and generally like a loose live wire thrashing about.

You are also crazy as a coot.

All this has nothing whatever to do with your being or not being a Lesbian, the best-balanced friend I have is one. So is the second-best-balanced, at least when last seen.

The reason you are crazy, intimidating and egotistically garrulous is because you are some kind of a genius, or part of one, or one part of the time. You are just so full of you and life. I can just see the picture, when you have that feeling you're among friends, someone who officially "shares" with you, a woman or a Lesbian or a writer—and you feel you can be yourself, or talk honestly to the point—and out comes this incredible flood of (a), (b), B1, B2, etc, which reminds you of (parenthesis) C, which leads on to E and F, which subsumes general principle G, having the subcorollaries H-prime illustrated by example VII, and what happened to me last week suggests that maybe we should turn the whole existential point on its head, which would lead to thoughts J, K, L—and what the hell have you crawled under the rug for when I was just *agreeing* with you and having a nice conversation?

Honey, other people, Lesbians, women, men, aardvarks—take a long time to go from A to maybe A-and-a-half, not to mention B, and when you open the curtains and invite people to share worlds, the other person is very apt to crawl under the rug or leap out the fire-escape—because they HAVEN'T GOT any such torrential inner world to share back.

While you're left feeling like you've been shouting down a well and why in christ's name didn't they *respond*, share back, even interrupt with their own views? . . . They didn't because they couldn't. They haven't any.

The lonely steam-roller.

And subconsciously you're so used to this, so used to being too fast and too much and seeing more and so forth, that you really don't take seriously any humble daisies offered to you. Other people have been stupid and wrong for too long.

Your doom is partial comradeship; any group will offer you companionship on only a portion of your perimeter, or heart. And you are going to have to learn to think with your mouth shut in those perilous moments when lesser mortals sidle up with a flower.

Further, you have to recognise that you are not, never, going to be "among your peers," part of a real "sacred band." You have to find your peers in this or that facet—as you really do—making a network of part-sharings serve the lonely need for a group of true fellows. It's the fate of the over-intellectualised even on the barricades. In action you're a Lenin, but your fate may be more like Trotsky's.

Now that is all I know about that.

But I should add that crazy egotistical rampantly talkative Joanna is also perfectly sane, kindly, just, luminously compassionate, and I would have no hesitation in exposing my deepest soul-quandaries to you. Please emphasize this paragraph—I was so amused—being, you know, older and having *seen* geniuses trying to make out in a world of trained poodles—that I went on and on. I know the bull-dozer aspect for what it is, and I don't for a minute confuse it with the core of you. I ache for you, Jo.

. . . The only real danger of your position is, like I said, that having had to learn to dismiss so much stupidity you get into the automatic habit of rejection.

Which brings up Ursula . . . I do think you reject too much there. You worry her work like a frantic puppy, and some of the pieces flying off the bones are real pieces. Of marrow, if we may carry this metaphor a bit unhappily longer. She's writing mostly about good and evil and death, you know. Motives which are as yet peripheral in your own writings, your good and evil are incidental to the life, life, life in your stuff. She's fundamentally an abstract thinker dressed in

178

the characters of fiction—witness OMELAS. And then she had this biological idea—LEFT HAND. She has a few genuine images, dragons and ice-fields and forests and mad kings in drafty scrubby keeps. But her most personal, odd, writerly thing was LATHE OF HEAVEN, where her characters started to run themselves. Truly, Doctor Haber in that is a real, real villain. And the strange upwelling of quietist hope showed up, the thing she tried to do more with in ATLANTIS. In LATHE it's a rather absurd but lovable salvation-through-aliens, and sea-images.

It is perfectly OK for a writer to be preoccupied with the neutral themes of mortality and virtues—only thing is, it makes for pallid writing unless one is an ecstatic . . . I kind of love her, as a baby philosophe more than fictioneer. [. . .]

Now sweetie go out and intimidate the world, suffer & study & convulse and talk, talk, talk, cook your week's stew, may the sun shine in your weighted curtains—above all may the writing go well. And may the world offer you some much-needed security.

Love,
Tip

* * *

James Tiptree Jr.
P. O. Box 315
McLean VA. 22101
S.F.W.A.   27 Oct 76

Dearest Jo,

Your letter awaited me on return from a journey so god-awful I won't go into it, except to report that my very aged mother finally died. It was odd; as the disfigured flesh in the bed started to cool, it vanished in my mind and gave way to the fleeting, brilliant picture of her as the vivid, highly intelligent, dazzling, adventurous young woman I had briefly known as a child. I am a total atheist and materialist, but just on the zillion-to-one chance that *something* lives, I spoke to that ghost . . . Only it wasn't a "ghost."

Old age is a bad practical joke, you know. If only we could all be of

179

an age, if Adolf Hitler exists somewhere as an appealing small boy, if all the pouched and crippled figures we see tottering off the stage could be for a day what they "really" are, young people sharp with hope and pain and love and interests . . .

Your letter was a lovely antidote. In it you are as usual "thinking with your mouth open," the total effort at definition and understanding going on right before my eyes. My impulse is to Xerox it and send you back the copy, I may do that unless you have a carbon. (*Do you???*)

In general, I agree, and of course life & death, good & evil, are in your works, but arising from the living characters. But they are in a sense still peripheral, you become beguiled with the living detail. Whereas in Ursula's work you have to allow for, or contend with, her "religion," the curious distancing effect. OMELAS is a perfect example of a story from an abstract base—is the happiness of a great public worth the knowledge that it is based on the terrible, unassuageable suffering of one innocent? (For one child, substitute the underclasses that made the remnants of Victorian life so idyllic for the "upstairs" world.)

Now you never write a story from or to illustrate a question like that.

I think it worthwhile to explore, as you think, exactly how the impulse to write a given story arises in your critical subject, and contrast it with your own. How did the story actually jell—around a vivid character, a situation, a question, an agony, what? (Many of mine start with a voice dictating from behind my pancreas.) I think it is relevant to your inquiry, the actual practical method of genesis of Ursula's stories, as, say, compared to yours. I bet, a huge difference.

Also recall that strange streak of mysticism, or quasi-hope, hopeless hope if you prefer, the odd fatalism of her mind. She has an area of belief in—I don't quite know what. Cosmic balance, the I Ching, something deviant maybe that came down to her through her anthropological progenitors. But there is a dim, vague—but real—immaterial *scenery* behind her tales, deploying itself like tentacles through the motivations of some of her characters.

By the way, you can't wean me from my love for her LATHE OF HEAVEN. Something in that spoke to me grippingly, still does. I think whatever kind of writer she will be is prefigured in LATHE, a voice in which she speaks more directly.

There are aspects of Ursula's fiction which cover pain she can't bear to handle, which muffle pain like a pot-holder to grip too hot a kettle.

You can handle pain, but you sometimes give the impression of not knowing exactly how much it hurts, or is hurtful to the vulnerable reader. You are, actually, a tough cookie. Maybe that is your ultimate quarrel with Ursula. You are vulnerable to empathy, but you have it under control, or rather, when you get into one of your Tsunami fits you leave all questions of the effect on the hearer far behind.

Ursula is like me, in that the problem of irremediable pain is one of the big "givens" in her world, we both spend a lot of fictional time tiptoeing around the sleeping dog—the never-sleeping dog—of hopeless hurt. Making a dash in to refer to it, which is all we can bear; retreating again knowing that certain kinds of reader know exactly what has been touched.

I suspect that empathy, or pity for the web of agony that underlies the living world, is a great drawback to a writer. I can barely stand life. And I find I can less and less manipulate fictional situations in which the reality of pain is one of the pawns . . . I may end up writing Peter Wabbit.

The more I think it over, the more it seems to me that not essencism or existentialism or anything so grand is the main problem between Ursula and you. (And maybe between you and me.) It is the difference between your very real toughness and viability and our "I can barely stand it" weakness.

Enough.

I wrote back to Jim Baen saying you had invented the Colonising equivalent of Malzberg's agonized psychotic astronaut, put a human reality into the standard cheerful-aluminum scenario. That a real colony would go far more as you describe than is commonly envisioned.

Do you want a Xerox of your letter-essay on Thinking About Le Guin?

By the way, I regard A.E. van Vogt as an android. Should I take him seriously? So far I simply can't. It is like a simulacrum of Calvin Coolidge writing fiction.

Again by the way, Tolkien—and, oddly enough, Wells, are writers who are writing around almost unbearable pain, too. A quite different affair from, say, Genet. Handling personal hurt—a motive for fantasy. In Wells you only see it indirectly, like that almost unreadable outburst, paean of hope, in, what was it, FOOD OF THE GODS? Where he for once lets himself describe what life might be like without it. (Without the needless, useless, omnipresent pain and cruelty.)

I think you would find it interesting to examine your own attitudes, and those of writers congenial to you, towards the pain and hurt of the world. Maybe you could divide us into survivors and non-survivor types. You would find a difference in the quality of the suffering. Something in you accepts, even is on the side of, pain and evil—perhaps you quite rightly feel it as a necessary ingredient. Even when you are howling in anguish it isn't the same as those of us who turn white, walk out and die. There is a tooth-gnash in your howl.

Now phones are ringing, I must go. My love to you, and special thanks for a letter that came into my life just when I needed to see my black swan flying.

Love
Tip

* * *

James Tiptree Jr.
P. O. Box 315
McLean VA. 22101
S.F.W.A.   7 Nov 76

Dearest Jo,

You are quite wrong; what I need is not "a back-rub and some comfort" but a fascinating, challenging letter and article like yours. Since I am most fascinated and helped by the letter, let us go into a few comments on the article first.

My first thought was that I better subscribe to the MLA Newsletter.

My second thought was that I understood exactly what you meant, despite the fact that I almost have never day-dreamed in the conventional sense, beyond a few obsessive scenarios age 14 centering around the idea of getting laid. (What took the place, with me, was compulsive reading—primarily stuff like the complete works of Kipling, with its hints of a mysterious grown-up world of understandings available only to the infinitely experienced; and don't forget I was partly raised in Colonial Africa and India.) What also took the place, with me, was lonely staring up at the stars, and feeling, with comfort, the utter indifference of, say, Sirius to the whole fabric of human existence, let alone my own small woes . . . I was, in short— still am—a kind of Loren Eiseley type.

But I realize that other people do have personal daydreams, and I think your analysis fits perfectly. What is so impressive about it, to me, are the concrete examples of what particularity, specificity, is and is not. Hot damn, you know a lot of literature.

Well, that is why you are a literary pundit while I know more than anybody needs to about rats.

Beautiful to see an expert at work.

[. . .] The whole relation of literature to subconscious themes. Gardner Dozois shook me, in his introduction to some new issue of my stories, by pointing out the revelations of my own terrible yearning for transcendence of the human condition, and my drive to somehow regain the lost Eden, the lost, forever yearned-for home. Even when it is also the place where things hurt . . . Are these "daydreams"? I was unconscious of the power of the motives driving my words and plots . . . I think my strangely-assorted readership includes primarily those susceptible to such wounds . . . How deeply I understand Tolkien's life-long grief and loathing for those who destroyed the beauty that he felt was "home." And of course his hatred of the forces—the almost impersonally evil forces—that slaughtered "all his friends but one."

Which brings us to your letter. What you have done with pain. "To shove it up your backbone and try to steal from it the iron we need." Extraordinary, your interpretation of "the iron has entered my soul."

That is what I can't do, and what I suspect Ursula can't do. It is not that we "do not face our anger." It is that the anger is unfaceable. How can you get angry with the Second Law of Thermodynamics, which has stolen from me most of what I love, and is in [the] process of killing me? How can I get angry with the nameless millions who had the extra children, decades ago, whose needs are now resulting in the bull-dozing of my home, and the destruction of the last beautiful wild lands? (I am, by the way, like C. Ain in my old story "The Last Flight of Doctor Ain," a very personal lover of the incredible natural web of beauty that was our unspoiled Earth. I have seen so much destroyed that can never come again, and must bear the seeing of more devastation every day. Can you understand that this can move a person to the same intolerable sick hatred as the forced daily witnessing of slaughter and rape?)

When you have anger—or rather, as you say, hatred which is helpless hopeless anger, of these dimensions, it is impossible to use it for strength. At least it seems so to me. I loathe man's fate, both in the Malrauxian sense and in the inevitable-interaction-of-large-social-

and-physical-forces sense. Unlike Ursula, I have no refuge in mystic hope.

You'll be amused to know that my therapist tells me to get angry. His own problem is anger, rage at "being told what to do," even in the most trivial way. How I envy him, and his ability to "distance" and denature pain. I simply go on hurting. And as for getting angry—I do have fantasies of machine-gunning deer-poachers—I rarely can. It is because I see behind the incident the huge impersonal chain of causality that brought about the confrontation. Behind the individual enraging idiot I see the idiotic parents, the idiot schools, the crumbling culture, the inadequate cortex. How to "get angry" when attacked by a virus? I think perhaps you could. I merely sadly see the imperatives of the virus, the chance vulnerability and accessibility of my own tissues; it seems a drama graven in the stone of impersonal causality.

And I have rather fragile connections with life. My impulse is to leave.

All quite unlike you, and your letter with its raging, engaging, positive tone was a bracer-upper.

Re Genet; haven't really read the man. Shied away, in fact; because I felt that I did not share his drives or pains or satisfactions. On your word I will look again.

Good for you, my dear fighter. I think you are forging your pain and fear into iron, and I cheer you on. But when you look at Ursula, re-member there are those whose pain literally cannot be so handled, either because it is diffused out to unmanageably large causalities—or because of some defect in the adrenals which simply dooms us to go on, as I said, sick-hearted and white-faced.

But your letter encourages me to try again, to weasel round somehow.

I still don't quite know what a "Platonist" is, chez you, but I am glad I am not one in my fiction. Actually in my writing I work from a strange self quite unlike my real, sick self; this artificial self has its gaze resolutely fixed outside, chuckles and damns reality, behaves in short as a producer of alternate view-points which might have some interest for the reader. I suppose the sickness speaks through—God knows it does in this novel Ballantine is supposed to be publishing—but I am aware that my own personal damnation is of not the slightest interest to the outer world until it has been forced up to form figures in the fire, dream-artifacts into which reader[s] can for a moment live.

Thank god your parents taught you that you were important.

I'll have to get Delany's book of essays. I've been afraid to read DHALGREN so far, afraid that it would be too alien. (Among other things the Billy-the-Kid mythologising I noted earlier in one of his things turns me off, and I gather there is some of that in DHALGREN) . . . I hope, hope, it is not one of those works like [the] GORMENGHAST Trilogy (Mervyn Peake) where all the blood and corpses and sufferings and appearances of other people add up to the denouement that one (male) adolescent has had some vague insight. But I will forgive Delany anything. By me, one of the greats.

By the way, someday could you do a bit of matchmaking? You occasionally say I'm "like" you and Delany, or on your general "side"— which I feel. But I've never been able to get a word out of Delany direct. Do you happen to know if he thinks I'm dreck, or what? At least I have the satisfaction of having let him know how grateful I feel for the work he's done . . . Funny; in this writing world it often comes down to writers making some terrific personal impression *on each other*. I feel an obligation to tell people when this personal sense of gratitude wells up—recall how I first wrote you.

Not that I expect you to "put me in correspondence" with D., or anything asinine like that, given the state of all our desks. I'd just like to be sure he knows he has a rather violent partisan in me.

Now, dearest Jo, your letter did the world of good here—outside of a vague dismal feeling like a weakling seeing photos of Charles Atlas lifting 500 lbs in each hand with a grin on his face—you too can be a hero. Well, I too positively can't, but at least I can grovel on a bit.

You can have no idea of the hideous complexities of settling Mother's estate, including material that goes to four museums—94 years of collecting mixtures of irreplaceable artifacts and memoires in a 26-room apt., complete with "secret" storerooms, all jumbled— letters from Carl Sandburg mixed with grocery bills, blank stationery, samples of curtain cloth, birthday poems by putative nonentities, greetings from Jan Smuts, historical memorabilia of Old Chicago, Old Africa, cloth of gold from Old Sumatra, lace panties, .38 calibre automatics, Marie Antoinette's tea-set, half-ton bronzes of gorillas, etfuckinginterminablecetera, 3 rooms of file cabinets—and all to be done by remote control, through a doddering ancient Legal Eminence known as the Executor who has to mull over every arrangement in triplicate. I was 4-plus-two solid hours on the long-distance phone yesterday, pausing only to type goddam letters confirming the conversations (in triplicate), etc more fucking crap. And all of it hurting, underneath, sending strangers in to paw over her private files and drawers. And it'll go on for weeks if not months. The part of my brain that writes feels like the Bulgarian Tank Corps was holding manoeuvers in it. Nothing left standing . . . not to mention what is laughingly called my "real life work."

I think I'm through. Love to my Lick-your-weight-in-wildcats.

Ever,
Tip

* * *

James Tiptree Jr.
P. O. Box 315
McLean VA. 22101
S.F.W.A.   4 Dec 76

Dear Joanna,

To say that this is a hard letter to write would be the understatement of some time.

How will you react when I tell you that the person you have been corresponding with as Traptroop is really Raccoona Sheldon, aka Alli Sheldon, aka Dr. Alice B. Sheldon—the doctorate being merely in a behavioural science, not the kind that does anybody any good?

The thing is, the last thing poor Mother did was blow Tiptree out of the water, I had no idea her obituaries would be splashed around. So Jeff Smith wrote me that Harlan had latched on to one, or something, giving me as sole survivor, and was busy telling the fans. So Jeff looked it up for himself and wrote me the question direct.

I don't lie, except for the signature—which has grown, over the years, into just another nickname—so I had to tell him yes. (That was good, actually, because I had always promised him he would be the first to know. I left a letter telling the truth in Bob Mill's safe, to be opened if Tiptree i.e., me, died; but I'm morally sure he hasn't opened it.)

The letter says that James Tiptree Jr. was born in late 1967 in the Import Food section of Giant, when I was looking for a name that editors would forget rejecting. It never occurred to me that everything would sell. So then everything just snowballed from there. I love the sf world, and I couldn't resist Jeff Smith's request for an

186

interview—figured I could skip over the bio details quickly without lying, because my curriculum vitae does sound male—and start waving Hello to all the people I've loved and admired for so long.

But then the epistolary friendships grew—especially with women; if you noticed Raccoona you understand I am deeply committed to women, and I thought in my innocence that this prank could help. (There are anthologists who have sharp inquiries from Tiptree as to why no women contributors.) But the friendships got real. But I never wrote calculated stuff or lies, what I've written you—or anyone—is true, true true. All of it.

So now it is time for me to stop being a brand of marmalade and painfully write those of you who have befriended Tiptree what the facts really are: A 61-yr-old retired woman—past adventures, I guess, life said to be "exciting" and "glamorous," but it just seemed like a lot of work at the time—6 ft 8 1/2, wt. 135, hair brownish going grey-streak, incurable open childish stare, lumpy writer's face, as I said, once said to be good-looking but really only animated; mostly wears jeans and cords, and worried sick that my much more aged husband of 30 years is going blind.

Jo, can you take it? God, the number of times I've wanted to cry out, dear Sister, how well I know, how well I know what you mean. But I am different, by reason of age and time of upbringing, from the feminists today. Maybe more pessimistic, more aware of the male power structure in which I've struggled for long years. (With their Queen Bees.)

Have I done anything evil? It didn't feel evil, it was just a prank that dreamed its way into reality. I think you were beginning to "see through," too.

Can I ask you to hold this "secret" a while longer, at least until Ballantine's stop sitting on that damn novel and decide to publish? I don't think they want an ersatz Tiptree . . . I had planned to establish Raccoona better and then kind of slide over, but with my low production and this damn novel I've only been able to give her minor stories. Funny though; editors screaming for Tiptree stuff return Raccoona with beer-can stains on the pages—not really that bad but almost.

(If you take this in the true spirit it happened in, there are quite a few laughs to share.)

The funny thing is, Tiptree has taken on a kind of weird reality; I'm beginning to believe something was awaiting incarnation in the gourmet food section. Tiptree for instance insisted [on] "Tip," would not be called "Jim." And he has shown himself a spiritual uncle to quite a few depressed people, mostly fellow pros. Alli Sheldon almost had to give up teaching for the same reason—all the outsiders, green monkeys, tearful young girls spotted me at once and made me into a kind of crying-shoulder or hot-line for troubles. I can't resist. I know too well how things hurt.

For your information, in addition to Jeff Smith, I wrote Ursula at once because of our long friendship, and then Quinn and Vonda because of ditto. Since we met later, I waited two nights to write you; it takes a sleepless night to write this. So you are the only ones who *know*, pace Harlan.

How I admire you who have made it openly as women.

I think I would have if I'd thought it through, but I was finishing my PhD orals at the time I wrote my first 4, and I wasn't thinking anything through except the evidence for and against rat learning—I'm a behavioural or "rat" psychologist. So I just tagged on the first male name that came handy and let it go. And then was stuck. You see, I am extremely shy and recessive.

I guess that's all the brute facts. If I should have put in more, let me know, if you're still speaking to your friend

> Tip
> Alli
> Raccoona

P.S. [O]ne thing I noticed, Tip was going to write you about. Have you noticed that we have always discussed writers not as technicians or the "art of writing"—but as their ethical, moral, political messages? Fascinating. Of course maybe you didn't want to discuss writerly points with me because neither Tip nor I really know *how* to write.

P.S.S. Another point; all of Tiptree is me; Ting (my husband) is a non-reader, hasn't a clue what I really do. An old friend, really; at 61 and 75 that becomes more important than gender.

Oh, Joanna, will I have any friends left?

* * *

James Tiptree Jr.
6037 Ramshorn Pl.
McLean, Va. 22101   16 July 77

Dearest Joanna:

[. . .] My mother once more or less openly invited me to bed with
her. I was 14, it was in a steamy little stateroom on a boat. I almost
did but the gleam of her gold fillings put me off. (I have this horror of
age, see.) Also, I didn't know how. This lack dogged me through all
the loves of later life. And since I looked and talked knowing, real
gays were always throwing themselves at my once-handsome feet,
and I hadn't a clue how to pick them up. Still don't really. I guess you
could call me a frustrated gay. God knows, the scene with men was
mostly pure havoc. [. . .]

                          Love
                          Tip/Alli

                    * * *

6037 Ramshorn Pl.
McLean, VA 22101   12 Mar 79

My dear, my dear—

[. . .] (God it was strange to come home to an empty, voiceless
room . . . where Tip had once lived and worked. Maybe refreshing,
we'll see.)
    Now really back to you. But what can I say to you, not knowing
"who" you are now? I suspect I know, of course. We are much alike
in many ways; you are having prematurely, because of your back,
what hit me ten years later in slow-motion . . . There is no answer,
no meaning. Life is death. Brief diagnostic: As long as you still *desire
anything*—beyond death at once, I mean—no matter how crazy; in
particular, if you still want to *do* anything, like writing, or washing
drip-dry, for that matter, *you* are still there and things will improve,
though it may take some technology. The sitting and staring dull-
eyed at horrors, and finally, at nothing, that is bad. That you do not

do. The sleeping 10-12 hours is partly physical need—things have exhausted you; partly an attempt to die, partly laziness and procrastination, and mostly the expression of a dilemma. You want A but you can't have A unless you do B, and you can't do B because you hate it or it bores you; so you sleep (which will do you no harm, so long as you are also physically active enough to halt atrophy).

The irremediable longing for lost youth and magic and meaning is of course the human condition—for those of us with minds; "Life is a process of disinheritance," my old-lady music teacher said to me when I was 14 and bowed down with sourceless woe. She was, I now realise, perhaps 38 or 42.

The physiological aspects of depression—which can sometimes be helped—are just coming into science. I was lucky in finding a shrink who finally found a "human" psychiatrist with a pharmacopoeia. (Most psychiatrists, as you know, are fossilised sophomores with stainless-steel heads.) When I find out if we're still speaking, we'll go into all that if you want. But nothing is clear-cut; among other things there is always our old friend the placebo effect . . . Something genuine is there, however. I've spent my life popping pills to try to live, or recapture life, and these pills seem better. (Luckily I had the sense to stay away from the hard stuff.)

Enough? Enough to show I know and care?

In a way, I'm glad I couldn't get your phone and had to write this. Scribble me a word, I know it will reflect only the current 10 seconds of your changeable soul, but do.

Love.
Nameless

* * *

6037 Ramshorn Pl
McLean VA 22101   25 Sep 80   0400hr

Hello Baby My Swan,

Listen, Love, due to circumstances too stupid to go into, I can't do a thing about the story you object to—(would heart trouble + 3 hunks of oral surgery do for starters?)—But this is about something else.

James Tiptree, Jr.

Just been reading The Coming-Out stories ed by Stanley + Wolfe (with a lot of Adrienne Rich) and it occurred to me to wonder if I ever told you in so many words that I too am a lesbian—or at least as close as one can come to being one never having had a successful love with any of the women I've loved, and being now too old + ugly to dare try. Oh, had 65 years been different! I *like* some men a lot, but from the start, before I knew anything, it was always girls + women who lit me up. (Oh, the sad foolish lovely tales I'm going to have to put down some day!)

I just thought I'd mention it, since you seem to have found yourself. (Possibly my reward for years of stasis + musing is to be the ideal confidante!) Anyway, I love you. Isn't this silly paper? How goes it?

 Alli/Tip

* * *

6037 Ramshorn Pl.
McLean VA 22101   5 May 81

Dearest, my much-experienced
Darling—

(The strange envelope is due to my crouching over my files, arms full of junk, in darkness due to a power failure, looking for something with your address on it. 6 months back I started a grand Reorganization of my address-book—one of those tear-pages things—with the result that said book is empty save for 3 neat pages for newspapers, dentists, and cleaners—while all the real people are in a kind of horrid paper salad in the bowl below. Such a procrastinator . . . do you?)

What you tell about female hatred and absolutism is so true. Oh god, I hate to say it—especially in the light of Belfast today—but we have some things to learn from men in the way of handling minor hostilities. The boxers who go after each other viciously—and then are found inquiring about each other's health and sending flowers, or caring for the loser's children . . . the US Congress, where a blistering floor-fight is so often followed by neutral* luncheons.

Is that the correct use of "neutral"? Always boggles me.

We women have no experience with fighting the issue, nor its exponent. (Result: men easily join forces to squash us.)

Not that they're perfect at it—just a *lot* better.

During WWII the bicycle dump-trucks in the Pentagon had signs on them: "We are fighting the enemy, not each other." And it took me some months to learn that when my boss in Intelligence* said "The Enemy" he meant (a) the British and (B) the Navy. A failure of the generality I just voiced—and reorganized as a failure by the Big Boys. In those days Air Intelligence was regarded as a dumping-ground for unassignables. (On some posts the Intelligence officer was also the special service officer who was responsible for storing the horse-shoe set, the badminton net, and the bean bags . . . one past commander fired his I.O. because the man could speak + read German.) Luckily this attitude changed soon, and never prevailed overseas, where Smiley and his kin taught us lessons A thru Y. (Z, or Zed, they failed on, as witness the UK moles now surfacing.)

Does all this free-association crap interest you at all?

No. What interests you is the dreadful view of "sisterhood" you are now getting. The *hatred*, the poisonous Leninism of the purges, complicated by personal envy. When that terrible fund of hatred turns from its proper target to focus on another woman, it's sick. And—never forget it—SAFE.

What would happen if you remarked, "Pretty safe, attacking me, isn't it? Always shoot down your allies first, it's such a help against your real enemies." Or, if they say you can't be an ally of theirs, wish them luck and depart to conduct your own lonely wars.

(Easy for me to say. But this crowd with their attractive doctrines evidently was quite a source of hope to you. Dammit—I wish I were there to lend a hand . . . Do you recall the lovely tale of the old Frankish king, who after being much moved by a Christian missionary's tale of the mob-death of Jesus, exclaimed fiercely, "*Ah—that only I had been there with my Franks!*" The dear old king would have ruined the martyrdom and set Christian history back a thousand years . . . Well, we don't need you as a *martyr*, thank fortune.)

Your other wonderful account is True Tales of Vampires I have known. (Oh god yes, gimme, gimme, gimme your talent, your fever, your secret, your blood, above all, your *time*.) Do you recall that little-mentioned story Harlan did in which the hero, Ellison virtually undisguised, discovers his pack of followers, of "good (Sorry for the

---

*His principal qualification was an award for saving the most gunny-sacks ever saved at Picatinny Arsenal in 1936.

writing—lights still out, scribbling by candle, lying down) friends," are actually out to suck his blood; it ends with them eating him alive. One of the penalties of Glamoor. I'm starting to get it, luckily by mail only as I've made myself very hard to reach. "Gimme—oh, *gimme*—" all carefully and quite unsuccessfully disguised, and wrapped in protestations about not wasting my time. A few are really egregious— "get me published"—but most, so far, start with the careful SASE, etc.

You're out there all exposed, in person. You must be damned magnetic flesh, too. Well, at this distance, and conscious as I am of my own physical decay + repulsiveness, I think you're safe with me. My only virtue is, you can say anything to me without ever changing my love, which is solidly based on what you *have* done, and the ongoing beauty of your mind. A totally risk-free lover. Who can only love you more as I curse your peccadillos.

Dull, what?

Well, this horrible position—I'm sore from sticking out my stomach to hold the notebook up—is clearly no place to even begin my promised saga of my attempts to genitalize my loves, or respond to others', and when I got thinking of it the other day this huge bag of history started dumping itself out—so I will just leave you with the last picture I was left with—a bathroom at 4 am, in the tub stretched out a red-haired girl of appalling beauty, under the grime of a week's debauch—I had just rescued her from the clutches of an assorted bag of faggots in an all-night eatery, who were visibly trying to make their weak brains figure out how to take financial advantage of Maggie, this wanderer from a very wealthy very upper-class gold coast family— the home had 9-foot cast iron gates mounted by a permanent Husky . . . she had called me to come get her. So at 3 am sucker me drives the old open top Packard through the grey, garish streets of the downtown red-light district, and was putting her back together—she addled with sex and some (to me then) unknown substance which stank up the car like turpentine—me addled with love. And as she lay there, lovely beyond words, letting me wash her all over, the only thing I could think of to do was to *lay peacock feathers over her.* Oh god, I can still see it.

May I leave you with that?

Love and a loving good night—
Ould Scrawly

James Tiptree, Jr.

* * *

Dearest Joanna—

I'm writing this when I should be working—Oh, for Chrissake,
which of us isn't?—but it's going to be a dull letter because I'm so
stuffed with medicaments, mostly pain-killers, that you're practically
being corresponded with by a bottle of pills.

Just wanted to tell you, I've been keeping alive by rereading your
EXTRA(ORDINARY) PEOPLE. Put together most ingeniously, of course—
but, Gods! Lady, you can write. Hard to believe that SOULS and the
MYSTERY OF THE YOUNG GENTLEMAN were writ by the same hand,
each so perfect, so enameled and ornamented in their diverse ways
. . . Of course, I like SOULS better, it may be the best, certainly one
of the best you've ever done. Oh, what reality. I don't see how you
knew what an abbess would say to terrified women confronted by
the Northmen. And those Vikings—how ghastly my forebears were.
There we were, itinerant murderers and bums, hacking people up
while elsewhere people were civilised. (Yours.) I used to take them as a
joke, until I saw the pathetic refuges built on the Hebrides islands for
use when they came. One great bee-hive of a building, walls around
a middle open space for livestock, and the people lived in the walls—
in a 5-foot space between the inner and outer walls. The whole place
reeking of blood after five centuries, and presided over by the gloomi-
est skies in the world . . . And all doors big enough only for dwarfs—
I never found out whether they and their cattle *were* tiny—look at
Shetland ponies—or whether it was to help keep the—I guess—taller
Norse out . . . Everyone was so small in those days, look at the old
suits of armour. (That was a shock to me, except I could now see how
a horse *could* carry an armed knight of that peewee size.) I guess a
modern basketball team would look like gods walking to them . . .

And THE YOUNG GENTLEMAN . . . Oh, but why should I go on telling you what you know? Just leave it at this—whenever you get to
thinking you've done some non-pareil stories—you're right! Take all
your most megalomaniacal musings and stamp them True. One picks
up your work in perfect confidence that one will be treated to a display of what one can't do . . . I'm savoring the book in slow readings

194

and retracements, so the fact that I haven't said anything about the stories at the end yet means nothing.

I've been a shade ill, but also trying to work hard, sort of dragging self from couch to type, back to couch, back to type. [. . .]

Is anything deadlier than being stuck with ~~an A~~ a B-minus story you simply *have* to finish because it's part of a set and no time to scrap it and begin anew? . . . I found I was so engaged with the setting of that novel (BRIGHTNESS FALLS FROM THE AIR) that I concocted a couple peripheral stories, and before I knew what was going on they got sold, pending a third, to Tor for printing together in a book. Tales Of the Starry Rift. Strictly good grade B.

I think I'll send you that novel with my love. *Don't* feel you have to read it.

I think I'll get to work. Or maybe lie down.

I think I'll end this . . . by telling you I miss you, Baby. I do. Of all the friends and acquaintances I've made in the last 15 years, you stand as the Authentic One.

Be good and write me a nice whiney angry note because I love you.

Your
Tip/A

The Showroom Variations
Michael Parrish Lee

We are now able to offer this esteemed series, compatible with most chambers and enjoying extensive replay value. Once within or returned to its chamber, the product can be fastened comfortably, and the Variations will proceed.

Variation 1. The Chamber
In a chamber the product waits to enter another chamber.

Variation 2. Daniel Arrives
A ringing scream pulls him into a chamber filling up with light and the chirping of birds. He wonders why he has again programmed the screaming to bring him here. He pushes his face into the spongy item that buoys his head as *the things to come* begin to shift and gurgle in his stomach. He wishes that for once he could return to the chamber he has left, or at least remember what happened there, but he knows that he will not allow himself to do so. Soon the chamber he hides his face from will fill with light completely and he will feel the air exit his lungs, knowing that he must enter other chambers where *the things to come* await him.

Variation 3. Breanne's Ritual
In a chamber filling up with light, she uses a metal instrument to push a concoction of milk-dampened flakes into her mouth, enabling her throat to tighten and produce a feeling similar to choking. She will mash the concoction with her teeth and contract throat muscles to pull the material deep within her, thus enabling the initial feeling to shift registers and become a feeling similar to nausea. She will repeat this process over and over, for what feels like an endless period of time, and then, the next day, she will begin the ritual again.

196

Variation 4. The Preparations of Alice and Jeff

As they prepare to leave a chamber full of light, she informs him that the product trapped inside her is moving again. But when he presses his hand to her belly, once again he can feel no movement. When he takes his hand away and resumes his preparations, she informs him that the product is moving again. But when he returns his hand, once again he can feel no movement. As they prepare to leave the chamber he will continue moving his hand to her belly and away again, wishing that the product were trapped inside him.

Variation 5. Barbara's Diminishing Returns

Before leaving the chamber, she checks to make sure that she has turned off the stove. After checking, she exits the chamber and locks it with a key. She begins to walk away but returns to make sure that she has locked the chamber. After checking, she unlocks the chamber and enters to make sure that she has turned off the stove. After checking, she exits the chamber and locks it with a key. She begins to walk away but returns to make sure that she has locked the door. After checking, she unlocks the chamber and enters to make sure that when she previously entered to check that the stove was turned off she didn't accidentally turn it on.

Variation 6. Trevor's Process

In an effort to leave the chamber he binds two squirming products in items that cover their feet and torsos. As he binds one product, the other frees itself, and he must begin the process again. With each new cycle the squirming products acquire more features: a soft stuffed donkey held by the ear, a paper crown, a carrot to feed the neighbors' rabbit, a sore finger, a bandage, a song to sing throughout the day. Trevor responds by making his own additions to the process: motivational chanting, juice bribes, puppet-based methods of distraction. He hopes these additions will help the cycles to accelerate and eventually bring about *the miraculous exit*, a sequence involving transport, body squeezes, and reluctantly depositing the products in another chamber where they will squirm amidst others. After a period of toil, he will return to collect the products so they can be fed, rinsed and rested, and the process can begin again.

Michael Parrish Lee

Variation 7. Timothy Spins

In a chamber there is a box, which he knows contains an item that is round and flat and pointy all at once. He sits on the floor and takes the item from the box. He whirls it between his finger and thumb and watches as it spins. He makes it spin but it spins without him. He feels it as a part of him. It belongs to him and him alone, and yet it spins on its own and belongs to no one. A mean product grabs the item and carries it away. Timothy weeps and begs a tall female product to have the item back. The tall product makes low sounds at the mean product, who moves his face into an alternate shape and returns the item. Timothy spins the item again, trying to forget that it was and can be taken away. But he knows that this mean product or another will come again to take the item. Now he cannot remember a time when the item was really just for him, when other products did not sneak up and grab it as it spun. And now he cannot be sure if he ever really spun the item for the pleasure that it brought or only for the hope that this time the others would not come for it. And now he cannot be sure if the way in which the others come for and take the item has not always been the main part of the item and the reason that he spins it. Soon another mean product grabs the item and carries it away. Timothy weeps and begs the tall female product to have the item back.

Variation 8. Xio Flees

In a chamber echoing with hard rubber squeaking and pattering against varnished wood, she enters a configuration of products fleeing a single product. If this product catches another, the old product will flee, and the new product will become the chaser. Xio is terrified by the screaming giggles that exit her mouth as she flees and by the possibility that she might stumble on the varnished wood or lose her breath and slow. Although Xio knows that products catch one another all the time, she fears that if she is caught she will become the chaser forever and never catch another product. But just as bad is the condition of fleeing, of having a product getting ever closer, its eyes fixed on her as screaming giggles exit its mouth. Xio wishes she could escape the configuration, but she will not, she knows, because if she does she will be forgotten and fade away as the configuration continues to make its patterns without her.

198

Variation 9. Ewan Replays

He sits in a chamber where it will soon be his turn to speak. But he cannot remember what he is supposed to say. A chirping bird chasing light tries to enter the chamber. He puts the crashing sound inside him and replays it over and over.

Variation 10. Natalie Imagines

Her acquaintance, Becky, lies in a chamber that she cannot leave, her leg immobilized in a hard white casing. Sometimes other products enter the chamber and write on the casing. Becky longs only to be outside in the sunshine amongst the flowers and the puddles. Natalie spends her days imagining that it is she, not Becky, who cannot leave the chamber; she, not Becky, whose leg is immobilized in the hard white casing that other products sometimes write on; she, not Becky, who longs only to be outside in the sunshine amongst the flowers and the puddles.

Variation 11. Allen Enters

In a chamber strewn with fabric, he enters a female product. He is excited, but he does not enjoy being here. Being here feels all wrong. Once the excitement and the feeling of nonenjoyment accelerate and combine to produce a cold spasm, he exits the female product and the chamber. He then enters a chamber furnished with metal cabinets and washing facilities in which he relays some of the details of his previous experience to a series of male products who strike his shoulder, slap his back, and recite a list of viruses that he might have obtained from the female product. The product reenacts the scenario as often as he is able. The only variation is the female product involved.

Variation 12. Jimmy's Procedure

He enters a chamber and sits in a rigid device, expertly designed to hold his body in place. He stares at something bright and maneuvers the bones and ligaments of his wrists and fingers into a series of damaging arrangements. The bright thing has been crafted to maximize a dull throbbing sensation in the backs of the product's eyes. The chamber is furnished with a number of other products engaging in similar operations. As far as we are able to deduce from the available data, the purpose of the other products is to inhibit the *emotional breakdown* facilitated by the operation. We therefore estimate that the overarching purpose of the procedure as a whole is to enable the product to achieve a prolonged proximity to *emotional breakdown* without attaining such breakdown—a process that we conclude produces an exquisite tension, since the product enters the chamber and enacts the procedure again and again and again.

Variation 13. Helen's Collapse

In a chamber furnished with a large plastic container of water, she encounters a male product at precisely 14:45. The male product wears a length of fabric tightened around his neck. The length of fabric bears the images of large-eyed quadrupeds wearing garments and standing on their hind legs. The male product says a series of words, presumably a code or incantation, and Helen makes a loud noise and collapses while still managing to remain on her feet. We infer, from his length of fabric, that the male product wishes quadrupeds to stand like bipeds. We therefore deduce that the collapses he facilitates in the product constitute his efforts to make her fall to the floor and go about on her hands and knees like a quadruped. Perhaps then he would embroider an image of her on some new length of fabric that he would tighten around his neck. But the product has him outmaneuvered. She only keeps her appointment five out of every seven days and thus gives her body time to recover so that she can enjoy the collapses without toppling completely and endangering her status as a biped.

Variation 14. Desiring Stuart

Within his chamber is a smaller chamber beyond a screen in which products desire other products and utilize many accessories. When he shuts the smaller chamber, he finds that he desires several of the products from the chamber as well as other products that resemble these. He does not know how to go about purchasing such products, but he finds that purchasing many of the accessories from the smaller chamber is very easy, so easy that he often does not recall desiring them or choosing to purchase them, but finds them already there in the larger chamber lurking around him, a discovery that cues him to push his face into his hands and then reopen the smaller chamber beyond the screen to look for more products to desire.

Variation 15. Astrid Makes a Mark

In her chamber, she makes a mark. The mark brings a feeling of exhilaration, so she makes another. The second mark brings a feeling of disappointment, so, trying to bring back the exhilaration, she makes another mark like the first. Although similar to the first, this third mark does not bring back the exhilaration, but instead produces a sickening feeling that this is only a stupid imitation of the first mark and does not even have the distinctness of the second. Now she looks at the second mark in a new way. It is not so bad, she sees. Caught between these three marks, she makes a fourth. This mark does not feel like anything. And yet, she sees, it is the best mark she has made. She wishes she could make another one like it— a mark that brings neither exhilaration nor disappointment nor the sickening feeling. But she knows the next mark will not be like this at all. Instead, it will carry the pressure of adding to the four marks she has already made, which now seem to possess a harmony that she fears she will never again achieve but that she knows is incomplete and still needs something more. But the mark after that, she decides, that will be something else altogether.

Variation 16. The Reenactments of Shirley and Renee

A chamber containing lights and machines causes them to shout at one another until fluid leaks from Renee's eyes. A seated male product speaks loudly and Shirley and Renee attempt to reenact what previously occurred as accurately as possible. However, some of the male product's words have infected their reenactment, causing slight variations, although they still shout at one another until fluid leaks from Renee's eyes. The seated product again speaks loudly, now using a slightly different strain of words, and the reenactment experiences new variations. The process repeats until the reenactment has mutated to the point where the male product produces no new strain of words but a copy of the final reenactment that he will play again and again, until he begins to feel that it is infecting him.

Variation 17. Product Removal via Mildred

Again returning to a chamber surrounded by curtains, she screams and heaves and spreads her legs until the cloaked attendant removes a small working product from inside her. She regards this as a favorable transaction, preferring to experience the removal of working products to the removal of products that no longer function.

Variation 18. The Parkers Animate

In a chamber normally reserved for meals, six products, some of which resemble one another, sit at a table with a cardboard box on it. Within the box they locate images of expired products that they resemble. The older the images they locate, the less they resemble them. The freer the products become from resemblance to the images, the more animated they get and the greater their efforts to locate prototypes of themselves in the products that have expired.

Variation 19. Billy Reassembles

As she moves from one chamber to the next, she dismantles and reassembles. Speaking to the products that occupy this chamber, she begins to feel as though it were not she but other products that have assembled her: the products in this chamber, the products she has shared beds with, a mother product far away. When she exits the chamber and enters another, she again dismantles and reassembles. But soon she will again feel as though it were not she but other products that have assembled her, and she will again dismantle and reassemble.

Variation 20. Matthew's Storage

On days of sun provision, small items usher him into a chamber that amplifies light and command him to store them in pots of soil. The product, in turn, stores these days within him and hides sun traces in his skin. When he is away from this chamber, at home with the product that he *retired* in order to spend more time with, he feels the commands of the small items and longs to be here performing his storage functions. But when he is here he imagines the day when, released from these functions, he will present a glistening bowl of sliced tomatoes to the product with whom he dwells, their dazzling light beaming back from her eyes. We deduce that the small items facilitate storage as a form of hiding, but from what we are not yet certain.

Variation 21. Franklin Repeats

He enters a chamber and sits in front of a wooden item. He knows that the item is a box. Lately he has been inside many similar chambers and sat in front of many similar boxes. The boxes contain products that no longer function. Each signals the removal of sequences from his remaining days and weeks and months. Without these, his hours have filled up with repetitions of sequences from the past and with his efforts, through repeating them, to make them transform and acquire new life. But with each new box this process becomes more difficult, and although the repetitions fill his hours, they are starting to feel like shapes without contents. Where once the products all seemed different, they are beginning to feel like variations of the same thing. And between the words repeated in front of him and the restless silence behind him, he feels himself becoming one with the series of products overtaking him.

Variation 22. Latisha Suspends

In a chamber there is a pit full of dense moisture that inhibits the movements of limbs through space. Here she suspends herself and climbs horizontally, gasping steadily at the air above. When she gets to the end, she turns around and begins her climb to the other side, and when she gets there she again reverses her trajectory. She continues climbing in horizontal lines, paying careful attention to her movements, trying with all of her effort to minimize the factors that bring exhaustion, and trying with all her effort to exhaust herself completely. Beyond the chamber, a decision awaits her, one that will affect many other products. She wonders how long she can keep making these lines, and whether, when she cannot, she will float or sink below.

Variation 23. Harold Relays

In a chamber at a table where products gather, he relays information about the product beside him. The information involves the second product's concern over baking a special cake for a special event. In her concern (he tells the gathering) she practiced baking the cake many times over several weeks, again and again, trying to get it just right; however, when it came to baking the cake that would be eaten on the day of the event, her concern led to unsteady hands and poor timing, resulting in an unsuccessful cake, a failure that no one at the event took notice of. As Harold relays this information his face illuminates and his hands wave in the air. Some of the products wheeze and buckle, some smile but look away. The product beside Harold nudges him under the table. Harold does not know why he is relaying this information or why he relays it whenever he gathers with products in chambers such as this. He does not enjoy the nudging of the product beside him or the way that products smile but look away. He once enjoyed the products buckling and wheezing, but he no longer does so. Each time he relays this information he finds himself wondering if this will be the final time.

Variation 24. Oscar's Recreations

In a cold chamber he cuts into a product that no longer functions. Through this technique, he attempts to induce internal sequences that recreate the nonfunctioning product's final moments. Once he has successfully completed the recreation, the nonfunctioning product will be taken away and a new one will arrive. Oscar's only concern, as he cuts through layers of flesh, is to make the recreation as vivid and precise as possible. The more vivid and precise the recreation becomes, the greater his sorrow, his hatred, and mistrust of the world around him, and his confidence in the value he adds, not to this world, but to a second world, a realm of products that no longer function and those that, while still functioning, will soon cease their operations.

Variation 25. Yolanda's Sculptures

She enters a chamber and sits in front of an item featuring a long line of black and white rectangles bound to small hammers obscured by wood and affected by pedals that she sometimes presses down with her foot. She pushes the rectangles with delicate fingers (sometimes at great speeds), a process that causes the hammers to strike metal strings and send vibrations through wood, producing a four-dimensional acoustic sculpture. She then produces another sculpture bearing a different shape but constructed out of similar elements. She then produces a third sculpture bearing a different shape but again constructed out of similar elements. She pushes the rectangles until she has produced thirty-one sculptures, each different in shape, but constructed out of similar elements. And then she reconstructs the first sculpture to make a thirty-second. She then repeats the process. She repeats the process again and again, day after day, attempting to bind herself so thoroughly to the sculptures that her previous attributes break down and dissolve, so that by the time she enters a larger chamber and produces the sculptures in front of a set of products adorned in colors that mimic the rectangles she pushes and the products rise to their feet and slap their hands together, the gesture will not be directed at the product, but at the series of sculptures that have overtaken her.

Variation 26. Aki Escapes

He looks out from a small chamber at the products that flail and squirm within the noise of a larger chamber. Some of the products are able to maneuver themselves so as to approach the smaller chamber and beckon him to join them. The product fears the larger chamber, but he also wishes to escape the smaller one. Eventually, he will discover a way to escape into a third chamber elsewhere. This chamber is larger than the first but smaller than the second. It makes the product feel at ease. But soon, lying down, he will imagine that he is back in the smaller chamber, looking out into the larger one at the products that flail and squirm and beckon him to join them.

Variation 27. Lauren and Steve Reconstruct

In times of sun closure after small products stored within the house are successfully relieved of consciousness, Lauren and Steve enter their chamber and, when not depleted of energy tokens, perform a binding of limbs, fingers, mouths, and genitals to attempt reconstruction of a fleshy sculpture that, in combination with a series of other binding methods, fastens their lives together, to this chamber, to the small products stored within the house. If the reconstruction is successful, Lauren and Steve will feel themselves overtaken by the sculpture and imagine the sound of hands slapping together in amazement.

Variation 28. The Binding of Hilary

In a chamber draining of light and the chirping of birds, she lowers herself onto the soft apparatus. Slowing her breath, she unhooks the memories of the day and binds herself carefully to *the things that she wants*. Once she is securely fastened, with her eyes shut and

Michael Parrish Lee

her head buoyed by the spongy item beneath it, suspension becomes possible: the apparatus falls away gradually and she can begin again to reconstruct sections of the sky that have been fractured or broken by the mechanisms of other chambers.

Variation 29. Michelle's Reentry

A ringing scream pulls her back into a chamber with no light. It is her fourth reentry since the birds stopped chirping, and this time the product beside her does not move. Through the darkness she will feel her way to the other chamber and bind herself once again to the screaming product that awaits her.

Variation 30. The Chambers

In the chambers the products wait to enter another chamber.

Payment Information

We are now able to offer this esteemed series, compatible with most chambers and enjoying extensive replay value. Once within or returned to its chamber, the product can be fastened comfortably, and the Variations will proceed.

The Process Is a Process All Its Own
Peter Straub

I HAVE THIS THING I DO because the thing reminds me of you know. You use these little deals, like the hearing-aid batteries that go into that thing deaf guys put in their shirt pockets, the thing with the wires that come out. You dump these batteries out of the pack and swish them around in three to four inches of water. Little bubbles begin to come up: in fact, little bubbles show up almost immediately. Why, I don't know, but they do. Maybe for reasons we will get into later. The batteries rest like little machine turds down there on the bottom of your ashtray or whatever. (I use an ashtray mainly.) Then what you do is, you sniff the bubbles.

Huh.

If you push your head right down next to the water, the bubbles open up right under your nose. Which is the point here, O Unseen. They give off this strange little smell. Those bubbles from Ray-O-Vac hearing-aid batteries smell like what happens when you shove your nose right into the middle of an old dictionary, the gutter where the two pages come together, and inhale. That's the smell you get from the bubbles out of hearing-aid batteries.

If the odor you get from the bubbles from hearing-aid batteries has anything in common with the odor you get from thrusting your nose deep into the seam of an open dictionary, particularly a dictionary of some vintage, then it cannot be inaccurate to say that the odor must be that of words. One comes across the odors of words in many, many contexts, and the odors of words are usually the same from one context to another. Only the strongest, most distinctly individuated, if that's a word, of individuals can control the colorations of the words that pass through them.

Nothing in this situation is odd, actually, odd given that we are dealing with words. Words are produced within the medium of air, and balloons and other empty spaces that produce bubbles do so because they themselves are filled with air. Air itself must be thought to be laden with words, to be word packed, word jammed. In fact, words tumble out of every orifice, panting to be born, screaming against the resistant membrane, trying their best to . . . Here's the deal. Words have plans. Ambitions. Goals. They are always trying to veer around us & zoom away. They wish to leave us in an abysmal darkness. You can think what you like about this.

Try the following experiment. Choose any old balloon you happen to see lying by the side of the path in a public park, even a balloon that may have been blown up for a child's birthday. (But make sure it's a *balloon* balloon, or you might not like the results!) When you thrust these poor old things underwater, pierce their hides with your knife, your hat pin, whatever, and then inhale the fragrance of the hazy penumbra substance that escapes into the water and bursts above it in bubble form, nine times out of ten, five out of six anyhow, there may be heard the off-key delivery of birthday songs, the chanting of inane good wishes, on top of these frequent invocations of the birthday child's name, and distributed through all of the intermediate spaces the names of his wretched friends and, guess what, lists of the silly birthday presents given and acquired on this date. *And* this tired, tired smell. All this verbal information can be detected within the exhalations to be had from these semideflated pastel-colored balloons. Once you really commit to this process, pretty much the same goes for gadgets like tape recorders, typewriters, old over-under cameras, headphones, microphones, everything like that. Once they have been plunged under water and agitated crushed berated abused destroyed, one can detect beneath the more prominent odors of distressed metal, rubber, and plastic, the ambitious stench of words that once passed through these various windows.

To a casual observer, dear little friend, all of the above may seem overspecialized, in fact obsessive. I can scarcely pretend that I am a casual onlooker. To illustrate the exact nature of my function, which at the moment I am perhaps a bit reluctant to do, I might allude to the properties of another set of bubbles and the nature of the inhalations contained within, which is to say, getting at last to the point, well, *one* of my points, the bubbles found in blood. Blood is particularly given to the formation of bubbles. Those with the stomach to lean over bubbles of blood and inhale their messages will find that they have in the process acquired a complex detailed subtle record of the life from which that blood emerged. It is one of the most delicate and moving instances of information transmission that I can imagine. It is certainly one of the most beautiful experiences that I have ever known—the catching of the deep, particular inflections within the bubbles of blood that issue from the human throat. Voices contain smells: all human structures carry—on their backs sides bellies feet cocks pussies scalps—stinks and perfumes. We cannot escape into any goddamn odor-free realm. Any such realm should scare us right out of our you know. Odors fasten us to our common world. Rot, fragrance, bud, and bloom exude the physical aura of the process that animates them. It does not take a scientist to detect a verbal motion, a verbal smell, within the bubbles of blood of a recently deceased beast or human. There is, however, perhaps only one given my particular history who may with a reasonably good assurance of being believed claim that when words are detected within the blood of human beings they generally have an English smell. It is the odor, and I understand that what I am telling you might seem arbitrary, of fish-and-chip shops on barren High Streets, of overcooked roast beefs, of limp, glistening "chips," of blank-eyed mackerel reeking on the departing tide, of dull seaweed and wet wool, of humid beards, of crap Virginia tobacco, of damp hair, likewise of cheap cologne and hair oil, also of flowers sold three days past their prime in Covent Garden, also of similar flowers wilting in the hair of neglected women—all of these structures are to be detected in the bubbles that form when blood is released from *any* human being, cart man, prince regent, or vicious greedy poxy trollop.

Those kinds of people I was talking about before, they do not produce these English smells. With them, it's all different, you don't know what you're going to hear. Fortunately they are very few in number.

Am I being fanciful? All right, perhaps I'm being fanciful. And yet what I tell you is on the nose. Most of the time, an English accent is what you get. What's more, it's usually a Cockney accent—turns out, words are blue-collar guys.

I don't want you to think that I mess around smelling blood bubbles, for God's sake. Nobody has that much time. Time is a luxury. And what human beings do with luxuries is very much their own business, thank you very much.

—*T.H., June 1958*

A man named Tillman Hayward wrote these words in a Hardy & Badgett leather-bound notebook, five by four inches, with pale-blue lined paper. He had purchased the notebook, along with three others like it, on sale for $9.95 at Ballantine and Scarneccia, a high-end stationery store in Columbus, Ohio. He "lived" in Columbus. His real life took place elsewhere.

Tillman Hayward, "Tilly," did not work in Columbus. He earned his reasonably substantial salary as a property manager in Columbus, but his real work—his "work"—was done elsewhere. This separation was self-protective.

He was writing with a German-made mechanical pencil purchased for $8.99 at the same store. Faber-Castell, its manufacturer, described it as a "propelling pencil." He liked the word "propelling": to propel sounded madly up-to-date. A propeller-pencil. (It, the word, not the pencil, smelled a great deal of Elmer's Glue.)

Tilly Hayward had been married for nine years to a blonde woman named Charlotte, née Sullivan. Tilly and Charlotte had produced three blonde daughters, each of them the replica of both her mother and their sisters. They looked like triplicates born in different years. These perfect girls were named Edith, Hannah, and Faith. The Hayward family lived in one of the apartment buildings owned by Charlotte's father, Daniel Sullivan, a flinty Irish immigrant in a flat cap, who had never known a moment's warmth or sentimentality. Tilly's job was to oversee the properties, keep them in satisfactory condition, check out whatever new might come on the market, and to make sure the rents came in. He deployed a full range of subcontractors to deal with the tenants' demands. With his father-in-law's approval, Tilly also had taken it upon himself to search for other properties to add to his holdings. He had convinced his father-in-law that the city of Milwaukee, his birthplace, was an excellent location for the long-planned expansion of the Sullivan company. Six or seven times a year, sometimes way more than that, Tilly either drove, took the train, or flew to Milwaukee (the handsome General Mitchell Field, where his tricky old Dad used to take the kids to watch the planes take off and land). There, he sometimes stayed with his brother, Bobby, and Bobby's wife, Mags, in the old brown-and-yellow duplex on West Forty-Fourth Street, where Bobby, Tilly, and their sister, Margaret (later Margot), had been born and raised. At other times, he planted himself in hotels, not always under his real name. "Jesse Unruh" and "Joe Ball" spent a few days at the Pfister, "Leslie Ervin" at the funkier, less expensive Plaza. Although Tilly appeared to be, and sometimes actually was, dedicated in his search for commercial properties, he had as yet to purchase a single one of these buildings for the Sullivan real estate empire.

It was in Milwaukee and under conditions of rigorous secrecy that Tilly's real "work" was carried out.

Tilly Hayward was one of those men in possession of two lives.

Either he was a dark, disturbing criminal sociopath who wore a more conventional person around him like a perfectly fitted suit of clothing, or he was a conventional person who within himself concealed a being like a wild animal. Tillman's response to his duality was not simple. He wondered sometimes if he were really a person at all. Perhaps he had originated on some faraway star—or in some other, far-distant time. Often, he felt *other*.

Many of the words whose odors Tillman caught as they emerged reeked of death and corruption. There were some words that almost always stank of the graveyard, of death and corpses. (These were words such as happiness, fulfillment, satisfaction, pleasure, also joy.) Tillman understood that these words smelled foul because the things they referred to were false.

In Tilly's sensitive nostrils, the word "job" often smelled like fresh vomit. People who spoke of their jobs evoked entire butcher shops filled with rotting meat. Tilly knew that if he ever permitted himself to speak in mixed company, away from his family, of the job he did for Sullivan Real Estate Holdings, the same terrible stench would attach itself to his vocabulary. Therefore, he never did speak of these matters except to his wife, who either did not notice the stinks that accompanied these words or, having grown accustomed to them during childhood, pretended that she did not. Words like sorrow, unhappiness, grief, these words that should have carried perhaps the worst stenches of all, did not actually smell so bad—more like rotting flowers than rotting meat, as though what had once been fresh about them was not so very distant. When Tilly went out in search of the people whom he dealt with as part of his real "work," he deliberately sought women who uttered the foulest words of all. He had an unerring instinct for women whose vocabularies betrayed a deep intrinsic falsity. He often thought that other people could do the same. He thought that a kind of politeness kept other people from speaking of this power, so out of uncharacteristic politeness he himself remained silent about it. There were times when he wondered if he alone could detect the odors that clung to the spoken words, but if that were true, and the power only his, he could never figure out what to do with it. Apart from being perhaps another indication of his status as an alien from a sphere far different, the power seemed a mere frivolity: like so much else, it had no relevance beyond its own borders.

Funny thing: the word "remorse" actually smelled pretty good, on the whole. The word remorse tended to smell like wood shavings and sunburnt lawns; at its worst it smelled of anthills, or something

211

sort of like anthills, sand dunes, Indian burial mounds. He never objected to the smell of the word remorse. In fact, rather to his surprise, Tilly tended to like it a lot. It was a pity that the word was heard so seldom in the course of ordinary conversation.

Tilly, of course, tended not to have ordinary conversations.

In October of 1958 Tilly once again found himself in Milwaukee. He had come not in pursuit of one or more of his many private obsessions, but because he had a genuine interest in a real estate property. Two years before, Tilly had acquired a real estate license. It had required considerable effort, but he managed to pass the qualifying exams on his first attempt. He wanted to be able to justify his trips out of town, especially those to Milwaukee, on commercial grounds. Now he had come to inspect a building, a four-story, mixed-use building on Welles Street. Its only problem was its single tenant: a sixty-five-year-old woman who had once worked for the mayor and for the past six years of her life had claimed to be dying from cardiomyopathy. Tilly had come to see if it might be possible to resolve this tenancy problem by means of certain efficient measures never to be revealed. Yet when he looked at it again, the building had become far less attractive—he saw the old lady, intractable, seated on her unclean old sofa, skinny arms extended as if for hundreds of feet, and chose not to negotiate in any way.

Late in the afternoon of the same day, Tilly decided to take a walk through downtown Milwaukee. He wanted to uncoil, perhaps also to allow passage into the attentive atmosphere some portion of his rabid, prancing inner self. Around the corner on Wisconsin Avenue stood the vast stone structure of the Central Milwaukee Library, and across the avenue from this big, dark building was a bookstore called Mannheim's.

Tilly had no interest in these buildings and could imagine no circumstance that would persuade him to enter either one. No sooner had he become conscious of this fact than he took note of someone, a young woman, who had no problem being in both. Through the slightly sunken and recessed front door of Mannheim's she floated, unencumbered by handbag, not to mention doubt, fear, depression, or any other conventional female disorder—perhaps thirty yards away, and already, instantly upon her entrance into his frame, rivetingly, infuriatingly attractive.

The girl was in her midtwenties, and perhaps five and a half feet tall, with dark brown hair and long blue eyes in a decisive little face with a flexible red mouth. She wore a green cardigan sweater and a khaki skirt. Her hair had been cut unusually short, to almost the length of a boy's hair, though no one could mistake her for a boy. He liked her suntanned fox face and her twinned immediate air of independence and intelligence. The girl glanced at him, and before continuing on displayed perhaps a flicker of rote, species-reproductive interest. (Tilly had long felt that women capable of bearing children came to all-but-instantaneous decisions about their willingness to do so with the men they met.)

She went up the stairs to the sidewalk, moved across the cement, and with a side-to-side flick of her eyes jumped down into the traffic moving north and south on busy Wisconsin Avenue. Delightful little twirls of her hands directed the cars that coursed around her, also to dismiss the few drivers who tried to flirt with her. It was like watching someone conducting an orchestra that moved around the room. She looked so valiant as she dodged through the fluid traffic. Who was this girl: her whole life long, had she never been afraid of anything? At first not entirely aware of what he was doing, Tilly began to move more quickly up the block.

The young woman reached the near curb and flowed safely onto the sidewalk. Without the renewed glance he felt he rather deserved, she sped across the pavement and proceeded up the wide stone path to the Central Library's massive front doors. Tilly began walking a little faster, then realized that she would be inside the building before he had even reached the pathway. He suffered a quick, hell-lit vision of the library's interior as a mazy series of tobacco-colored corridors connected by random staircases and dim, flickering bulbs.

Once he got through the main door, he looked both left and right in search of the girl, then straight ahead down the empty central hallway. At the end of the hallway stood a wide glass door, closed. Black letters painted on the pebbled glass said FICTION. This was almost certainly where she had gone. She was imaginative, she was interested in literature: when the moment came, she'd have things to say, she would be able to speak up. Tilly enjoyed flashes of spirit in his playmates.

At the you know. During the. Maybe. If not then, what a pity, never.

Tilly strode through the glass door into the fiction room. The girl could have been bent over a book at one of the wide tables or hidden behind some of the open shelves at the edges of the room. He did a quick scan of the tables and saw only the usual library riffraff,

213

then moved toward the shelves. His heart began to beat a little more quickly.

Tilly could taste blood; he could already catch the meat-sack stench of "please" and "mercy" as they slid through the girl's sweetheart lips. Better than a meal to a hungry man, the you know . . . except the you know *was* a meal, finer than a T-bone fresh from the slaughter-house and butchered on the spot. . . .

Tilly stopped moving, closed his eyes, and touched his tongue to the center of his upper lip. He made himself breathe softly and evenly. There was no point in letting his emotions ride him like a pony.

Twice he wandered through the three stacks of books on the fiction floor, going in one end and out the other, along the way peering over the cityscape tops of the books to see if his target was drifting down the other side. Within a couple of minutes, he had looked everywhere, yet had somehow failed to locate the girl. Girl walks into room, girl disappears. This was a red-line disappointment, a tremble, a shake-and-quiver. Already Tilly had begun to feel that this girl should have had some special place in his grand scheme—that if she were granted such a place, a perfection of the sort he had seldom known would have taken hold. The grand scheme itself borrowed its shape from those who contributed to it—the girls whose lives were demanded—and for that reason at the moment of his fruitless search the floating girl felt like an essential aspect of his life in Milwaukee. He needed her. The surprise of real fulfillment could be found only in what would happen after he managed to talk her into his "special place" out in the far western suburbs.

After something like fifteen minutes, Tilly finally admitted to himself that somehow she had managed to escape from the fiction room. Baffling; impossible. He had kept his eye on the door the whole time he'd been in the room. Two people, both now bent over their reading, had entered, and only three people had left—a pair of emaciated women in their fifties and a slender Negro girl with glossy little curls in her hair.

For a moment, Tilly considered racing out and following the wide central hallway wherever it went. He saw, as if arrayed before him on a desktop, pictures of frantic Tillman Hayward charging into rooms where quiet people dozed over books or newspapers. No part of balance and restitution could be found in the images strewn across the desk. Something told him—everything told him!—that none of these people half asleep under the library lamps could be his girl.

He had lost her for good. This wonderful young woman would never be permitted to fulfill her role in the grand design of Tillman Hayward's extraordinary life. For both of them, what a tragic diminution. Tilly spun around and dropped himself into an empty chair. None of the pig-ignorant people reading their trashy books even bothered to glance at him. He continued to try to force calm upon himself, to take control of his emotions. Tilly feared that he might have to go outside, prop his hands on his knees, and inhale deeply to find calm. Eventually his body began to relax.

The girl was gone. There was nothing to be done for it. It would always be as if he had never seen her. For the rest of his life he would have to act as though he had never sensed the possibilities with which this young woman, so alive with possibility, had presented him. Tilly knew himself to be a supreme compartmentalizer, and he did not doubt his power to squeeze the girl down into a little drawer in his mind, and there quite nearly to forget her.

Two nights later, he had planned to get some rest before going back to Columbus, but the idea of Mags and Bob sitting in their miserable living room thinking God knows what and remembering too much of what he might have said made him edgy. Probably he should never have given that *True Detective* to poor little Keith. It was like a secret handshake he could not as yet acknowledge. It was like saying, *This is my work, and I want you to admire my achievement, but it is still too soon to for you and me to really talk about it. But you're beginning to understand, aren't you?* Because that was true: the kid was beginning to put things together.

Tilly tried stretching out on the bed and sort-of reading his book, which was a novel based on the career of Caryl Chessman, the Red Light Bandit, who had been sentenced to execution in the gas chamber at San Quentin. Tilly loved the book. He thought it made Chessman seem at least a little sympathetic. Yet his attempt at reading did not go well. The image of Bob and Mags seated stiffly before their television, and that of Keith doing God knew what with *True Detective* in his bedroom kept dragging his concentration away from the page. Finally he decided: one last night, maybe one last girl. Good old Caryl kept himself in the game, you had to give him that.

He checked his inner weather. A sullen little flame of pure desire had flared into being at the prospect of going out on the hunt one last time. He tucked the book beneath his pillow, took his second-favorite knife from its hiding place, then put it back. He would play it All or

215

Nothing: if he could coax a girl out to his Special Place in the suburbs, he would use his favorite knife, which was stashed in a drawer out there; if he failed, there'd be one less corpse in the world. All or Nothing always made his mouth fizz. He lifted his overcoat off the hook on the back of the door and slipped his arms into the sleeves on the short distance to the living room.

That coat fit him like another skin. When he moved, it moved with him. (Such sensations were another benefit of All or Nothing.)

"Why do you do that, Tilly?" Mags asked.

"Do what?"

"That thing you just did. That . . . shimmy."

"Shimmy," a word he seldom used, stank of celery. "I have no idea how to shimmy, sorry."

"But you are obviously going out. Aren't you?"

"Oh, Mags," sighed Bob.

"Last-minute look at a property. I shouldn't be superlate, but don't wait up for me."

"Where would this property be, Tilly, exactly?"

He grinned at her. "It's on North Avenue, way east, past that French restaurant over there. The next block."

"Is it nice?"

"Exactly my question. Be good now, you two."

"What time is your train tomorrow?"

"Eleven in the morning. I won't be home until midnight, probably."

When he got outside and began walking down the street to his rented car through the cool air, he felt himself turning into his other, deeper self. It had been months since he had last been in Lou's Rendezvous.

Formerly an unrepentant dive, Lou's had recently become a college joint with an overlay of old-time neighborhood pond scum. Ever optimistic about the possibility of having sex with these good-looking youngsters, the old-timers kept jamming quarters into the jukebox and playing "Great Balls of Fire" and "All I Have to Do Is Dream of You." That the neighborhood characters never got disgusting made for a loose, lively crowd. Supposedly a businessman from Chicago, a man who had been at Lou's several times before, the Ladykiller dressed well, he was relaxed and good-looking. Knew how to make a person laugh. The man wandered in and out, had a few drinks, talked to this one and that one, whispered into a few ears. Some thought his name was Mac, maybe Mark. Like a single flower in a pretty vase, the girl from the library was parked at the corner of the bar. Her name was Lori Terry. She called him Mike and slipped out of the bar with him before anyone had time to notice.

So not Nothing. All. A final present from the city of Milwaukee.

After he had driven west some fifteen minutes she asked, "So where are we going anyhow, Mike?" (Young avocado, peppermint.)

Like very few people he had observed, Lori Terry had the gift of imbuing words and even whole sentences with fragrances all her own. His nephew had a touch of this ability too.

"This place a little way out of town," he said.

"Sounds romantic. Is it romantic?" She'd had perhaps two or three drinks too many. ("Romantic" kind of hovered over a blocked drain.)

"I think it is, yes." He smiled at her. "Tonight wasn't the first time I've ever seen you, you know. I was in the library this morning. I saw you walk from Fiction right through into Biography."

"Why didn't you say hello?"

"You were too fast for me. Peeled right out of there."

"Must have made quite the impression." (Some lively pepperminty thing here, like gum, only not really.)

"I looked at you, and I thought, That girl could change my life."

"Well, maybe I will. Maybe you'll change mine. Look what we're doing! Nobody ever takes me out of town."

"I'll try to make the trip extra memorable."

"Actually, isn't it a little late for going out of town?"

"Lori, are you worried about sleep? Because I'll make sure you get enough sleep."

"Promise?" This word floated on a bed of fat green olives.

He promised her all the sleep she was going to need.

Trouble started twenty minutes later, when he pulled up into the weedy dirt driveway. As she stared first at the unpromising little tavern next to his actual building, then at him, disbelief widened her eyes. "This place isn't even open!" (Rancid milk.)

"Not that one, no," said the Ladykiller, now nearly on the verge of laughter. "The other one."

She swiveled her head and took in the old storehouse with the ghostlike word clinging to a front window. "Goods?" she asked. "If you tell me that's the name of the place, you're fulla shit." (Gunmetal, silver polish.)

"That's not a name, it's a disguise."

"Are you really sure about this?"

"Do you think I brought you all the way out here by mistake?" He opened his door, leaned toward her, and smiled. "Come on, you'll see."

217

"What is this, an after-hours joint? Like a club?" With a gathering, slow-moving reluctance, she swung the door open on a dissipating cloud of rainwater and fried onions and moved one leg out of the car.

"Private club." He moved gracefully around the hood and took her hand to ease her delivery from the car. The temperature of his resolve was doing that thing of turning hot as lava, then as cold as the flanks of a glacier, then back again, in about a second and a half. "Just for us, tonight."

"Jesus, you can do that?"

"You wait," he said, and searched his pocket for the magic key. It glided into the lock and struck home with the usual heavy-duty sound effects.

"Maybe we should both wait." (Chalk-dusty blackboard.)

He gave her an over-the-shoulder glance of rueful, ironic mock regret. "Wait? I'll get you back into town in plenty of time."

"We just met. You want me to follow you into this old building, and it's already past twelve . . ."

"You don't trust me?" Now he was frankly pouting. "And after all we've meant to each other."

"I was just thinking my father would be really suspicious right now."

"Isn't that part of the whole point about me, Lori? That your father wouldn't like me?"

She laughed. "You may be right."

"All right then." He opened the door onto an absolute darkness. "Just give me a sec. It's one flight down."

"A basement? I'm not so . . ."

"That's how they keep the place private. Wait, I'll get the light."

He disappeared inside and a moment later flipped a switch. Watery illumination revealed floorboards with a sweeping, half-visible grain. She heard the turning of another vault-like lock. He again appeared in the doorway, took her hand, and with only a minimum of pressure urged her into the building. Shivering in the sudden cold, she glanced around at the barren cell-like room she had entered. It seemed to be perfectly empty and perfectly clean. He was drawing her toward a door that opened onto a rectangle of greater brightness. It gradually revealed the flat, dimpled platform and gray descending handrail of a metal staircase. No noise came from the dark realm beyond the circle of light at the bottom of the steps.

"Ladies first," he said, and she had reached the fifth step down before she realized that he had blocked any possibility of escape. She turned to look at him over her shoulder, and received, as if in payment, a smile of utmost white seductiveness. "I know, it looks like no one's here. Works in our favor, actually. We'll have the whole place to ourselves. Do anything we like, absolutely everything."

"Wait a second," she said. "I want to have a good time, Mike, but absolutely everything is not in the picture, do you hear me?" What he had here, Till realized, was a clear, straightforward case of a specific fragrance emerging from a sentence as a whole, instead of blooming into the foreground of a lot of other, lesser smells. And in this case, the fragrance was that of a fresh fruit salad, heavy on the melons but with clean, ringing top notes of lime, just now liberated from the grocer's wrapping. Dazzled, he felt momentarily off-balance, as if his weight were on the wrong foot.

"Loud and clear. I don't have those kinds of designs on you."

"You don't?" In spite of everything, it was a kind of shock. He could smell it too: the fruit salad had been topped with a layer of thin, dark German pumpernickel. From *two words*. He was going to kill this wonderful girl, but part of him wished he could eat her too.

"Just wait at the bottom of the stairs. There's another door, and I have to get the light."

The habit of obedience rooted her to the floor as he squeezed past and pushed a third key into a third lock. Again Lori took in the heaviness of the mechanism, the thunk of precision-made machinery falling into place. Whatever made Mike happy, he had taken pains to keep it safe. Mike grasped her elbow and drew her after him into the dark room. The door closed heavily behind her, and Mike said, "OK, Lori, take a gander at my sandbox, my pride and joy."

He flipped up a switch and in the sudden glare of illumination she heard him relocking the door. In all the sparkle and shine she thought for a moment that she was actually looking at a metal sandbox. When her vision cleared, she glanced over her shoulder to see him tucking a key into his pocket.

"Oh my God," she said, and stepped away from him through a briefly hovering cloud of old saddles and baseball mitts.

"Lori Terry. Here you are."

"You're him."

"I am?"

"You're the Ladykiller guy. Goddamn." (Concrete sidewalks. Steel girders, plus maple syrup. She imprinted *her own* odors upon the words that issued from her, and she had the strength of character to shape entire utterances within that framework. He was still reeling.)

He spread his arms and summoned a handsome smile. "Like what I've done with the place?"

"I'd like you to take me home, please."

He stepped toward her. "In all honesty, Lori, this could go either way. Whichever path you choose, you're gonna end up in the same place. That's the deal here."

She moved about three inches backward, slowly. "You like blow jobs, Mike? I'll make you come like a fire hose." (Oh, exquisite, in fact almost *painfully* exquisite: when she must have been dropping into terror like a dead bird, her sentences came swaddled in clove, and ginger, and yet again the kind of maple syrup that came from trees bleeding into pails way up in Vermont and Maine, that area.)

"I always come like a fire hose. Of course, most of my partners aren't alive anymore. I like it that way. Come to think of it, they probably do too."

"You think a woman would have to be dead to enjoy making love to you? Let me prove how wrong you are."

He was inching toward her, but the distance between them remained constant.

"You're an unusual girl, Lori."

"What makes me 'unusual'?" (Marshmallow and chocolate: s'mores!)

"You're not cowering on the floor. Or sniveling. All the other girls—"

She took one fast step backward, spun around, and sprinted toward the center of the room. Amused by this display of nerve, he lunged for her playfully and almost deliberately missed. Lori ran around to the other side of the second steel table and leaned on it with stiff arms, her eyes and mouth open, watching him closely, ready to flee in any direction. For a couple of seconds only, she glanced into the corners of the shiny basement.

"To get out, you need my keys," he said. "Which means you ain't gonna get out. So are you going to make a break for it, or wait for me to come get you? I recommend the second one. It's not in your best interest to piss me off, I promise you." From across the room, he gave her the openhearted gift of a wide, very nearly genuine smile.

She kept watching him with the close, steady attention of a sailor regarding an unpredictable sea. On every second inhalation, she bent her elbows and leaned forward.

"Because right at this moment? Right at this moment, I admire the hell out of you. All kinds of reasons, honest to God."

He waited for her to break for either the right or the left side of the metal table so that he could at last close the distance between them and finish the gesture he had begun at Lou's Rendezvous, but she did not move. She kept on leaning forward and pushing back.

"You remind me of something I can't really remember. That FUBAR enough for you? Doozy of a story. About someone who won't stay dead but doesn't live." He lifted his arms, palms up, and all but uttered an involuntary sigh. "People keep telling me this shit, like they want me to remember! My brother, that stupid Henry James story . . . It's no good. It doesn't actually *mean* anything . . . but shouldn't it mean *everything*? A person who won't stay dead? Plus . . . someone else, a boy? An *old* boy?"

He shook his head as though to clear it. "Say something. Say anything. I love what happens when you talk."

"Oh?" Not enough to be measured: something about peanuts in a roaster . . . peanuts rolling in an oiled pan. . . .

"You know how words have these smells? Like 'paycheck' always smells like a dirty men's room? You know what I'm talking about, yeah?"

"You smell what I'm saying?" Without relaxing her attention, Lori leaned forward and narrowed her eyes. "How would you describe the smell of what I'm saying now?"

"Like butter, salt, and caramel sauce. Honest to God. You're amazing."

Lori exhaled and straightened her arms, pushing herself back. "You're a crazy piece of shit."

The Ladykiller kept looking at her steadily, almost not blinking, waiting for her to move to the right or the left. He told himself: *this resurrection stuff is all bullshit to lull her into breaking away from the autopsy table.*

Unless . . .

Something dark, something unstable flickered in his mind and memory and vanished back into the purely dark and fathomless realm where so much of the Ladykiller was rooted. Once again he shook his head, this time to rid himself of the terror and misery that had so briefly shone forth, and after that briefest possible moment of disconnection saw that Lori had not after all been waiting to bolt from the table. Instead, she had jerked open the drawer and snatched out a knife with a curved blade and a fat leather handle wrapped in layers of sweat- and dirt-stained tape. He loved that knife. Looking at it, you would be so distracted by its ugliness that you'd never notice how sharp it was. You wouldn't fear what it could do until it was already too late.

"Oh, that old thing," he said. "What are you going to do, open a beer can?"

"I'll open you right up, unless you toss me those keys." (The worse it got, the better it smelled: a bank of tiger lilies, the open window of a country kitchen.)

He pulled himself back into focus. "Jeez, you could have picked up one of the scalpels. Then I might be scared."

"You want me to swap it for a scalpel? It must be really lethal."

"*You'll* never find out," he said, and began slowly to move toward her again, holding out his hands as if in supplication.

"No matter what happens, I'm glad I'm not you." (Dishwashing liquid in a soapy sink, a wealth of lemon-scented bubbles: in his humble opinion, one of the world's greatest odors.)

Lori Terry moved back a single step and assumed a firmer grip on the ugly handle. She was holding it the right way, he noticed, sharp side up.

"You're a funny little thing." He straightened up, laughed, and wagged an index finger at her. "You have to admit, that is pretty droll."

"You have the emptiest, ugliest life I can imagine. You look like you'd be so much fun, but really you're as boring as a cockroach—the rest of your life is a disguise for what you do in this miserable room. Everything else is just a performance. Can't you see how disgusting that is?" This whole statement emerged clothed in a slowly turning haze of perfumed girl neck gradually melting to a smellscape of haystacks drying in a sunstruck field. This was terrible, somehow shaming.

"I thought I heard you trying to talk me into a blow job."

"That's when I was scared. I'm not afraid of you anymore." (Spinach, creamed, in a steakhouse.)

"Oh, come on." He moved across the room on a slanting line, trying to back her into a corner. "I know you're scared."

"I was afraid when I thought I had a chance to get out of this cockroach parlor. But I really don't, do I? I'm going to die here. At best, I'll cut you up a little bit. Then you'll kill me, and it'll all be over. You, however, will have to go on being a miserable, fucked-up creep with a horrible, depressing life." (Who knew what that was—horses? A rich man's stables?)

"At least I'll have a life," he said, and felt that he had yielded some obscure concession, or told her absolutely the wrong thing.

"Sure. A terrible one, and you'll still be incredibly creepy." (Astonishingly, this came out in a sunny ripple of clean laundry drying on a line.)

"I believe you might be starting to piss me off."

"Wouldn't that be a fucking shame." An idea of some kind moved into her eyes. "You thought I might change your life? I think you were right, I think I will change your life. Only right now you have no idea how that'll happen. But it'll be a surprise, that I can tell you."

Amazed, he said, "You think you're better than me?" (*And you just said four or five sentences that smelled like cloves and vetiver.*)

"You're a disgusting person, and I'm a good one."

She feinted and jabbed with the curved blade. It was enough to push him backward.

"I see you're afraid of this knife."

He licked his lips, wishing he were holding a baseball bat, or maybe a truncheon, a thing you could swing, hard, to knock in the side of someone's head. Then, before he could think about what he was going to do, he ducked left and immediately swerved to his right. Having succeeded in faking her off-balance, the Ladykiller rushed forward, furious and exulting, eager to finish off this mouthy bitch.

Before he could get a proper grip on her, Lori surprised him by jumping left and slashing at him. The blade, which had been fabricated by a long-dead craftsman in Arkansas and honed and honed again a thousand times on wet Arkansas stone, opened the sleeve of his nice tweed jacket and continued on to slice through the midriff of his blue broadcloth shirt. In the second and a half it took him to let go of her shoulder and anchor his hand on her wrist, blood soaked through the fine fabric of the shirt and began to ooze downward along a straight horizontal axis. As soon as he noticed that the growing bloodstain had immediately begun to spread and widen, he heard blood splashing steadily onto the floor, looked for the source, and witnessed a fat red stream gliding through the slashed fabric on his sleeve.

"Damn you." He jerked her forward and threw her to the ground. "What am I supposed to do now? Hell!"

She looked up at him from the floor. Crimson stains and spatters blossomed on her opened skirt and splayed legs. "The sight of your own blood throws you into a panic," she said. "Figures, I guess." (Tomato soup, no surprise, with garlic. Was she actually controlling the smells she sent out?)

"You *hurt* me!" He kicked her in the hip.

"OK, you hurt me back. Now we're even," she said. "If you give me the keys, I'll bandage you up. You could bleed to death, you know. I think you ought to be aware of—"

Both her words and the renewed smell of laundry drying in sunshine on a backyard clothesline caused rage to flare through all the empty spaces in his head and body. He bent over, ripped the knife from her loose hand, and with a single sweep of his arm cut so deeply through her throat that he all but decapitated her. A jet of blood shot from the long wound, soaking his chest before he could dodge out of the way. Lori Terry jittered a moment and was dead.

"Bitch, bitch, damn bitch," he said, "fuck this shit—I'm bleeding to death here!"

He trotted across the room to a pair of sinks, stripping off his jacket as he went and leaving bloody footprints in his wake. Though his wounds bled freely, and when first exposed seemed life-threatening, a matter that made him feel queasy and light-headed, soon he was winding bands of tape around a fat pad of gauze on his arm. The long cut on his stomach proved less dangerous but harder to stanch. While simultaneously stretching toward his spine with one hand and groping with the other, he found himself wishing that Lori had not been such a colossal bitch as to make him kill her before she could help him wrap the long bandage around the middle of his body. Of course, had she not been such an unfeeling bitch, she would have obliged him by curling up in whimpering terror even before he explained in free-spending detail precisely what he was going to do to her. The tramp had escaped the punishment she had craved, down there at the dark center of her heart. She got to fulfill her goal, but she had cheated herself of most of the journey toward it! And cheated him of being her guide!

While he was mopping the floor with a mixture of bleach and soapy water, the Ladykiller remembered his admiration of Lori Terry—the respect she had evoked in him by being uncowed. Instead of bursting into tears and falling down she had offered him a blow job! He had approved the tilt of her chin, the steadiness of her voice. Also, the resolute, undaunted look in her eyes. And the odors, the odors, the odors, in their unfathomable unhurried march. In farewell to her spirit, he dropped to his knees at the edge of her pooled blood, pursed his lips, and forcefully expelled air, but although he managed to create a row of sturdy little ripples, for only the second or at a stretch maybe third time in his life as the Ladykiller he failed to raise up even a single bubble. He nearly moaned in frustration, but held back: she had

224

refused to speak in Cockney, she had held to her dignity.

For the first time in his long career, the Ladykiller came close to regretting an obligatory murder, but this approach to remorse withered and died before the memory of her ugly dismissal of his life. Why, he wondered, should a sustained, lifelong performance be *disgusting*? Couldn't the cow see how interesting, how clever, his whole splendid balancing act had been? After this consoling reflection, his pain, which had been quietly pulsing away, throbbed within his lower abdomen and left forearm. This was a sharp reminder of her treachery. When the floor shone like the surface of a pond, he rinsed and stowed the mop, reverently washed the curved knife in a sink, and approached the long, cold table where Lori Terry's naked body, already cleansed and readied, awaited the final rites.

Two hours later, with everything—tables, walls, floor, switches, the dismembered body—rescrubbed and doused yet again in bleach, he stacked Lori's remains in a cardboard steamer trunk: feet and calves; thighs; pelvis; female organs from which his traces had been washed; liver, heart, lungs, stomach, and spleen in one bag, the long silver ropes of her intestines in another; hands and forearms; upper arms; rib cage; spine; shoulders; and as in life the open-eyed head atop all in a swirl of bleached hair. At the end, she had smelled of nothing but washed corpse. He locked the trunk, lugged it up the stairs, dragged it to his car, and with considerable effort wedged it into the car's trunk.

On his journey back into the city, he found that the care he had given her body, the thorough cleansing, the equally thorough separation of part from part, its arrangement within its conveyance, brought back to him now the respect he had learned to feel for her once the final key had turned in his serial locks. For respect it had been, greater and more valuable than admiration. Lori Terry had displayed none of the terror she, no less than his other victims, felt when she saw the pickle she was in: instead she had fought him from the beginning, with, he saw now, offers of sex that had actually promised something else altogether. She had wanted him exposed and vulnerable, she had wanted him open to pain, *in* grave pain—she had intended to put him in agony. It was true, he had to admire the bitch.

A momentary vision of the dismembered body arrayed like an unfolding blossom in the cardboard trunk popped like a flashbulb in his mind. He heard words begin to flow through his throat before he realized that he was talking out loud—talking to Lori Terry.

As he spoke, he had been removing the girl's remains from the

Peter Straub

cardboard trunk and placing them this way and that on the cobble-
stones of backstreet downtown Milwaukee. It took a while to get
them right. By the time he was satisfied, gray, early light had begun
to wash across the cobbles and the garbage cans behind the clubs.
Lori Terry's porcelain face gazed up at him like a bust in a museum.
Then he was gone, yessir, the Ladykiller was right straight outta
there, clean as a you-know-what and on to pastures new.

An Interview with Kelly Link
Conducted by Elizabeth Hand

IT IS RARE THAT ONE SEES a literary supernova explode upon the scene. Yet with the 1995 publication of Kelly Link's first story, "Water off a Black Dog's Back," anyone who happened to be scanning the artistic horizon at the time witnessed just that: the debut of an astonishing writer who from her opening sentence—*"Tell me which you could sooner do without, love or water"*—compelled a reader's attention, immersing her in the "vivid and continuous dream" that John Gardner believed was the achievement of great fiction.

Connoisseurs of Fantastika might have been early adopters of Link's work, which first appeared in small magazines such as *Lady Churchill's Rosebud Wristlet* (founded and edited by Link and her husband, Gavin Grant) and the short-lived 1990s reboot of *Century Magazine*, but her 2001 collection, *Stranger Things Happen*, exposed her work to a wider audience, winning the trifecta for fantastic literature (the Nebula, Tiptree, and World Fantasy Awards) even as it was chosen as one of the year's best books in mainstream venues *Salon* and the *Village Voice*. Her later collections, *Magic for Beginners* and *Pretty Monsters*, received equally rapturous reviews, and her most recent collection, *Get in Trouble*, was one of two finalists for the 2016 Pulitzer Prize.

At once oneiric and constructed from the brick-and-mortar details of ordinary life, Link's fiction renders the mundane transcendent and often terrifying: the dissolution of a marriage and family in "Stone Animals"; the revenant as babysitter in the deeply disturbing, ambiguous "The Specialist's Hat"; microparenting elevated to an absurd (and unnervingly plausible) degree in "Valley of the Girls." Her stories often read like urban legends spun by a contemporary Scheherazade. Tales within tales, told forward or backward or sideways, they can feel like portents of what might actually happen to the reader once she finishes the story.

We often speak of being changed by our experience with a book— one is kinder to orphaned children or learns never to venture alone into the woods after dark. The sublime unease that radiates from

227

Kelly Link

Kelly Link's short fiction derives from the fact that the reader knows she's been changed—but she doesn't understand *how*. It's literature as virus, mutating inside that part of the brain that processes language and memory. One never reads a Kelly Link story the same way twice, and one is never the same afterward. You've been warned.

ELIZABETH HAND: A hallmark of your work is an exquisite, often terrifying, transfixing strangeness. Have you ever had a real-life encounter that resembles something out of one of your stories? Do you know anyone who has?

KELLY LINK: I've always suspected that my antennae for recognizing strangeness and the uncanny in real life is poor, much like my ability to tell when someone I'm interacting with is drunk. So if I've had that sort of encounter, I didn't know it (like the husband and wife in Edith Wharton's ghost story "Afterward" but without the consequence). Wouldn't that be the strangest ghost story of all? That there was a ghost but you never discovered that a ghost is what it was? The strangest things in my life have been only a little strange: meeting, falling in love with, and marrying a man who, as it turned out, had lived for a year in the same small Scottish town as me and attended the same university. We each wrote something for the same ghost-story competition. But never met during that year. I do love other people's true stories about the inexplicable. I save them up and tell them when the situation is appropriate, and then other people will share their own stories, which means I have an even bigger repository to trade and pass on. Surely you have a ghost story or the equivalent, Liz?

HAND: I did experience something inexplicable when I was fourteen, with my two best friends in eighth grade. To this day I'm not sure what happened—I wrote about it in "Near Zennor." So, what about aliens? Do you think they exist, and there's any chance we might make first contact in your lifetime?

LINK: This seems to suggest that it's all up to me. If I say yes, then any terrible results are my fault, and if I say no, I exclude so many possibilities. Right now, my daughter, when you ask her to make a choice between any two things, will yell, "Both!" Anyway, luckily it isn't up to me.

HAND: Ha! She has the makings of an artist, being able to see both sides. Or a politician. What was your first encounter with an alien, real or imaginary?

LINK: The ones that I remember most vividly are all movies or television. E.T., and the crew of the Nostromo encountering the eggs in the ruin of the spaceship, and before that, of course, *Star Trek*. I watched *Star Trek* with my dad. I was deeply in love with Spock for most of my childhood. Also I wanted to be him.

I watched *Alien* for the first time the same summer that Lady Diana married Prince Charles. My sister and I had been at camp and my mother recorded both the wedding and *Alien* for us. It seemed as if we were supposed to watch the royal wedding, and so we did. *Alien*, on the other hand, was something that my mother made clear we weren't supposed to watch, but it was such an extraordinarily good movie that we had special permission. She said that we might want to look away from the scene in which John Hurt begins to cough, because it was disturbing. And so, for years, I would cover my eyes whenever the alien burst out of his chest. In fact I didn't watch that scene until I was maybe forty.

Except for *Alien*, most aliens always felt a little disappointing. And even the alien in *Alien* I liked because the bones of the story were the bones of a ghost story. The malignant presence in a haunted house. Years ago, Slate.com had a contest to come up with titles in the same style as *Snakes on a Plane*. The best was "The Creature Lurks in the Structure." Which describes most succinctly my favorite genre. Perhaps all of art. But aliens: the mashed potatoes were more interesting to me in *Close Encounters* than the aliens. If not the first, then near the first aliens I came across in books were the Martians in *The War of the Worlds*, or possibly in some of the short stories in Helen Hoke's anthologies, or the Alfred Hitchcock anthologies that Robert Arthur edited.

HAND: I didn't see *Alien* when it first came out, I was so nervous about watching that scene. Waiting didn't make it any easier when I did see it. You channel the perils and sheer weirdness of childhood and adolescence better than just about any writer working today, some of which make *Alien* seem tame in comparison.

LINK: I don't think that can be true. I don't even know if that's what I'm aiming for. I think that I'm trying to get something true *enough*, accurate *enough*, that I can get away with the kind of invention or

229

entertainment that I want to tackle. The emotional stuff has to echo with the reader, or blindside the reader in the right way for the uncanniness to have verisimilitude. Everything is in service of the uncanny or to allow an easier approach to a certain kind of structural difficulty. I'm not entirely sure what the uncanny is in the service of: representing life as it seems to me, I suppose. So we've come full circle.

HAND: What was your own early life like? Were you interested in writing then, or did that come much later?

LINK: I was interested, when I was a teenager, in writing but only in the most dreamy kind of way. It seemed like it would be *neat*. It seemed as if there wasn't anything else that would be more interesting. But it also seemed like a lot of work, so I put off doing it for as long as possible. I'm still very good at putting it off. As for what kind of person I was, I was a mostly happy child who didn't fit in. I was interested in the same kinds of things that I am interested in now: books, music, horror movies, pattern making and pattern recognition, people who make and do things that are surprising. The difference between child me and adult me is that I have to organize my own life now, that I have lived in the same place now for fifteen years, and that I have many friends whose preoccupations are congruent with, or at least neighborly to, my interests. I spend less time catching snakes. More time designing book covers.

HAND: Was there ever a book or story you were afraid to read at night?

LINK: No and also yes. I read H. P. Lovecraft and M. R. James and Stephen King at night in bed when I was ten or eleven, and then I would go tell my mother I was too afraid to go to sleep. But I kept on reading them anyway because it was pleasurable to lie in bed and be so terrified by a story that I couldn't go to sleep.

HAND: So you were both terrified and there was an element of pleasure involved too? How do you think that fear can generate the frisson of pleasure we get from reading the best kind of eerie story? And did that girlhood reading help inspire you to become the kind of writer you are today, scaring other girls as they read late at night?

LINK: The idea that I might cause anyone at all to lie in bed at night feeling uneasy about things that don't exist is almost overwhelmingly gratifying. I suppose it's an addictive thrill, the feeling of all of the senses prepared to detect strangeness in the absence of tangible stimulus that would justify the effort. The satisfaction of an eerie story is that it gives a shape and a narrative arc (even if it isn't one which completes/resolves) to something that we have a capacity for— or even a longing to experience.

HAND: Shirley Jackson is another great American writer who decamped to northern New England. Her relationship to the small town where she lived was somewhat complicated, as evinced by stories like "The Lottery" and "The Summer People." What if any impact has that part of the world had on your own work? It certainly attracts a lot of artists.

LINK: It's had tremendous impact on my working life in that I regularly meet up to work with the writers Holly Black and Cassandra Clare in this area. Jedediah Berry and Susan Stinson and John Crowley are also more or less local. In terms of what I write about, I think that I've now lived in one place (Western Mass) for so long that I can now comfortably write about the other places that I've lived: Florida, North Carolina, and Boston.

HAND: Is there anything in particular about New England that resonates with you?

LINK: In my day-to-day life, I find it easier to live here. I wasn't great at being southern, in the social sense. Here we live in a place with terrific music too: the Winterpills and the Fawns are local bands and I often listen to their songs while I'm working. There are a lot of bookstores in barns and old mill buildings. Pretty idyllic.

HAND: You admire Shirley Jackson's work: what story or novel of hers would you give to a first-time reader?

LINK: *The Haunting of Hill House.* I can't imagine anyone reading the first paragraph, and then the first page, and not wanting to know more. As much as I love Jackson's stories, there's something luxurious about getting to inhabit her imagination, be under the influence of her sentences for a whole novel.

HAND: You've taught creative writing at places like the Clarion [Science Fiction and Fantasy] Writers' Workshop. Are there any habits of student writers that you like to unteach?

LINK: I don't know that there's anything that I think of as unteaching. I usually start by asking a workshop what books/work they respond to as writers and what they respond to as readers. I used to frame that second question as "guilty pleasures," by which I meant the kinds of things that they wouldn't feel represented their best writerly impulses, but which they were drawn to anyway. I taught at Clarion again this summer, and I came away thinking about patterns of storytelling. It's useful to consider the kinds of patterns that you find interesting which are generic/often replicated. You should use those. But you should also think about the kinds of narrative/structural/technical problems that you haven't seen solved. Many writers will do interesting and compelling work with generic patterns. But the problems that, as a writer, you are interested in solving—and their solutions—are more likely to be particular to you. Conversely, the things that you object to most strenuously are also tender places and you should consider those as well and why you have an emotional reaction to them. There can be a kind of recognition of self in the things (techniques, modes, ambitions) that we most loathe.

HAND: Pop culture ripples through many of your stories, sometimes like a secret tributary. Were you and are you a comic-book fan? If so, who's your favorite character?

LINK: Referencing pop culture is a way of rendering landscape. Right?

HAND: "Rendering landscape" through pop culture is such an intriguing notion—how does that work? By giving readers a hook into your own imaginary landscape?

LINK: The kind of spaces and communities that people inhabit now aren't solely defined by a particular physical place or landscape. And even physical landscape (if, like me, you've moved around a fair amount) is defined, in memory, by the person you were when you lived in that place; by the things that you read, that you discovered, that you loved, that you later abandoned. In a piece of fiction, particularly a short story, every detail tells you something about the characters and their community. How they define themselves, how they want other people to see them, what they love and are ashamed of loving, what is vital to them. I spent not quite a decade as the member of a very active youth group in a Presbyterian Church in Miami, watching movies about the Rapture, listening to Amy Grant, playing Capture the Flag, and making out with other people on church buses. I went to malls every weekend and spent my allowance at Spencer's Gifts, B. Dalton, and a novelty candle shop. All of that, I think, is as much the landscape of Florida to me as the Everglades and Coral Gables and catching snakes and iguanas.

The first comic to get me into a bookstore, literally, was the cover of an issue of Dave Sim's *Cerebus*. Or, more accurately, Gerhard's background on the cover of an issue of *Cerebus*. But I don't know that I have a favorite character. I love Hellboy and the manga *Twin Spica*. *Scott Pilgrim*, *The Land of Nod*, Emily Carroll's *Through the Woods*. I loved Bill Sienkiewicz's art. I loved Lynda Barry's *Ernie Pook's Comeek*. I love Joann Sfar and Lewis Trondheim's *Dungeon*, Ryan North's *Dinosaur Comics*, Kevin Huizenga's Glenn Ganges. That last one is probably closest to my life.

HAND: I adore Lynda Barry. She got me through a brain-numbing job in the 1980s. What really grabs you about the folks you mention—their artwork? Narratives? And what did that Gerhard background depict?

LINK: I think I have that envy, particular to writers, of artists who work in mediums that are more immediately accessible/economical. Musicians, artists, screenwriters. My daughter draws a lot of comics at the moment. There isn't much text, but you can tell, in a flash, what the rats are feeling. Fear, sadness, exhilaration, rage. The text is almost extraneous. I love black-and-white comics, maybe because even with that limitation, so much life, so much narrative and emotional information is available. *Cerebus* was about a warrior aardvark who becomes a kind of pope. A ridiculous premise, but Gerhard's backgrounds were somber and luminous. The contrast between the aardvark and the kind of art nouveau backdrop behind him was intriguing.

HAND: Many of your stories—"The Specialist's Hat" or "Lull," to name just two—are profoundly unsettling but also kind of funny. Do you think about balancing humor with terror when you're writing something? Or do you just decide you want to really creep out the reader?

LINK: Humor and horror are both approaches that dislocate or disarrange. They jar. The person experiencing them is necessarily surrendering control over their response. They're pleasurable, or can be, for the person having the experience, and as a writer, if you discover that you can produce that effect, it's addictive. I was the kid who liked to jump out of the closet to scare people. I still like slapstick.

HAND: I can definitely see that slapstick, "Boo!" element in some of your stories, also that sense of dislocation. "Lull" is a perfect example, I think. And "Stone Animals" remains one of the most disturbing

233

stories I've read in the last twenty years. Do you know how you produced the effects in that story? Is it more of an organic process, or do you have a particular technique or techniques that you deliberately make use of?

LINK: "Stone Animals" took over a year to figure out, by which I mean revising over and over again. The last couple of pages I wrote in the space of a couple of days, and I don't think I had to rework them quite as much. But the premise of the story seemed so comical to me (it started with the ending) that I spent a great deal of time reworking for pacing and description, in order to provide weight. Eventually I began to move in and out of tenses as a way of increasing discomfort. And because the premise was comical, I had to think about comedy differently. Goofiness is more my natural mode, but anything that I might be tempted to handle in the manner of a soufflé in other stories is, in "Stone Animals," more somewhere between dour humor and inexorable nightmare logic.

HAND: How do you feel when you finish writing a story?

LINK: Relieved! Slightly euphoric. The desire to jump into a pool and go sit at the bottom. (I grew up in Florida, we had a swimming pool. I miss having a swimming pool.)

HAND: Let's say our planet has somehow miraculously survived the current electoral cycle and made contact with an alien race. You're one of the six people chosen to first meet them. You also get to choose the five other people who will accompany you: who would you bring? (In addition to making ET contact, we've also developed a time machine, so you can choose anyone from anywhere anytime on earth.)

LINK: I'm sure that this is a terrible list, but Tove Jansson, Grace Paley, Queen Elizabeth I, Michelle Obama, and my mother, because she can talk to anyone.

HAND: So why these particular women? And why no men?

LINK: If I had listed all men and no women, would you ask why no women? General preference, I suppose. Five is a small list. I could come up with probably another fifty lists of five people who could go meet aliens. I'd love to hear Ted Chiang's list.

HAND: You also get to be the Decider on the aliens' first contact with world literature. What five books would you give the aliens?

LINK: Oh, boy. Don't ask me to justify my choices, but I guess I'd go with Sei Shōnagon's *Pillow Book*, Samuel Delany's *Dhalgren*, Frank Stanford's *What About This*, Zadie Smith's *White Teeth*, and *Brat Farrar* by Josephine Tey. Or maybe there should be a graphic novel in there. Scott McCloud's *Understanding Comics*? *Garfield*? I don't know.

HAND: Some of your tales read like brilliant variations on a camp-fire story or slumber-party story. There's always a kid who everyone wants to tell the scary story. Was that you? Or were you just listening very closely to that kid?

LINK: I wasn't that kid, but I am that kid now. Although I'm also just as thrilled now to be the one listening.

HAND: Do you listen to audiobooks? I always find the experiences of reading and listening to a story to be very different. Do you?

LINK: I'm terrible at listening to audiobooks. The only one I can re-member enjoying was the audiobook of James B. Stewart's true-crime book, *Blind Eye*, because it was so harrowing. I don't typically enjoy listening to recordings of books, perhaps because I read so much faster from the page. Having said that, I really love "Selected Shorts," especially if I don't know the story. And I love listening to writers read their own work.

HAND: This is a golden age for literature of the fantastic. Who are the emerging writers you're most excited about reading?

LINK: I'll mention two writers whose work I love, whom I've also been lucky enough to get to publish, Alice Sola Kim and Sofia Samatar. Carmen Maria Machado! I loved two recent debut novels. One, *The Loney*, by Andrew Michael Hurley, which is a very old-fashioned Satanists (or the equivalent)-in-an-isolated-English-countryside set-ting, is just out. The other is *Rawblood* by Catriona Ward, a really gorgeous Gothic novel that skips around in time. I think you'd really like that one too. And here are two more writers whose first books I loved, Ben Rice (*Pobby and Dingan*) and Jen Banbury (*Like a Hole in the Head*), and ever since I've been waiting to read something else they've written.

HAND: Two last questions about your writing process. Do you work from an outline, or do you work in a more instinctive, organic fashion?

Kelly Link

LINK: I don't have any sort of formal outline, but I tend to have a particular kind of structure in my head, and I usually have a firm idea of the ending that I'm working toward. The first three to ten pages is usually the trickiest part, and the piece that I spend the most time revising before I get anywhere else. The middle I figure out as I revise the first bits.

HAND: So why are those first pages the trickiest part? It's funny, that's the one part I find much easier than writing the ending. Can you give us an example from your recent collection of one story that was especially difficult (or easy) to write?

LINK: I have about seven significantly different versions of the first six pages or so of "I Can See Right through You." That is, I saved seven separate, distinct versions. There were probably another two dozen slight variations. Each start felt as if it would work to build on, and yet I couldn't build on it past a certain point. So I revisited it off and on for about a year, until I had versions of the two main characters that were dimensional enough to me, a kind of tonal quality that felt sustainable, and movement between time periods that suggested as much as I wanted to suggest about the entanglement between the personal relationship and the supernatural element. On the other hand, I wrote most of "The Lesson" in about a week, assembling it out of components that I'd had in my head for many years.

HAND: Do you create a playlist for whatever you're working on, or do you prefer silence?

LINK: Oh, a very long playlist that I add or subtract things to as I start new stories. Currently it's lots of the Kills, TV on the Radio, Winterpills, Prince, the New Pornographers, Lady Lamb, Wolf Alice, Santigold, Jenny Lewis, and Lucius.

HAND: Are these old favorites, or do you add new music and musicians all the time? What is it about the artists you mention here that helps you write? (I'm trying to do a kind of musical forensics and see if I can guess what story might come out of this song mix.)

LINK: I used to switch between playlists once I moved from one story to the next, so that I could imagine that I was resetting a kind of aural prompt. But at the moment, I've moved on to writing a novel, and so I've kept most of the last three playlists and just added on a bunch of old/new material. A kind of security blanket!

HAND: One last question: You and your husband, Gavin Grant, run Small Beer Press—what's it like to wear two hats, writer and editor/publisher? (Maybe that's three hats?)

LINK: It used to seem to me that I would be miserable if the only work that I had was writing. My year used to break down into teaching/writing/editing and Small Beer, and I liked being able to move from job to job to job. Teaching/workshop is the most purely pleasurable/gratifying. What's better than being useful? With Small Beer, I get the fun work: editing and cover design. Gavin does all the heavy lifting. I hope that being a writer makes me a better editor and teacher. Now if I only had a bookshop as well, I'd be set.

Fallout

Madeline Bourque Kearin

IT HAS BEEN TWENTY YEARS since the last bomb dropped and his skin still prickles in the open air. From far away he looks like an impressionist rendering of a man, drips and dabs of pink and brown and beige molded into humanoid form. Close up, the illusion breaks, and in its place, the skin asserts its rugged intricacies: the taut geography of cells that have lost their substance, dissolving the boundaries between fingers, between features, between his face and neck. His body is anarchy, anthropomorphized. Yet his two brown eyes, round and glossy, are preserved perfectly, fixed like wet marbles in tight rings of scar tissue, and somehow their presence calls the rest of the face to order. He is proud of his eyes, and of his half head of hair, which grew back brown and lustrous after it fell out. He has every one of his fingers and seven of his fingernails. He wears his grandfather's clothes, flannel shirts and moleskin pants and cabled sweaters that nearly fit him, and his mother's wedding ring on a chain around his neck.

He lives in the house he was in when the last bomb fell. His house, with his parents in it, had been blown away two weeks earlier. He was ten years old that day and can still remember the way that his skin felt—smooth and pliable, tailored to every bone and joint—as well as the way he moved, the liquid gestures of his arms and legs, the painless molding of clothes to flesh, and the way the sun bristled along the tips of his eyelashes. When the sirens wailed he went with his sister and their neighbors into the basement. It was over in a couple of seconds. The narrow window above their heads enclosed a rectangle of pure fire that shattered the glass as it blazed into the room, converting everything into a jigsaw of white light and black shadows. They felt the hairs on their arms stand on end, then fizzle into nothingness, along with the first few layers of skin. Skin that rose, he remembers, like the top sheet of a pad of paper, blackening as it fell away. The cover of the book his sister was reading cleaved to her face, leaving the title printed on her cheek.

The blast made no sound.

Life was never the same. There were no more bombs, and those who survived were free to come and go as they pleased. After long, excruciating months, during which more people died, more layers of skin fell off, and he spat teeth bloodlessly onto his pillow every morning, their conditions stabilized. What was left of their community rallied. Like their bodies, they have spun out ropes of scar tissue to build a web between them, filling in gaps and covering naked joints as best they can. They hear little from the outside world and are glad of it. Before the last bomb, when the end of days seemed imminent, they stored enough provisions to last them a hundred years, and now it's more than they need. The bomb rounded off their population. The very young and the very old died immediately or shortly thereafter; now everyone is about the same age and in the same condition: scarred but stable. They are also universally sterile, likening themselves humorously to the trees at the university that survived the blast intact only to lose their fruits, one by one, over the course of the next weeks. He recalls the hollow punching sound of rotten peaches as they fell, detonating in slimy masses on the ground. But it's all right. Spared from the anxieties of procreation, they found other things to do. To begin with, they relearned each other's faces, mentally grafting the purple welts and waxy white scars over the features they once possessed. Now they guard their damaged skin against the sun and wind, bandage their weeping wounds, and rake the fallout that continues to descend, like black leaves, slowly and silently over the city.

It shouldn't have been me. It wasn't supposed to be, but LeRoy lost his nerve at the last minute and so here I am, the balm for a public relations nightmare that is now seven centuries old.

I'm sitting on the steps of the Rockefeller Library, knee to knee with Ernest Gracey, the young man whose marbled hands with their seven gray fingernails are laced in his lap like the legs of a large, barnacled crab. There is just enough light in the thready dusk to plant shadows in all the little canyons of his skin. Behind us, the wind curdles in the empty eye slats of the Rock and peels feathers of ash from its black face. When I stumbled into the revolving door as a first-year graduate student, sending the contents of my bag pinwheeling across the floor, the Rock was taupe colored and there was glass in every window, admitting bands of autumn light that crisscrossed through the stacks.

I've explained it to him three times and he still won't believe it.

239

"I was so sure it was a fortress," he says, snorting a breath through his pinched nostrils as he shakes his head. "What with all the cement, and the narrow windows, and the subterranean chambers—it even has a perfect vantage point to see invaders coming."

"Well, I never saw any invaders when I was here. Lots of weary students, though, lugging backpacks up the hill."

"But what about the railing along the top—surely that's defensive. I imagined sharpshooters balancing their rifles on it, picking out targets a thousand yards away."

"Actually, it's just decorative," I tell him, and hear how ridiculous the words sound only in the course of saying them. He and I steal a glance back at the building, at the strips of cement pieced like Tinkertoys to form a squat ledge along the cornice, and both burst into laughter. He gives me that look, communicated through spasms of his eyebrowless forehead: *Sure, Dr. Hamblin, sure.* And I have to concede, as I always do, that his well-reasoned theories, built upon years of observation and study, make a lot more sense than my clumsy explanations, although the latter are, ostensibly, the truth.

The city is not all that different from how I knew it, for thirteen years in the first half of the third millennium. Its architectural underpinnings have barely been touched; the bones, as one of my old professors might say, are still there. But the skin and musculature are not simply aged but mutilated. Like the Rock: recognizable enough to those who knew it when (that is, only to me), it would not occur to anyone who saw it now for the first time that it had ever been a library. The golden letters at the entrance spalled from their surface so long ago that not even their shadows remain. And of course, the entire contents—every one of the millions of volumes—were atomized by a bomb before Ernest's grandparents were born, leaving nothing but a shell, another scorched jungle gym for neighborhood children; another theater for a young man's imagination.

In the absence of a future, he has wed himself to the past. Twenty years of searching, and all it took was one loud-mouthed time traveler to capsize all of his visions. So far not one of his theories has proven correct. He thought that the Graduate Center dormitories were barracks for slaves and that India Point Park was a wildlife sanctuary for dogs, which he surmised must have been a highly endangered species. He imagined that the soaring white spires of the Baptist and Congregational Churches were landing docks for flying machines and that the Van Wickle Gates barricaded against wild beasts. Finding statues of bears across the campus, some still erect, others toppled, he assumed they had been the objects of a shamanistic cult that ascribed mystical power to animals. He based his conclusions on careful induction and attributed any phenomenon that resisted easy categorization to ritual.

"You're an excellent archaeologist," I tell him.

I'm not lying.

We walk down from the steps and lean into the steep climb up toward Prospect Terrace Park. Once, half a dozen lifetimes ago, a pair of rabbits darted across the street in front of my husband (then boyfriend) and me in this very spot, chasing each other between cars until they came to a stop on a grassy patch near Lovecraft Memorial Square. I shrieked with laughter at the sight of them (I was young and carefree once, not that anyone would believe it now) and made sure that James was aware: it was the first time I'd ever seen wild rabbits in Providence. And it would be the last; no animals survived the bombs. Burnt-out cars lie stranded, one or two on every road, like the scorched skeletons of beached whales. Utility poles dip wearily, resting the pendulous arcs of their fried lines on the black cement. And the soft strands of the sunset wend smoothly up the hill, undiluted by electric lights, kindling an iridescent glow on the crumbling rooftops.

I wasn't prepared for how changed it would be—not the city itself but the natural environment, the phenomena that I considered to be eternal and detached from time. The bombs scrambled the substance of the city on an atomic level. The air feels different, heavier, and somehow sharp and shiny, as though there were diamonds lodged inside every molecule. Darkness is not dark; it resonates with a radiant substance, colorful spots that occasionally resolve into patterns, triangles and pinwheels and castellations that brand the inside of my eyelids. And the sun and moon, refracted through nuclear residue, conjure kaleidoscopic visions: a different hallucination every morning, noon, and night. Just now, the barbed tail of a green aurora lashes across the horizon, lancing the sky from seam to seam. For a moment it appears to bleed, great red clots that glaze the hollow silhouette of the Omni Hotel and pool in the State House's punctured dome. Then the entire canvas halts and dips, and slips like a reel of film into a fresh image, this one purple and blue and crushed like velvet, pilled with soft yellow stars like the holes in Ernest's face.

He casts a toothless smile at me over his shoulder as we walk, ropes of scar tissue pulling his mouth like the strings of a marionette. Two weeks after I arrived, sweaty and wild-eyed from the pod, he apologized for looking at me so much.

"That's not the way my parents raised me, to stare at someone like that," he said. "It's only that it's been twenty years since I saw a face like yours. A normal human face."

He was the only one to apologize, but he wasn't the only person to stare. They all do. It's been an adjustment. I am no great beauty; I never was. For most of my life I slipped under the radar, relying on my words to draw people's attention across a room. But now attention clusters around me. They marvel at my full head of glossy black hair, my seamless brown skin, my flat pink fingernails. They admire the fluidity of my joints. One man always asks to see my ears. His name is David Arnold, but naturally I think of him as the Ear Fetishist—not that I think there is anything lewd in his desire. It has been twenty years since any of them has seen a human ear that wasn't melted. They all want to see, but most are too polite to ask. They look at my lips instead; lips are almost as rare as ears. Most of their mouths are undifferentiated openings, scarred-over slits that look as though they've been cut into their heads with a knife, and some must continue to cut them regularly to keep the scar tissue from pulling them shut.

When we take meals together (always the same gray nutritious paste, derived from a concentrate resistant to radiation and decay), I eat slowly, in order to keep pace with their labored movements, and I never begrudge them their stares.

There was a time, not long before I came here, when I loathed company. I accepted this one-way mission—five centuries in a metal pod, one hundred feet square, in which time would be slowed to a fraction of its normal rate—partly out of scientific interest and partly out of a vague and idiopathic misanthropy that had left me feeling empty and annoyed with the human race. To others, I would always attribute this feeling to the sudden death of my husband; in truth it had come about long before then, descending like a veil, then deepening until it settled beneath my skin. And now it's gone, I suppose, back to the place from which it came. I suppose that's what half a millennium in a pod will do to you.

I could say that it was my admiration for the patient suffering of the people of the future, their willingness to hope in the face of hopelessness, that finally lifted my melancholy, but that would be another lie. In truth it was Ernest Gracey: his wide-eyed curiosity, his stupid optimism, his undeterred joy for all the strange little things of the world. He reminds me of all the reasons I was drawn to cultural anthropology in the first place. Because I am, first and foremost, an anthropologist—the twenty-first century's natural second choice for an ambassador.

When I first listened to Ernest spin his fantasies across the blackened landscape, I was struck by their divergence from the city as I had known it. Now, after seven months, I'm not so sure that his vision of the past is that different from mine. The absence of flying machines and bear cults aside, there was always something fantastical about Providence, some mystical current surging beneath the surface, rioting beneath the weathered bricks, and when it was dark, every old house glowed purposefully, as though it were lit from within by its own secret soul. Perhaps it was the lingering afterglow of Lovecraft, or perhaps it's something deeper, which Lovecraft was able to tap into: a sense of wildness and vastness; of a universe that resists all attempts to impose order upon it; of the staggering depth of human vulnerability, like staring down into a black and bottomless well.

These fantasies are what sustain us; it's no fun seeing what's behind the curtain. And while I would never tell an outright lie, there are things about which I will never tell the whole truth. The people of the future think that the people of my century were just and noble, and that my passage here was orchestrated out of a pure-hearted desire to advance human knowledge. They think that I was the ideal candidate, hand selected from a pool of millions. They think that I volunteered for altruistic reasons, not because I was sad and frustrated and bored. And they think that more people from my time are coming.

I'm not sure yet whether that last one is false. There were supposed to be more, a year or less from my arrival. Even if they had taken decades to build another pod, the end point would be the same, rendering any passage of time between starting points insignificant. They could even have sent someone before me, to meet me when I arrived. It's true that the calibration was thought to be imprecise. I was told that I could find myself a decade later or earlier than when I was expected, but I arrived exactly on time, within hours of my target. And here I remain, stranded in this century, my vessel having reached its programmed obsolescence.

Less than a year, they said, but the year is winding down—not that you'd know it. There are no seasons. Untethered from its accustomed rhythms, time spills where it once flowed, forming tributaries that grow into oceans where you can easily lose yourself. I try to reconnect to time, but it is difficult. I am living in a colony of ageless souls, whose skin sloughs off before it can sag, where youth and

243

age cohabitate on a single face: those living patchworks of skin that evoke Frankenstein's monster and faded quilts and the blood-colored rawness of something just hatched all at once. They are simultaneously more and less than human, and in my own way, so am I.

I live in University Hall. The entire building is mine: four stories, five chimneys, and thousands of bricks, some placed there by African slaves; two smashed pediments, a toppled cupola, and a hundred empty windows; gutters that dangle from splintered cornices; and all that's inside too—dusty rooms, crumbling fireplaces, ceilings that sheltered Revolutionary troops and nineteenth-century undergraduates and Horace Mann, along with the little refuge I've carved into the top floor, furnished with my few possessions.

My pod was anchored in the middle of the Main Green with University Hall framed in its only window, a bubble of glass through which I watched the years peel back from the skin of the world. I saw oceans rise and fall: red oceans of leaves and white oceans of snow and, much later, black oceans of ash. I watched the buds on trees open and close like grasping fists and watched the pink blooms of rhododendrons yawn in and out of existence. And below the sun and the moon, taking turns scoring bright channels into the sky, millions of bodies swept like smoke up and down stairs and along the paths. Occasionally, they pressed their diaphanous faces into my window, though they were gone so quickly that I couldn't tell what they looked like. I often wondered if they were still human. But more so, I wondered what they thought of me: the woman they observed frozen in the same pose every time they looked in, like a natural-history diorama, simulating the act of eating toast or reading a book or typing on my computer. With the years, the scene would seem increasingly strange. Students wouldn't recognize the food I ate or the objects I used. The clothes that I wore would look dated, then retro, then exotic, until they passed the threshold of museum worthiness. I imagined a placard next to me: *Anthropologist. Twenty-First Century. Please don't tap the glass.*

As it turns out, they had erected something, evidenced by the metal marker I found when I emerged, but the top had broken off. In the place of this explanatory statement, the people of the future maintained a mutated memory of me, a mythology cultured from scraps of the truth. They even had a name for me: Thalia Tamerlane. It felt like a betrayal—or at the very least a disenchantment—to introduce myself to them as Sarah Hamblin. Sarah Hamblin, PhD. No one knew what the letters stood for, but of course Ernest was ready to offer his best guess.

I walk home alone after leaving him at his place, which he still refers to as the Pagets' house, though the elderly Pagets died shortly after the last blast. It's a mid-nineteenth-century, mansard-roofed mansion that may at one point have been green. The inside is sparsely but tastefully furnished in pieces plucked from the wreckage: a chipped dresser, an assortment of tables and chairs, and a startlingly well-preserved four-poster bed salvaged from the RISD Museum; a leather sofa, ravaged with tears, which he has painstakingly stitched with the same oily catgut the populace use for their wounds; and in every room, one or two of the Oriental carpets he found sealed in a Wickenden Street basement. The carpets act like rouge on the skin of the dead house, maintaining a facsimile of life over the decaying floorboards and gutted walls.

I take one last glance across the green as I enter University Hall. The first time I was here, I was with James; it was the end of summer, and cicadas scribbled their vibrations on the heavy air.

And the last time, the green was crowded with fanfare as I stepped into the pod. I took one last glance to survey the faces of all the people who would be dead before I needed to trim my toenails again: President Roberts and Dean Eyles and the entire Anthropology Department, including the one weasel-faced graduate student whom I hoped would be *especially* dead; a sea of undergraduates wielding smartphones and journalists wielding cameras; and John LeRoy, whose place I was taking in hell.

At least, that was how he appeared, his face awash with the species of relief native to the convict who receives a last-minute call from the governor. But it didn't feel like a death sentence to me. I was already comfortably ensconced in my afterlife. Likewise the newspapers described mine as a willing sacrifice, verging on martyrdom; one said, *She will enter into the small womb-like capsule on September 16, and close the door on the twenty-first century.* They implied that I had all of the agency. But what had I done, day after day, as the walls pieced themselves together around me? Nothing but sit in my house, reading or writing, glancing through the door of my office to James on the sofa as the television spun electric skeins inside the lenses of his glasses; always alone, even when I was in a crowded room; always apart, even when I lay next to him. It was as though a sudden guillotine-like violence had severed the vessels that connected me to the world and left me raw and mutilated. Through my ribs I could see the empty engine of my heart spinning, still working tirelessly to send out warmth and affection, but its wasted efforts spattered on the ground. Likewise all the meaningful gestures of other people kept on hurtling toward me, only to spill before they could reach their mark. But hardly anyone noticed; my reflexes guided me aptly enough through the act of being human.

My departure from the twenty-first century was not a separation. It was a last-minute, life-saving procedure, intended to treat an ancient and mortal injury. In burning down the world around me, I hoped to cauterize my wounds.

I would emerge from the pod intact.

"Will you open the chamber soon?" Ernest asked while we were walking in the North Burial Ground. The gravestones there are black on one side from years of air pollution and white on the other where they were bleached by the bomb. White spikes dart over the brim of each white side and onto the black, forming a jagged fringe like the mane of a lion around illegible inscriptions and partly effaced cherubs. The stones are luminous in twilight, their faces imbibing notes of green and orange from the spangled sky.

I had no idea what he meant, and vaguely wondered if he was beginning to show symptoms of the brain sickness that overtakes most of them before they die. I've seen several dozen cases now, but my first encounter was the most severe. I had asked Ernest to introduce me to the oldest person he knew. He led me up Hope Street, to the Ladd Observatory, which sits on a shallow hillock circled by a bristly crown of splintered houses. Inside was an emaciated man, folded accordion-like against the wall, with his angular knees drawn into his chest and his arms tented on his knees like defleshed wings. The vault of the observatory above was pitted with holes, emitting channels of light that blistered his bald head with blue and yellow boils and pooled in the alcove of his missing nose. He didn't move, except to roll his dust-colored eyes from the floor to the wall to the worm-eaten vault and back again.

"How old is he?" I asked.

"Forty," said Ernest.

His name is Charles Dexter, and he was a junior at the university when the last bomb dropped. He had first started acting strangely in the weeks afterward, but it was only five years ago that he took up living in the observatory and wouldn't let anyone near him, not even to clean the pile of filth he sits in or to brush away the ash that sticks to his clothes. Now he's encased in it, like a bird bristling with black feathers. Emeline Gracey—Ernest's sister, better known as Jane—brings him food and water twice a day.

We went to the North Burial Ground to look for graves belonging to people I knew in the twenty-first century (we haven't found any, but in most cases the stones are too difficult to read). Ernest was in poor spirits. His remaining ear fell off yesterday. The other, the one that had sat beneath the curtain of his brown hair, fell off a week before that.

"Just when I thought I couldn't lose any more parts of myself," he told me.

But they are all losing parts, rapidly. They look worse than they were when I arrived; worse than they were a week ago, like paintings whose colors are running in the rain. Each of them takes a different approach to the situation. Mary Ward planted her toes in her backyard like tulip bulbs, all ten in a row. Geoffrey Emlen keeps his right eyeball in a mason jar, where it turns like a murky planet in a blob of formaldehyde. And Jane tied her detached pointer finger back onto her hand with a bolt of ribbon until the flesh dried off and fell away; then she wrapped the ribbon around the naked bones to keep them in place.

All this time, they've let me know them; let me share their meals, and lifted their shirts to show me the angry red ulcers where the tips of their lower ribs shred their skin from the inside out; they've idolized me, even apotheosized me, and fixed me inside loving and lingering stares, all the time thinking that I had something to give them in return, some secret panacea from the past hidden in plain view in a windowless vault on Brown Street.

"Why have you never brought this up before?" I asked him.

"They all cautioned me not to," he said, as he wilted onto a box grave to catch his breath. "They said that I shouldn't push it, that if you were planning on doing it, you would bring it up. And they thought maybe you were waiting for the others to arrive."

I hear the word *others*, and the force that implies—the people of my own era, my cohort, my comrades, with their smooth skin and supple joints and memories of Internet culture, of 9/11, of *South Park* and WaterFire and Blue State Coffee—skewers my gut and stays there, twisting, reeling my intestines around it.

"Ernest, for the last time, I don't know if there are going to *be* any others."

"But, Dr. Hamblin—"

"Can't you ever call me Sarah?"

But I know he won't, and the irony of my fury isn't lost on me; I once spent half an hour ranting to James that I was never addressed as *Doctor* in professional correspondence, whereas my male colleagues consistently were. But that seems small and petty now, compressed like carbon from a mass of gargantuan portions into something small, hard, and shiny, rolling alone in some back corner of my brain, like everything else from the cold, vitrified past.

And so we go back, tracing the swells and hollows of the heaving earth; through plains of slate tablets worn to nubs like rows of rotten teeth; out through the gate and down the dusty corridor of Hope Street and past the observatory just in time to see the red moonlight open its wilted dome. The wind twines together the sounds of nuclear static and the splitting of dry timbers and Charles Dexter's sonorous howls. We don't talk, hardly even look at each other, until we pass the ruins of the Moses Brown School and Ernest trips over his wobbly knee. When I catch him by the arm he pulls away from me, tears beading in the corners of his eyes.

"We all thought you were sent here to save us," he says. "I suppose we must seem like a bunch of half-witted freaks."

He keeps walking and I follow, my hands held out, pleading, my palms printed with his sloughed-off skin, like bloody leaves.

"That's not how you seem at all. I just don't know where you got the idea that I was anything but an ordinary scientist—an ethnographer, really. If I knew some powerful secret, I would have told you. Ernest!"

He's lurching on his long, unsteady legs, out in the intersection of Hope and Angell with the mound of gray bricks that was once the Lippitt House looming in front of him like a pyramid, vast and shaggy with shadows. Then he buckles and sits down on the pavement, his sweater rippling over his back, and stares into the distance, toward the spot where the street winds down into a puddle of soft, roaming lights. It's the fractured glow of all of Providence, tossed back to us on the river.

"You think it's all fun for me," he says, between ragged breaths, "this digging around in the past. But it's everything. We're already dead—you must know that. We have nothing of our own."

I kneel beside him, and my shadow mutes the glare of the light on his scars. For a brief moment, the mask of his deformity breaks, and I see him as he should have been: young, intelligent, roguishly

248

handsome, with a spark in his eyes that is not simply curious but searching, longing, aching. He recognizes the look on my face, as though I am caught in a spell, and as if to prove that what I have seen is real, that handsome rogue darts through the darkness—straight out of his skin—and presses his thick, lipless mouth to mine.

I don't reciprocate, but I don't pull away either, and for a moment my eyes close, shutting me inside the busy universe behind my lids. The tips of my fingers and toes are tingling, so powerfully that it is almost painful. This, I think, must be what regeneration feels like: the stinging heat of nerves reasserting their pathways through paralyzed flesh.

He pulls back, and sweeps a stray lock from my brow with his knobby finger.

"Go on," he says, in a low whisper. "Kill my last fantasy."

An hour later, punctuated by a brief detour to University Hall to bandage his arm and retrieve a few tools, we stand together in front of the chamber.

It's a long wedge of a building, one story, pieced out of granite blocks—once gray, now blackened and roiling with hints of the fluorescent blue air. The low, hipped roof bristles with layers of ash and dead leaves and long tendrils of scorched ivy. A short row of steps fans open in front of us, then narrows into the entrance: a pair of enormous bronze doors, spiderwebbed with rusted chains, beneath an unadorned lintel and an unintelligible inscription.

Ernest plucks the bolt cutters out of my hands and skips up the steps, as quickly as he can manage in his clipped, puppetlike gait. He trims back the chains, slowly and painstakingly, until they rattle into a pile at his feet. When the dust settles, he sweeps the black filth from one of the doors with the back of his bandaged arm.

"There it is, just like my grandfather said—a woman," he says, stepping back grandiosely, as a manic grin splits the scars on his cheeks. "She's beautiful."

His gaze traces the cast bronze relief: a classical figure with a book in one outstretched hand, standing *contrapposto* so as to assert the forms of her shapely knees through her long, gauzy dress. Then he looks at me, his eyes scanning in sequence over my gray sneakers, torn jeans, and pilled green sweater, before finally settling on my face: oily and sunburnt, wreathed with frizzy, cropped hair, and soured by my permanently grim expression.

"She looks a bit like you," he says.

I laugh, then realize he is serious. "Jesus, Ernest. Your imagination has taken a turn for the worse."

"Is it supposed to be you?"

"It's an allegorical figure." I brush past him, the heat in my cheeks rising, as the threads of two opposing emotions coil together in my gut: anxiety, on the one hand, and on the other, embarrassment about the pinprick of juvenile pleasure that his words arouse in me. It isn't simply the absurdity of feeling flattered by the attentions of a man who has spent his entire adult life amidst disfigurement; it's also the absurdity of feeling anything at all in this dead universe, when all the vitality of the twenty-first century could not penetrate my cold, apathetic armor.

I grab the doorknob. Several minutes of dedicated twisting and pushing and we are inside, transported into an expanse of dark so pure that only a few stray particles of light strain through, dipping over our shoulders toward unfathomable depths.

Ernest brandishes his flashlight and jumps ahead, bolting through the long tunnel of rooms, the wan light glancing over grimy wood and peeling plaster and glass that glistens dully beneath a pall of dust.

"It's all here! It's all here!" he chants as the flashlight exposes the rows of paintings that hang from the crown molding: portraits of gray-haired men in starched collars and women in ruffled bonnets, some intact, others with curls of canvas weeping over their shoulders. "It's exactly how my grandfather said it would be. He said on the eve of the Third World War, all the brightest people in the university got together and gathered the most valuable knowledge and things they had, just in case they lost everything—so that it would be safe. And that's why they sent you—isn't it? To show it all to us in case we'd forgotten it. There must be enough material in here to remake the world."

I'm still in the entryway, one hand on the doorknob, while fractals of electric light, sweeping in from behind me, trace the profile of my body onto the darkness. This is a sanctuary of the past, but not in the way he thinks. It doesn't belong to him; it is my own. Every surface is textured with memory, preserved like the frescoes of Pompeii and Herculaneum under layers of ash. As I look around, a sort of calibration occurs. The contours of the room conform to the landmarks marked out in my mind, and along with that specimen of mental cartography come the emotions in which its lines were drawn.

James died in August, in the year I was on sabbatical to finish my second book. My publisher and the university were generous in allowing me time to mourn, but I was not. I pushed myself to my outer limits, too anesthetized to feel the pain of overwork, the ache of grief, or anything at all besides the dull weight of dread. I dreaded the places on campus where I was bound to run into some colleague whose mouth would instantly invert once I was in sight. I came to see the pinched face of sympathy as a type of disfigurement, an ugly mask of feigned emotion stretched over an uncaring interior, and so I shunned it, along with all of the corners of the university that held artifacts of my happiness, and sequestered myself inside the Annmary Brown Memorial.

The word *memorial* implies a kind of peaceful, sanitized vacancy, but this one is not empty; it's a proper tomb, containing a dead couple and the relics of their lives. Annmary Brown died in 1903, and her husband, Rush Hawkins—a lawyer and book collector, made famous in the Civil War as the colonel of Hawkins' Zouaves—built an elaborate mausoleum for her on the outskirts of the university. Almost simultaneously, the Italian diplomat Paul Bajnotti built the ninety-five-foot-tall redbrick clock tower in the corner of the Quiet Green in memory of his own deceased wife, Annmary's sister, Carrie. It seems the Brown sisters were the sort of women who inspired extravagant postmortem expressions of devotion.

By virtue of its dual identity as a tomb and a museum, the Annmary Brown Memorial was, in my time, open to the public, though it was almost always empty. And so I settled there to write the rest of my book, all five hundred pages of it, erecting a temple of words to my sorrows because I couldn't build one of stone or brick.

I am on the verge of stepping forward and telling Ernest everything when he peels off the surface of the darkness like a specter, the glare of his flashlight crawling frenziedly in the hollows of his face.

"There's something back there!"

He grabs my hand and pulls me through, all the way to the very last chamber, and I brace myself for the sight of the two stone sarcophagi, their edges furred with dust.

Instead, his light flickers over something large and lustrous.

I step forward and fish my own flashlight from my pocket. The markers in my memory have been scoured from my sight, and the forms that replace them refuse to come to order, bobbing and shaking like silvery liquid on the surface of my vision. I put my hand out and feel it—sheets of smooth metal knobbed with rivets; flanks that

251

bulge gently, like the contours of a submarine; and a single round glass window, winking in Ernest's trembling light. The voice that comes out of me feels like it belongs to someone else.

"It's another pod."

I glance around wildly, but there is no one. The dust on the floor is pristine, with no footprints but my own, and Ernest's trailing close behind. But there is something written—engraved—on the pod door. I step forward, and shred the dust with my fingers, and read it aloud.

> To Dr. Sarah Hamblin,
>
> I'm so sorry, but no one is coming. The government shut down all time-dilation programs, and the university lost almost everyone in the war. I couldn't stand the thought of you being stuck in some horrible future, but I'm still too much of a coward to join you. So I have spent the last decades of my life and my remaining sanity disassembling the one pod we had secreted away and reassembling it, piece by piece, in the place where you see it now. I never knew anyone to come here but you and hopefully it will stay that way. I can't promise the future you find next will be any better than the one you have found, but at least you will have the choice to go or to stay.
>
> My sincerest apologies,
> John C. LeRoy

Beneath his name, there is a date: four decades past my departure from the twenty-first century, almost to the day.

"He would have been pushing eighty," I tell Ernest, as he completes his second turn around the pod with his flashlight.

When I sit down on the floor, he comes and sits next to me, and turns the flashlight off. So many radioactive particles have infiltrated the tomb that it is now possible to see clearly in the dark. They envelop the pod in a technicolor swarm, mustering along its seams until it looks as though it's been outlined in static. Soon enough LeRoy's words have been rewritten in light, nuclear blues and greens and yellows rippling from side to side along the length of the inscription.

"Nothing is what I thought it was, is it?" says Ernest.

I don't answer. He's known it all along.

After a moment, he asks, "What are you going to do?"

I still say nothing, but I suppose I've known that all along too.

*

It's early morning in Providence, and its residents are clustered on Brown Street, swarming beneath a sea of umbrellas intended to fend off the razor-edged sunlight. We've dragged the pod into the middle of the road, where it gleams in the shadow of the tomb from which it came. Its single window captures the short approach to the university. From inside, Ernest and I can see the fluted columns of the John Carter Brown Library and the dead tree that bends precipitously toward it like a skeletal hand with its fingers probing an open window; the bronze lampposts, with their exploded bulbs, weeping green rivulets down the short flight of steps; and beyond that, the ragged outlines of other buildings: Sayles Hall with its trio of vacant windows and Faunce Arch, beneath which dust clusters like cobwebs.

The entire population—all six dozen or so who remain—gather to watch as we finish loading the pod with keepsakes and supplies, Ernest's salvaged paintings and ancient sweaters, and my collection of things from the twenty-first century: anthropological texts and my parents' silver wedding porringer and James's favorite blue teapot.

My eyes scan the sea of faces, fractured by bolts of shadow and light, of the people who will be dead before Ernest needs to change the bandage on his arm. They are a ragbag patchwork of humanity, sewn together from scraps; the threads that hold them in place are fraying quickly and they know it, but they smile broadly with their lipless mouths and raise their hands—those knobby, fingerless clubs—to wave at us as we enter the pod.

After I close and lock the door and before I set the controls that will stretch the fabric of time down to the warp, I ask him, playfully, how he imagines the future.

He shakes his head at me.

"I want to know what you imagine," he says.

And so I tell him, as I set the dial to the year of my two thousandth birthday, turn off the safety mechanism, and flip the switch. My words, echoing inside the pod, pattern the churning of souls as they swell and disperse, falter, and peter out, and the nuclear glow falls like a curtain over the city.

Cartoon

Jean Muno

—Translated from French by Edward Gauvin

ON APRIL 18, 1977, AROUND 8:00 A.M., when Cecile Angenot had drawn the garnet drapes that hid the windows of her dining room, she noticed, in the middle of the lawn, between the red cedars and the edge of the decorative well, something like an oblong splash of light. *An illusion*, she thought, *the sun in my eyes*. Error: the irradiation was quite real. It was coming from a small Class 3 UFO, roughly cigar shaped and squamous in appearance; truth to tell, a bit screwball, with its tuft of slender antennae and its three crutch-like struts, one of which was patched up with a crude ligature. But Mrs. Angenot saw none of this: she had mislaid her glasses.

"When you've mislaid your glasses," she was fond of saying, "the bothersome part is you need another pair to find them."

Ten minutes later, as she was coming down the stairs, clinging tightly to the banister, her gaze aimed at her feet, she heard a knock. Two, in fact, quite distinct, as sharp a rap as wood on wood. Without undoing the safety chain, she opened the front door and saw no one. In back then? Not a living soul. . . . She ventured out on the deck.

Someone was standing down below, by the dog's pen. A man, apparently, in motorcycle leathers all white like his boots and helmet. A biker, white from head to toe! Probably for nighttime visibility. He had his back to her and was busy imitating Balthazar, matching his every yap, trading retorts. *Young people today*, thought Mrs. Angenot. *What breeding!* And why hadn't Balthazar alerted them?

"May I help you?"

No answer. Had to raise her voice.

"Quiet, Balthazar!"

The stranger turned around abruptly. A foreigner, South American, North African, they were everywhere these days. Beneath the dazzling whiteness of his helmet, a dark face of a singularly olive hue.

"Pardon me, Misangenot," he drawled. "We just plumb run dry. Could we borrow some water off you? Liquid water."

254

Borrow water? *Liquid* water? What nonsense! But his Belgian accent was reassuring.

"There's a spigot in the ivy, to your left."

"Don't got a jug, Misangenot."

She retreated to the kitchen, locking the door behind her. Had her doubts. A small favor, sure, but stay on guard. Especially when her glasses were missing. With his "Misangenot," he was trying a little too hard to inspire trust. Sure, he sounded like a Belgian and kept a respectful distance. But why, after reading her name off the doorbell, had he knocked at the back door? Oh, if only I could find those silly glasses!

The blindingly white biker stood waiting, perfectly still. It considered the bizarre house, all gables, the trees with their aerial roots, the quivering nebula of spring flowers. . . . The natives seemed gentle and naive; no doubt they could be tamed. Still, like the plantigrades of 384N7, they seemed to suffer from ophthalmic scotoma; that'd be in its report. Also the fact that their behavior bore signs of anxiety typical of oxycoicoids. Now and then, the traveler moved its head, a brusque, precise, almost instantaneous twitch, and each time, like a stinger, its tongue shot out and crackled.

(In fact, there was no proof that it was, strictly speaking, a tongue at all, that *mobile, elongated muscular organ in the buccal cavity*, but the biker's face, or rather *facies*, or maybe even mask, covered in tiny gray scales, made this term more or less plausible.)

"There you go!" said Mrs. Angenot, setting her oldest pitcher on the low wall. "Remember to turn off the water when you're done, and please don't make a mess."

"Don't worry, Misangenot. If we need an oil change, we'll resinify first."

"You're not from around here, are you?"

"No, Misangenot. Took a wrong turn."

"It's not rocket science. At the next roundabout, go right, and then right again. You'll see a sign pointing the way out of town."

"Thanks, Misangenot. Very kind of you. And Mr. Balthazar too."

About to step back into the kitchen, Cecile stopped short. *Mr. Balthazar!* Really, did he think he was in some kind of children's cartoon?

"You and Mr. Balthazar sure make a good pair. Plain to see."

What a boor! What an oaf! Oh, if she'd only had her glasses, goodness gracious, she'd give him what for!

*

Later on, during the few weeks when, not yet recovered from her fright, Cecile would blather on nonsensically, we would hear her say, "I was worried right off the bat, you know. Why didn't he ring at the front door, like everyone else? Fine, so he was a foreigner; that's slightly more understandable. In some countries people live on top of each other. But take him and the dog, for instance—I could tell there was something abnormal going on. A kind of fraternizing, if you will, an intimacy. When I walked out on the deck that first time, I had the clear feeling I was interrupting them. Yes, interrupting their conversation! Go ahead, call me crazy! But that man, I mean, that . . . creature! His voice . . . well, it wasn't coming from his mouth, but somewhere lower, straight from his throat—his chest, even. To put it simply, it was like hearing a radio with faltering reception, fading in and out. Of course, when I found my glasses again—silly me, they were right in my good old apron pocket—and I saw that things were normal, I told myself I'd been dreaming, my nearsightedness had been playing tricks on me. Oh! We all just want a logical explanation, don't we?"

No trace now of the biker in white. Nor of his "oil change." If the old pitcher hadn't been set right back on the wall, she'd have thought she'd been seeing things. And yet he'd said, "We'll *resinify*," she was sure of that much. She could still hear the metallic timbre of his voice. Maybe Pascal also *resinified* his old motor oil, but that wasn't the word he used. She couldn't have come up with it.

Cecile went about her chores: putting the dishes away, making the bed, sorting the laundry. Don't forget to water the papyrus in the dining room! From time to time, she would go into the kitchen and scribble something down on a pad. The radio provided unobtrusive company, coming and going like a pet. . . . Words, music, words again . . . fighting in Kolwezi . . . a strike in the public sector to protest . . . two farmers in Pas-de-Calais confirmed having seen . . . Cecile cared not a fig for what they might have seen; her thoughts turned to organizing her day, her virtuous day as a model housewife, which didn't really begin till Irene showed up. Then she'd give instructions and the work would start in earnest. Work that was its own religion, one of whose fundamental laws was not to hinder the whims and predilections of the masters of the house, its Lares, but rather to honor them, anticipate them devoutly. Oh, if Pascal had only been home this morning, the visitor might have seemed less bizarre!

Irene should have shown up ten minutes ago. The clock on the kitchen wall, the grandfather clock in the foyer, the alarm clock in the bedroom all confirmed her tardiness. "With what I'm paying her!" Mrs. Angenot sighed. As she did whenever she was upset, which was rarely, she lit a cigarette. Irene came from town on a moped; every morning she'd go round the house and park her moped by Balthazar's pen, and he would start barking. A minute later, she was in the kitchen, tossing out her "Hello, Mrs. Angenot!" even if no one was there to answer.

At least, that was how things should have gone a good quarter of an hour ago—seventeen minutes, to be exact. *Now, really,* thought Mrs. Angenot. *This time she's gone too far!* And to show she meant it, she threw a shawl over her shoulders and went to station herself at the prow of the deck, lookout and judge. . . . What was that strange smell? Her cigarette? No. It smelled like roses . . . better, even! Subtler, rarer, more . . . fetching, that was the word! But she couldn't seem to put a name to it. Surely the smell of springtime, what else? It had been ages since spring had smelled so powerful, so youthful, so . . . edible! Balthazar was sitting in a splash of sunlight, like a dog made of porcelain, at once silent and ceremonious. True, he was smiling, maybe because of the smell? It was enthralling, like a memory. . . .

But over there, in the grass . . . Why, there was Irene's moped! Abandoned. Toppled on the grass like scrap on a landfill. Now, really! Was her backyard to be a gypsy camp?

"Irene? Irene! Where are you?" Smooching in the bushes? For this long? Impossible! "Irene!"

Or maybe at the far end of the yard, hanging laundry? Loafing, goofing off! Because of a sweetness in the air, that terrible aroma of spring, so unexpected.

"Irene! I've been calling your name for the last ten minutes!"

No answer. Something must have happened to her. And me too, if I keep pressing forward, something will happen to me. . . . I'm past the well now, and I can feel it. . . . Like that other time, with Pascal, in the Bay of . . . We knew there was a sudden drop, that we'd lose our footing, but we kept pressing forward anyway, and surprise! Suddenly, we were floating! Side by side, without lifting a finger, just Pascal and me. The water, filled with sunlight, buoyed us aloft!

Cecile had passed the well, the red cedar, and was heading down the great sloping lawn, in a fragrance that grew ever more intense, as if lovingly simmered at length in the gentle sun—so enthralling, really, that she stopped, spellbound.

"Good Lord!" she said. "Goodness gracious me!"

Later on, she would say, "I couldn't believe my eyes! But this time I had my glasses on! No more lawn, just a big circle of dirt! And in the middle of that burnt patch, a huge pile of . . . I don't know, Jell-O, bluish jelly, shining brightly in the sun. I didn't see Irene at first. She was on the other side of the mound, flat on her back on that . . . stuff, which was sagging softly under her weight. Seeing her like that, you'd have thought she was dead, though, to tell the truth, the thought never crossed my mind. . . ."

Another time, still during those aforementioned weeks, she would say this (and we can all see how such words might lend credence to rumors of menopausal confabulation): "That smell! I could feel it in my belly, it was pulling me closer, it was like a kind of vertigo. At the same time, I wanted to touch things, to be a little girl again—the one who, at the village grocery, when her mother wasn't looking, would surreptitiously plunge her hands into the big sacks full of dried green peas, cool as springwater, and sink her arms in all the way up to the elbow! Irene was far from dead; she was smiling, all smeared with blueberry jam, drunk on jelly! Goodness gracious me, what a child! And so lovable. . . . How happy I was to see her like that, and happy the encounter that morning hadn't been a dream, and that this . . . this! Was their *oil change*, this . . . opulence, this royal jelly, this . . . turquoise afterbirth! Forgive me, I wasn't myself anymore, the thought of afterbirth seemed delectable to me, shameful and delectable. . . ."

Almost evangelically, Mrs. Angenot caressed her maid's brow: those peacefully shut eyelids, that naive smile of a medieval Virgin. "My poor child. . . . Who will do all our chores? What will the man of the house say? Come now, on your feet! If we have time, we'll come back later, when everything's shipshape. . . ." Come, come, my darling little girl, my humming girl whose sleepy hands are dreaming in Jell-O blue as deep water in a well . . . a well of green peas. . . . Up, up! You've no right to come over to my house and dream without me! My serving girl, my serving darling, in that sad little green dress you wear every day.

Cecile knelt down. That aroma! Good Lord, that aroma! I'm in it up to my elbows! Green peas, green peas. . . . She raised her hands to her face, as if to pray; her features hardened, her face took on a ferocious expression, the grocer's dried green peas! Then suddenly, fingers spread, body abandoned, she dove into the indulgence.

Dove right in.

When the man of the house came home two hours later as usual, he was surprised to say the least. An empty, messy house, windows open to the four winds. Admittedly, there was a smell of something cooking, but it wasn't coming from the kitchen. *Curious,* thought the man of the house. Strange, even a bit outlandish. The radio, which was playing for no one at all, was like a glimmer of light at the end of a mine shaft. He turned it off, and the silence seemed menacing. Thoughts of kidnapping, of ransoms, crossed his mind.

And yet, to smell it, there was something invigorating about that aroma. Leaning out the upstairs window, Pascal was astonished to find the entire backyard redolent as a richly laid table. Was there a picnic surprise in store for him? A banquet, even—legs of lamb, pâtés en croûte, truffles and melons, stuffing and beignets, rare sauces, exquisite cheeses. . . . That vast aroma had a little bit of everything. Beverages too: fine wines, precious liqueurs . . . with a deliciously robust hint of staleness he would have been hard put to name, a pinch of rot. . . . "How hungry I am!" sighed Mr. Angenot, who at that moment thought he glimpsed a bright splotch (linens? a dress?) between the low boughs of a pine.

"Cecile! I'm home!"

No answer. The yard lay still, silent, unmoved by his cries. Seized with genuine panic, Pascal ran downstairs, dashed through the kitchen, and sprinted toward the bright splotch. The sight of the massive jellyfish brought his headlong hurtle up short. What on earth? Cecile and the maid lying side by side, lolling higgledy-piggledy in the stuff. Asleep. Intoxicated! You could see their underwear and, on Irene's immodest thighs, petals from the cherry tree clinging like glitter. This detail put the finishing touch on Pascal's embarrassment.

"You should be ashamed," he whimpered, bending over his wife.

She opened her eyes, staring at him fixedly, unblinking. "It was ready," she said, her voice thick, "so we started without you." Meanwhile, Irene, no doubt the devil on his wife's shoulder, began murmuring even as her thighs shivered with pleasure, "I'm a fly, a giant flutter-fly, naughty, poopy fly! Irene, queen of the flies, naughty fly, poop-poop-de-doop!"

"You make me sick," said Pascal Angenot. With difficulty, he had straightened up and was now removing his accountant's vest. "Frankly, you make me sick, both of you!"

"Blue poop, gold poop, the battle for the golden poop!"

Now he was in his shirt, his undershirt, and then, still repeating, "You make me sick! You should be ashamed!" he was naked. In his age-worn, donkey-like skin. And now he was taking off his shoes without even bothering to untie them.

"I'm a fly, a fly to poop, a poop to flies, fly to fly . . . how I want you, you blue poo! Poop of gold, you'll never get old!"

"Debauchery and depravity," said Pascal Angenot with grim conviction. "The decline of moral conscience!" Even as his pants slipped down, revealing the bloodless tubercles of his hairy legs.

"Come, my man of the house! Meatfly mine!"

Later, when his sense of decorum had wholly returned, he would confess, "I lost my footing, I'll admit. But it's a long way from losing your footing to falling for some childish science fiction. Look, we've all known forever there are such things as stimulants, even euphoriants. I, for one, am still convinced the labs will give us an explanation once they've thoroughly examined that suspect substance. What else can I say? Maybe they'll even find it's some phenomenon resulting from pollution that produces an effect like running amok. You're up, science! Ball's in your court!"

But during this time, Cecile would tell her seamstress, her podiatrist, the women in the PTA, my wife, myself—in short, anyone at all: "When I saw Pascal next to me, I felt fulfilled. Before then, I'd felt remorseful. I told him, 'Pascal dear, you'll catch cold.' And he replied, 'Let's slip inside, dear Cecile.' He was right. We got inside the Jell-O, only our heads sticking out. Did we feel good! Nothing could happen to us now, nothing better or worse. It nourished us, protected us; we were at home. Like two maggots, two huge maggots cozy inside food!"

What a shameless image! And she said it unabashedly, the wife of the town comptroller! With such evident retrospective relish. People were embarrassed for her. Especially us—my wife and I—who only meant her well.

That was where things stood on April 18, 1977, when chance and a sense of professional duty threw someone into the mix—someone who should never have been there, who belonged even less than everyone else. Firmin had always elevated discretion to the status of a sacrosanct principle. "It's nobody's business but your own" was his favorite expression, and unlike everyone else, he never used it to preface malicious gossip. True, sometimes his job as a mailman got in the way of his fondness for happy innocence. In fact, on the day in question, he had a certified letter for Mr. Pascal Angenot, 4 Turtledove Lane.

After ringing at the front door and waiting a reasonable amount of time, Firmin went around the back of the house and into the yard in hopes of finding someone. Five whole minutes went by before he reappeared, but given the circumstances as we now know them, that mere reappearance was a kind of miracle in and of itself. Pensively, he got back on his bike and pedaled hard, all quite as usual, except for one thing: he was riding the opposite way from his normal route.

When Firmin walked into the little post office in Malaise less than fifteen minutes later, Antoinette was in the middle of doing addition, her mouth full of figures.

"There's a problem," he said.

"Forty-seven . . . fifty-two . . . what? Carry the two . . ."

"Certified letter. Pascal Angenot, Turtledove Lane . . . undeliverable."

"Forty-four . . . sixty-six . . ."

"But they *were* home. In the backyard. Angenot and two women . . . naked! In a blue bubble!"

"What is this, some kind of kids' cartoon?"

(It should be noted that Antoinette was merely voicing a thought that, but a few hours earlier, had crossed Cecile's mind.)

"No, I swear! Naked, in a blue balloon! Look, here's the letter. Pascal Angenot, Turtledove Lane."

She started at him, a wicked gleam in her eye, a mocking grin. "And you claim you saw them?"

"With my own eyes!"

"And they were having sex?"

"I didn't say that! They were lying down, not moving."

"It's their business, isn't it?"

"Well . . . of course," Firmin could only concede. He seemed to hesitate, then, having walked right up to the window, he leaned toward the clerk and whispered, "Sure. Their business. You're right, Antoinette. It's just . . . I think they're dead."

*

"Indeed," remarked Inspector Jacques as he stepped from the van, "quite a peculiar aroma."

"Carnations," said the taller of the two patrolmen.

"Verbena," said the other.

They walked into the backyard, passed before Balthazar, who harassed the boys in blue; then, with the mailman in the lead, all four of them headed for the red cedar, whose shadow was invading the lawn.

"The culprit!" Firmin declared.

Before them: the heap of bluish Jell-O, still brilliant and firm, it tenants intact.

"The naked guy," Firmin specified, "is the addressee, Mr. Angenot."

"And the others?"

"His wife . . . their maid, Irene . . . those two over there are neighbors, and the smaller young man is Martial, the butcher's boy. As for the priest and the cyclist, I have no idea. Probably people passing through."

"At any rate," said the inspector, "contrary to your allegations, they don't seem to be dead."

That much was obvious. Irene and the butcher's delivery boy, in unison, were humming something like:

> *Come, my darling little fly*
> *Dally in my lullaby*
> *We'll flitter-flutter fly to fly*
> *Darling little fly!*

"They don't even seem to be in pain! Should've called narcotics!"

There was something like a sigh, an easeful cooing, an ample swoon: one of the patrolmen, the one who'd said it smelled like carnations, had just lain down, arms spread wide, hugging the maternal substance.

"He slipped," said his fellow patrolman, a glazed look in his eye. "But he didn't hurt himself."

"If you ask me," Firmin piped up, "I don't think you're going about this the right way."

"Oh, really? Is Mr. Know-It-All the Postman going to teach us how to do our job?"

"Look, don't fly off the handle—"

"Ahhh!" bellowed the other patrolman, the one who'd smelled verbena, tumbling into the elastic bliss.

Come, my darling little fly
Dally in my lullaby
Flitter-flutter fly to fly

"You shouldn't criticize them," said the inspector. "They're just civil servants, like you . . . employees of the state. . . . They're doing their job . . . just like me. . . . Professionally, I am . . . forced to give this closer . . . examination. . . ."

Firmin grabbed his arm. "Don't go! Don't leave me all alone!"

"You can come with."

"Detective, I don't think you're going about it the right way."

"Well, don't you just think you're the bee's knees! So what *is* the right way?"

"Hold your nose!"

"Hold my nose? If that doesn't fly in the face of all—" He burst out laughing, reeling like a wino, legs akimbo. Firmin, still holding him by the arm, delicately pinched his nostrils shut. For a moment, they stayed like that, anxiously awaiting whatever was to come.

"You're right," said Inspector Jacques. "My mind's clearing up."

He couldn't get over it.

"How very right you were! That aroma is a drug! May I?" Relieving Firmin, he took charge of pinching his own nose, and straightened up with assurance. "But my dear fellow, however did you resist?"

"I suffer from anosmia, Mr. Inspector. Do you know what that is?"

"Yes. Not exactly."

"I can't smell a thing. No olfactory sense. Especially in spring, when the almond trees are in bloom."

Come, my darling little fly
Dally in my lullaby
Flitter-flutter fly to fly

They made a slow circuit of the bubble, stopping several times, nodding like experts.

"Curious, isn't it? Ten victims, but who's behind it? Or what? Not to be too on the nose—heh—but no violence or indecency. . . ."

"Except the naked guy, Mr. Inspector."

"He's at home, on his own property. Careful, don't step on the cyclist! Have you noticed that the grass all around is burnt? Maybe some kind of chemical fertilizer in blue plastic packaging that

263

somehow mutated? Just a theory. And right in the middle of the lawn! What a bunch of nincompoops!"

Dithering nasally, in utter agreement, coldly eyeing the mysterious orgy, they experienced an intense feeling of superiority. Men, men they were, and upright! All they had to do was hold their noses.

At their feet, from the mush sparkling in the sunlight, came a higgledy-piggledy humming. And in the air was a strange tension, more than vernal, a new pigment, as if life hung suspended a bit above itself, suddenly glistening with a surfeit of obviousness.

In his pen, the dog was gazing at the sky.

There's nothing left to tell that isn't utterly ordinary. Really, we should stop here, on the image of Balthazar gazing at the sky. The rest, alas, is but denouement.

The bubble was removed by men from the Department of Public Works equipped with mentholated breathing masks. In the hour that followed, each of the ten victims recovered his or her verticality and dignity. It might be observed, on this occasion, the degree to which the average Westerner, no matter how conceited, refuses to be a celebrity of the inexplicable. As we have said, Mrs. Angenot was the only one who gave in to the temptation for wild confession, and for just a few weeks—up until the day when the mayor, who was almost a friend, summoned her to his office. The meeting lasted more than two hours.

"I wonder," Cecile admitted the next day, "I do wonder if I didn't dream it all. At least a little bit. I didn't have my glasses on, so . . . They say it's pollution."

And why not? Who is to say she didn't dream it, that we didn't all dream this little episode? The grass has grown back on the lawn, the man of the house is back in charge, Irene is busy sweeping and Firmin pedaling. As for the bluish Jell-O, it's long since been sealed in lead-lined drums and sent off to high places for study. Places so high we've quite lost it from sight. Just like the biker in his white leathers. No one's ever seen him again. Has he too—who knows?— gone to a higher place?

"Just like my childhood," Mrs. Angenot reflects dreamily, gazing at the sky. Those stars, by the thousand, unattainable as little green peas.

Two Poems
Jonathan Thirkield

SUPER FRAGILE CATALYST

our child was the size of a hummingbird
neatly glued to the stomach lining

blur of liquid metal sunshine
purring through apse and radial cells

a gently rising submarine
in the unsettling before sleep

a hologram of your next self
will break into a new body

building a raceme hierarchy
from which the hummingbird sips

*

a race disappears around the corner
I hear their voices another two blocks

colors at sunset go from the schoolyard
skin dusted shades of cobalt

river sounds flow out of eyeshot
a heart-based curvature of time (language)

a contraction of time (systole) in the heart
hearing the kids fly from imaginary beings

Jonathan Thirkield

the filling of time or blood (diastole)
in a name you dream walks by you

*

new love flutters at seventy wingbeats
a new movie flickers at twenty-four flames

a thousand fine gradations of happiness
performing a lice check on my daughter

testing all twenty-six teeth
in the Latin alphabet

the tongue like a Ouija planchette
points to the letter it licks

a silverleaf-faced angel pricks
her finger with a sterile need

*

missing rivers of bodies flow
through channels of the blood

are you so different having seen the second
beating of a wing across the shoulder

a woman once came to our apartment
all the bones in China wouldn't bend

a vivid pink against the cheek that way
a swan rustles in the neoprene

our minds better at absorbing
fictions than new realities

*

shivering snare drum
phantom living lung

flawless sun-like figurines
sea-level dreaming azimuths

synthetic hyacinth junk derivatives
finite winter maize red party

black famine roulette station pilgrims
live hierarchical prunings in the brain

diving bells locked in palatine eardrums
a serpentine train set carries us off

*

decidual trans-cysteine life machines
cosmetic metalinguistic surgery prongs

sword forged consanguine molecular
carbon substitutions on a benzene ring

polyphonic fucking data strata erotics
sugar tongs orange gin red sangria

funny how gallium melts in the palm
how a human head melts in the mind

anything can be anything else after burning
the key to metamorphosis is turning

Jonathan Thirkield

*

drawn without learning the lettering
the alternate editing the director's cut

written in heaven among the bodies
of the 24 episodes to come

and bead upon be cloned among
other things a turnip plant an explosive device

the impulse to cloak the exposed girl
super fragile catalysts

to rout to expel the red cross
wear whiteface be cow-eyed to desert to echo

*

a corpse looks nothing like a robot
the sight of corpses is commoner

in less industrialized nations
the presence of the illusion

of distance deepens the assimilation
of the angel's silver leafed plane

the wind's a substitution for the sonic gulf
where water ran above us

but then again upon waking I lose
the conviction

*

where the wind farm is now
not far from the radiowaste tanks

a man once returned to the edge
of a battlefield made silver

by meadows filled with bodies
whose noses or ears were severed

as tokens by victors and carried
in sacks to later match to the kill

the man filled with hunger
held a yuzu rind against his teeth

*

the unimaginable being
the reality I choose

not to process the eyes'
aversion to the thing I

cordon off whole sections of
the body rendered herded

speechless unheard of zoned
imagining reality as it cones

in the quarter-second brain delay
by the phenotype's deficiency

Jonathan Thirkield

*

where does the mapping end
all the thoughtless forms formed from foam

glaring indifferently like 1000 toys
glaring happily like 100000 toys

unimagined casualties
rolling through watery air

freshly minted tongues for kissing
behind the schoolyard

fuck and dream of continuities
between impassable mirrors

*

I worry when you lift your eyes to this you
won't find a satisfying mirror

I was reading about kindness last night
the currency in the early minds of kids

I thought the animals outside
were dressed in human conditions

I thought of writing a treatment
for an animated sitcom

in which everything is normal as hell
but everyone's all dressed up as animals

THE ATLAS OF VIRTUAL

Constantly recorded, listening through loops
Of string of blue with fraying fibers webbing
The walls of the kitchen, climbing like ivy
Into the ears of our loved ones, channels
Playing whales and spinning light-up
Jellyfish, lipstick headed tubers by the ocean's
Vents, music making modulated intimations

Of the lives of minor species, brown and golden red
Across the white-paged sky, a tablet
Of numbers spiraling out from one like trapdoors
Beneath a stage where a table stands with settings in Dutch blue
Of Japanese castles, cypresses, blue brick walls
Dividing the pastures, cows, sheep, a stray deer
Nibbling at an apple, and a huntsman in sandals

Drawing his bow, the feet of children showing
Beneath a fence by the stable playing
Harpsichords, samisens, and sitars on the service
Platter, tiny sketches of robotic spy insects
Twitching in the marsh, and I grew hungry, I ripped
The greenest lowest branch and loosest chips,
The skin of moss at its foot, forgetting that trees

Are others, forgetting people are always close
And listening, the mountains drilled through for
Fiber-optic trains, hidden suns speeding a desire for
Water, speeding the sleepless heart with particulate
Matter, the regions of dust in the visual apnea where
Mother and starlet and cow blend within the segmented
Caterpillar rushes, all seeping into the deepest troughs

Of the river systems of Mars, beneath the Olympus
Mons, the pyramidal tracts, a system of green men
With leaflike pinnate ears harvesting root crops
In the sub-rosa villages. During my abduction, the one
I'd prayed for all those years under the painted girl
Whispering, you are special, you really are,
Not an apparition in my night window, the six lights

From the hydroelectric plant making a crown
Above her many eyes. I toured the catacombs
Under the sandy planetary face, nothing was
Illusion, they called my guide Virtual, their towers
Modeled on a neurotransit system, trains
Passed from axon to dendrite, the supple liquid
Walls teeming with krill-like ground creatures,

They said, snack as you please. The taste bordered
On pork rinds and blueberries, the redder ones were
Sweeter, almost cotton candy, for a minute every
Word rhymed with every other one, the poison ones
Are irresistible and equally unstable, they said,
Approaching the planet's nuclear heart or amygdala,
Its marzipan scent covering field upon field of dark

Tentacular flowers or ideas, I couldn't tell, the smell
So enveloped my senses like a boat crashing through
The snowy skullcap of a Western child, I thought
Briefly the Martians wore Japanese teddy bear
Suits, even heard the zippers close up their spines and felt
Myself being enclosed in one as well, it was difficult
To see through the pinhole eye, my head became

A camera obscura, I watched the film of a mariner
Eating bodies he carved with an LCD glass machete
That played video collages culled by a spider
Algorithm: a roulette of babies, cats, mirror
Soliloquies, violinists in short dresses, cooking
Instructions, nuptials, snake v. mongoose, poverty
Trials, cucumbers on the eyes, centers getting

Posterized, and a very long song about May. I may
Have been in the bear head for seconds or years being fed
By the mariner. The many men, so beautiful,
I feared, but I ate and ate, because they reassured
Me it was a dream, all of it, the scented watermelon
On the shoulders of the women, the scent of quinine
On their feathers, the myriad reductions—wine, cherry,

Anise—bubbling up from the skin, the fading purgatory
Impulse as my hunger and joy took hold. I felt perfect
Complicity with the mariner, he was the reason
I thought, the reason words gave way to pictures again,
He was the manager of the bodies. I came to
An oasis, Virtual let me surf the liquid plasma,
The buttons on her face went purple-pink, the doctor lost

His horse in the snow, and a trainer applied oleoresin
To his client's thighs. The answer to every office pool,
The runoff from every dye job, the diminishing, ever
Diminishing trees and catalysts and rare earth
Materials seemed to extend their private wilds
Into an infinite number of vanishing points. It
Was or it wasn't. I was told a girl in the farmlands

Of China had lied to her friends about owning
A horse, said her brother put him down just yesterday
And showed them the patch of grass: blood, hoofprint
And all. I was told to visit her with a lead-glazed heart filled
With aphids. I was told to write things down with a Sharpie
Every morning on the surface of the water,
And when I did, the words became affixed to my

Forehead. For days I wrote *anabasis*, thinking it
Meant something else. Virtual was pleased. Thirty
Days or hours or lives of purple sky passed over
Me, lambs and squires rested in the fields like
White chocolate daubs on a macaroon, my skin
Broke out in gray eruptions, I was told this was
A common reaction to snow. The stars finally cut

Through the purple silk, I was told this too
Happened to visitors, visitors who forced
Their memory of Earth's weather and atmospheric
Anomalies on the entoptically dense ferry terminals
Of the Martian life terrines. I was told stories
Of microcuisines, services in petri dishes, blue
Liquid racing down from droppers to make things

More palatable. I was told of the 47 facial expressions
And the withdrawal of love after the first 108
Days of life, the phloem and xylem that mediate
The memory hinges. Virtual was curious about all
Those home movies, film ones, from the seventies
With the bleached light, memory light, those silences
And vacancies, roadside hotels of killing music,

Polypropylene quilts, white kids and black kids
In matching T-shirts, the owl brown of the trees
Corroding the film stock, the centripetal desire
Of watching the endless false battles in Cantonese
On Saturdays, and the difference between moths
And paper as both emerge from tree life, and pattern
Themselves on language, and die when wet.

Mysterious Strangers: A Conversation
John Clute and John Crowley

JOHN CROWLEY: WHAT THEN is our topic?

JOHN CLUTE: Our topic, very briefly, as I take it, is the concept or motif of alienation as found in contemporary speculative fiction—not traditional renderings of alien/alienating intrusions that one finds in vampire stories or ghost stories or tales of revenants, even though they can be insinuatingly seductive; but a more contemporary alienation, more intimate, more threatening: more like the world itself with the shades off.

CROWLEY: And not restricted to the science fiction alien—

CLUTE: Not restricted to science fiction and open to fictions that engage other forms of alienation.

CROWLEY: So let's begin.

CLUTE: There are two entries I've done recently for *The Encyclopedia of Science Fiction* What I Wrote. The one is a working definition of "Fantastika," which implicitly incorporates models for the recognition of something we might call the alien, and the other, just drafted a month ago, is about how to think of aliens as Mysterious Strangers.

CROWLEY: Mysterious Strangers—yes.

CLUTE: For a complex of reasons not really relevant here, for several years I've been using Fantastika as an umbrella term to refer to the literatures of the fantastic in the West from around the beginning of the nineteenth century until now. But among the various conditions for Fantastika I laid down in my entry, one does seem particularly to the point here: that nonmimetic stories, at any rate those written within my time period, are normally best understood when they are read literally. I'm channeling Chip Delany here, of course. That—for something like a second—what you read is what you get. In more traditional understandings of stories, metaphor or thematic understandings can be understood as *preceding* the raw glimpse of something

Other, of something we do not already have words for. In our context here, that which we did not have words for before we read it on the page is alien. So though 99 percent of Fantastika is otiose, there is always a chance we will encounter in some story a flash of something that has no prior convictions. To see something as literal is to see something before the jaws snap shut. Attempt to read Kafka's *Metamorphosis* with eyes only and you may smell the density of the terror.

CROWLEY: Isn't there a third category? There is the metaphorical, on the one hand, in which in a realistic story someone could be a "bloodsucker" and "vampiric" in very many realistic ways and still have the structural impact of a vampire; or on the other hand, somehow retrofitted by imagined science, so that their blood corpuscles are described as different, or whatever. The third category merely posits a literary device, a literary artifact that we do not expect to have explained to us—why such a thing can be in the modern world—nor accounted for as metaphor, but is simply stated. I recently read Richard Matheson's 1956 SF novel *The Shrinking Man*. It occurred to me halfway through what a wonderful—or much better—book this would have been if the author had never tried to attribute the shrinking to an accidental release of radioactivity. He would have then ended up with a book about a guy who's getting smaller and smaller and smaller for no reason whatever—whose world was becoming alien to him—and it would have ended up being more Kafka than Heinlein.

CLUTE: Pre-translation of story into what "explains" it is deadly. It's what many mainstream writers do when they think they're composing Fantastika. It's deadly in most of the literary criticism that I've read in the last fifty years.

CROWLEY: Criticism of fantastical literature?

CLUTE: What I mean is any kind of academic criticism that purports to use a story to illustrate a theme, without attempting to experience the story first, and without attempting to convey that central epiphany. If you cannot paraphrase a story, you should not try to make it fit an a priori assignment of meaning. Period. Raw story is central, it is not accidental: where it appeared, how it appeared, how it was understood, how it went. And that it is told with *intention*, or do I blaspheme? But maybe I'm flogging a dead horse here.

CROWLEY: I think that tendency is fading away to a certain extent, but one of the reasons for it lies in the teachers who don't know how to talk about literature, and in trying to understand a story ask children, "What is this about? What is this story (or 'this writer') trying to say?"—implying that the story has a meaning, a moral, a significance that a reader is to set out to find. But having to extract the significance or moral of a story leads to a sense of, "Well, why didn't the writer just say that?" If the significance is "We should all try to be kinder to one another" or "Things change and become bad and they can become good again" or whatever it is, that could have been said in a sentence. This form of understanding writing and reading has been very pervasive, at least in America, for the last fifty years.

CLUTE: Kafka's *Metamorphosis* should seem to come unbidden into the world, without context, like an epiphany. What it *is* should stare you in the face, for something (as I said a moment ago) like a second (Leonard Cohen). And then almost before we can blink we begin to reread, to retrofit: we cannot help doing so. We begin to embed that alien is-ness into our consoling knowledge that *Metamorphosis* is a novella written by Franz Kafka right before World War I and published in Prague then as a real book; it is part of our record of the apprehension of the war to come.

CROWLEY: Would this apply as well to stories in which storytellers (Marlow, in Conrad's stories) are out to convince listeners in the story, as well as readers of it, of the truth of it?

CLUTE: In *Conjunctions:39, The New Wave Fabulists*, I remember going on about how Club Stories enforced witness, urged the reader to understand that a story being told cannot in a sense be gainsaid. What I'd add here is that the first glimpse of *any* story is a witness. Only afterwards does it fixate in our minds as interpretable. Or so we pray. This instant of witnessing is a paradigm for proper apprehension of the alien in 2016. So if *Conjunctions* is exploring the theme of the alien in this issue, I think it is a good idea if we start with the apprehension that the alien on the page has never been seen before. To see something never seen before but almost instantly recognized seems a good way to begin to define Terror. To experience Terror is to experience the malice of the world.

CROWLEY: That's true of science fiction, and can be extended to alien beings of other kinds, as well to the kinds of monsters that have inhabited our imaginations forever: that are sent up to outer space only to return to us in the same form or to be encountered on other planets, still in similar form. But I'm also thinking about Vladimir Nabokov, who said that "all great realistic novels are fairy tales." *Anna Karenina* is a fairy tale, *Madame Bovary* is a fairy tale, *Little Dorrit* is a fairy tale, because they're worlds inhabited by imaginary beings—aliens, in effect. They're not facts in the world, they're objects of words. They are fairy tales in which anything can happen, even though they have delimited what can happen by their realistic assumptions. He says, "They are fairy tales without which our real world could not exist."

CLUTE: That is Nabokov having a concentrated thought that I'm no way going to deal with myself very cogently, except that it seems to be intuitively spot-on and certainly a very good way of describing how his own novels feel.

CROWLEY: Absolutely. The intentional fallacy of those schoolteachers is that an author should set out a reason for his or her book to exist in the world, with a lesson and a meaning to be extracted from it, and a generally acceptable sort of form in which to put the lesson, maybe with dramatic and interesting events, but with the ultimate intention of teaching us that all you need is love—or whatever it is.

CLUTE: And that is, I think, almost certainly bullshit.

CROWLEY: It is bullshit, yes. It may not even be the way most writers work to create things. Upton Sinclair probably worked that way.

CLUTE: Both of the Sinclairs, Upton and Lewis, with their lessons that nobody can remember.

CROWLEY: Well, that's the problem with lesson stories. Once the lesson's learned or is no longer useful, the book vanishes.

CLUTE: That takes us back to Aesop, which is full of lessons, but there's always a story from which the lesson is subsequently extracted, and sometimes the lesson has a surreal relationship to the actual story.

CROWLEY: And in fact we have learned that the lessons at the end of Aesop's fables were actually added long after the fables themselves were told. In the original form, some of them just remain very strange stories.

CLUTE: So then there are stories that incline to be stories, which you read to find out what happens. Within that story, an alien has to be understood as it is uncovered, and we can talk about these implications, after the story is at great length unpacked, without needing an Aesopian appendix attached. There's also the obvious fact that any kind of narrative is inherently nonmimetic, inherently fantastic, because any continuous presentation of data fantasticates the world. "There is more than one history of the world," as you've put it, without I think claiming that a particular one of them might be true, but certainly, I think, implying no one story *is* the world.

CROWLEY: Well, I think that to make new, or other, histories of the world almost certainly generates worlds in which the familiar becomes alien. It certainly isn't unique to me.

CLUTE: Which brings a question to mind. There is a sentence in the justly esteemed final paragraph of your novel *Little, Big* which has long intrigued me. As you punctuate it—"It was anyway all a long time ago; the world, we know now, is as it is and not different."—it conveys an apodictic certainty about the news it tells. It's not as though I thought (because I did not so think) that you should have punctuated it like this—"It was anyway all a long time ago; the world we know now is as it is and not different."—even though as revised it might give us a loophole to dream through about the incarnation of something better. I guess the question is a terrible one to ask: do you think that thirty-five years after *Little, Big* was published the world is as it is and not different? That the sentence with two commas means we're goners for sure?

CROWLEY: I actually love that emendation, or its possibility. The sentence was intended to close down possibilities: we know that different worlds once were, in which beings exist that no longer seem to. Our present wish that it might be different is passé: it is as it is. But of course all that other world *does* still exist—in the book. And it's the same for all aliens we accept at face value, who are ghosts, AIs, centuries-old beings who persist, soulless people of the vampire and serial-killer varieties. There are all kinds of possibilities, and we can always pick up the book and find them there still.

CLUTE: Including extraterrestrial beings themselves, because it's less and less of a conceptual leap to think of inhabiting a more complex universe than we had previously thought plausible. This all connects with the epiphanic moment of one's first glimpse of the Other, which I was talking about before as something enabled by the *exposure* to the world characteristic of Fantastika as I try to think about it. And

279

there's another kind of epiphany: the flash realization that what you think you are seeing in a text is something almost identical to what you thought you were seeing, but also immensely Other. This may be the heart of what we call Uncanny Valley.

CROWLEY: This morning I read an absolutely wonderful story by Jeffrey Ford called "The Word Doll," about something strange and alien coming to be in an ordinary Ohio world, a farmland of the last hundred years. The story is of alien beings who've had to go away because they didn't suit the modern world. It's indescribable—except to say that it is almost entirely about words creating aliens. John, you have considered alienation and usurpation in a work, *The Darkening Garden*, that treats horror fiction. Can you speak to the question of how a genre that's *devoted* to the eliciting of fear and loathing in characters (and readers) can be understood in the terms we're deploying here?

CLUTE: Well, the first thing to note about what I tried to do in that book (though I was insufficiently clear in my head about this at first) was to distinguish Terror, which I defined more or less as recognition of the malice of the world, from Horror, which I pretty well defined as what I called Affect Horror: stories built on conveying an emotion of Horror, Horror tending to be defined by its effect on readers (which, of course, is circular). The heart of the four-point model of the discourse of Terror I suggested in the book—Sighting, Thickening, Revel (or Recognition), Aftermath—lies in the *beat* of epiphanic heightened awareness, the passage from Thickening to Recognition, the instant where the naked eye sees into, or acutely apprehends, the time and place of the truth of things. This is also rather terpsichorean, of course, the truth of things being apprehensible through a dance-like leap out of the Thickening of the prior. Like the ending of *Billy Elliot*, *The Darkening Garden* does not deal directly with the Other or the Alien as such, but it is through that leap that we see the Other undomesticated. Literally understood, aliens in twenty-first-century stories may tend to represent our insecurity in ourselves, in our societies, in our planet, in the universe. This insecurity is something that is manifestly required of us if we're going to remain sane.

CROWLEY: Have you not just articulated a reason to read these stories that goes beyond simply accepting them as stories? Did you just fall on your own petard there?

John Clute/John Crowley

CLUTE: We can only apprehend pure story in glimpses. As soon as we begin to talk about what we've read, that story is belated, it is fair game. The epiphanic leap of apprehension of the new lasts about as long as the moment of sexual bliss in Cohen: for as long as a second, as I think I said a ways back. As soon as you take a breath you begin to remember. Memory (as has been argued more than once recently) is intrinsicate with cognition. We are memorious creatures. We cannot say a word without memory. Guilty as charged then.

CROWLEY: I will not hold you to it, though I see exactly what you mean. What may be the case is that the environment and moment in which aliens appear has to serve partly as a metaphor for how we understand their nature.

CLUTE: If we try to figure their contemporary meaning, which it *is* fair game to do, Aliens and/or the Other manifest themselves uncannily in worlds where tenure is insecure. I did an entry, a month or so ago, in *The Encyclopedia of Science Fiction*, on the Mysterious Stranger motif in Western literature. In his *Enter, Mysterious Stranger* (1979), Roy R. Male describes narratives of the Mysterious Stranger as "cloistral fiction," as enclosed and closing; and he made a case for understanding nineteenth-century American stories and even Mark Twain's posthumously published *The Mysterious Stranger* (1916) in those terms. I started there, but thought as well that the motif might be used in a more extensive way to point to a characteristic of the literature of the West, written and mostly set as it is in a peninsula at the edge of the world whose history is a history of constant claim jumping. From this angle, the literature of the West can be scryed as a set of tales told by usurpers, but within that frame the prototypical Mysterious Stranger is not a fellow usurper but a *revenant*. The Mysterious Stranger story always threatens to reveal someone who has *returned* to claim back his or her heritage.

I think you can unpack a lot of the stories of earlier centuries in these terms: vampires, werewolves, ghosts, reborn magi with a grudge; any one of them may fulfill the role of the Mysterious Stranger. But there is something to note here: that traditionally those "imposed" upon (you and me and Dad) have been very much realer than the figures who disrupt our world with their presence and/or their claims for restitution. We are a conquering civilization. We do not give up easily.

John Clute/John Crowley

CROWLEY: I think that's true, but I think the Mysterious Stranger in most stories has more self-centeredness, more basal sense of authority than the people around him, whom he unsettles and makes to understand their unsettledness merely by his own absolute sense of self.

CLUTE: This seems increasingly evident as we approach the present day; I really don't think it's only the speed with which I'm becoming venerable that makes me feel that the old days were more *real* than they are now. I really do think that the fragrant analogue *difficulty* of the world we once knew has become increasingly simplified—or bar-coded—into fungible product; and I think this is reflected in an ontological reversal in the stories we write now. *Density of being* is a characteristic I think I may actually add to my entry as one of the ways of identifying a Mysterious Stranger (which is to say an Alien or an Other) in the twenty-first century. The terror of the alien story today is that aliens are no longer less real than we are—that they are now *more* real than we are.

CROWLEY: I think that's really interesting. And the Paul Park story in this issue of *Conjunctions* is exactly that: the alien is more real than the humans and knows it.

CLUTE: The first Mysterious Stranger in fiction that I could identify (over and above "The Serpent in the Garden," which is kind of a joke) is Odysseus in *The Odyssey*. We see his narrative mostly through his eyes, though he may be lying because he tells his own story three or four times in different ways; but certainly as a Mysterious Stranger he is a prelude to our own times, for he is ontologically more dense than the suitors. He is returning, he is reclaiming, he is upsetting, he is ready to breed again with his wife. He is a massively paradigmatic Mysterious Stranger. And I think it odd that he hasn't been described in exactly those terms for centuries. Maybe it's because we have not wanted to have our homesteads reclaimed by the likes of Odysseus.

CROWLEY: He has certainly become monstrous in the course of his returning. But can a Mysterious Stranger remain mysterious when seen from his own point of view?

CLUTE: Sections in *The Odyssey* are told through omniscient narration.

CROWLEY: I think the Nausicaa scene is like that: she and her women come upon a being that they don't understand.

282

CLUTE: Parts of the story almost seem to be channeling Pallas Athena. We are teased because we know its dramatic irony, we know what they don't know about who this beggar is, but we see the beggar quite often from the viewpoint of the suitors and from other viewpoints. So it squeaks into the Mysterious Stranger paradigm.

CROWLEY: Powerful magician figures who show up in Victorian novels or even hypnotists and mesmerists and others of spiritual power drawn from popular culture seem to have that same quality of being able to project—until they are unmasked, which they sometimes are—an entirely solid being, unlike the people whom they unsettle and change and whose lives they upend with their supposed powers.

CLUTE: Part of the defensive posture of European popular literature of the nineteenth century is that you can unmask the Mysterious Stranger as a fraud.

CROWLEY: Or as one of us.

CLUTE: That is a defense mechanism.

CROWLEY: I think it is. And though they are sometimes unmasked, those they deceived are not then restored to their sense of self.

CLUTE: A subcutaneous implication of early fantasies in which a Mysterious Stranger is reborn, or revealed as immortal, or just mysteriously arrives, is that the prior is more real than the present. A Mysterious Stranger typical of relatively recent science fiction, the forerunner character who's part of the race that founded us and then left, may be *clearly* realer than we are. Once again we have a sense of astonishing insecurity, an upwelling of what one might call the ontology shakes: a sense that reality is suffering osteoporosis, the old load-bearing world weakening into broth.

CROWLEY: Reality is conditional, while the Mysterious Stranger does not depend on conditions. Bram Stoker's Dracula arriving in England is definitely a Mysterious Stranger in exactly the terms you're talking about.

CLUTE: And in Cooper's *The Dark Is Rising*, Merlin is a Mysterious Stranger.

CROWLEY: You could even call the big bug in *Metamorphosis* an alien, a Mysterious Stranger who suddenly shows up one morning. Its parents assume that their son is gone, but we know better. In a violation of the trope, we see that story from inside the Mysterious Stranger.

CLUTE: The story form itself is violated and I keep on violating it in my descriptions because it's necessary to do so to extract this terrifying figure out of stories that coat them over. You can't easily describe something that is more real than you are, or that has a terrifyingly better right to the farm you just claim jumped than you do. There's a term *nostos*, which I think is etymologically related to nostalgia and is defined as the drama of return. *The Odyssey* is a *nostos*. The drama of return is a very threatening drama for a usurping culture. In essence, I guess, what I've been saying here is that the Mysterious Stranger story is a *nostos*.

CROWLEY: But Odysseus, like all the people he returns to, was a Greek, and it would seem to me that the aliens that we're talking about are going to be not of our makeup in any way. They will have come to confront us. They may not speak our language, or they may speak to us in ways we fend off because we can't understand them or because we worry that they will challenge us. The magicians of those nineteenth-century novels were Jews or Jewish Italians or some other species or "race." Will the ones we are talking about now, who come to talk about usurping what is ours or about what we usurped from them, have that same element of difference?

CLUTE: Maybe creating stories that project an element of difference could be seen as displacing our inner apprehension that the Other is realer than we are. You and me, we're elderly white males with no particular gender issues, and are in general well-behaved. We kind of float, or I think I do. I think I kind of float on the osteoporosis of the fungible world, hoping not to stamp too hard. But I kind of dread to think of the moment when I find somebody more real than me.

CROWLEY: Then you have to unmask him, John, show him proof that you're more real than he is, watch him crumble before your eyes.

CLUTE: I would not look forward to that contest. We are very wise not to think we can win. The light at the end of the tunnel may be brighter than we are.

CROWLEY: The Mysterious Stranger also has something to do with the punitive, as do aliens when we come upon them. They're out for something even if they don't end up expressing it; we assign it to them. There is this story by Steven Millhauser, "The Slap." In a small, ordinary suburban town, a character, an ordinary human dressed in an overcoat and hat, comes up to somebody on a train platform and slaps him in the face and then walks away. He appears again and again to one person after another, delivers the slap, and walks away. Now there's a Mysterious Stranger, purely punitive, who sets up uncertainty and blame and can't be characterized. He's perfectly normal, meaning that he's not in any way different from me, he's not from outer space, he's not creepy, and yet he is out to punish people. At the end of the story the plague of slapping diminishes and he's gone, he just never appears again, which I'm not sure I think of as a quite satisfactory ending—but in another sense it's key to the Mysterious Stranger, who appears, shakes everything up, calls into question the basis of the other characters' existences, and then goes away to leave them to deal with it.

CLUTE: That would be the good news. The bad news would be that the Snark *was* a Raven, you see.

CROWLEY: Is it common for Mysterious Strangers to pose riddles? I think it is. Having taken a pause here to ponder, I decode this as: an episode of sly or nasty upbraiding may be salutary—even comic—but if the alien becomes one that departs nevermore, we are in a different and far worse case. It will be interesting for readers of the issue to see where the majority of writers are aligning on this.

NOTE. The authors and editors wish to thank B. Diane Martin of the Readercon Committee for making the documentation of this conversation possible. The authors have edited this transcript, and are responsible for the form it now takes.

Undocumented Alien
Very Rough First Draft Report PROJECT JRD
Joyce Carol Oates

LOST IN TIME

TEST SUBJECT #293199/Joseph Saidu Maada (undocumented alien, home country Nigeria, b. 1990, d. 2016).

Most immediate and long-lasting effect of the neurotransmitter micro-chip (NTM) inserted in the cerebral cortex of the human brain appears to be a radical destabilization of temporal and spatial functions of cognition. (See Graz, S. R., "Temporal and Parietal Functions of the Human Brain," *Journal of Neuroscience Studies* 14:2 for a detailed description of normal functions.)

In test subject #293199 temporal destabilization was immediate and (seemingly) permanent; spatial destabilization was sporadic and unpredictable.

For instance, upon several (videotaped) occasions in the PROJECT JRD laboratory (Institute for Independent Neurophysiological Research, Princeton, New Jersey), test subject #293199 J. S. Maada demonstrated confusion and panic when asked to list events in a chronological sequence. Even those events that were made to occur within a single hour in the institute laboratory, which he had observed, were virtually impossible for Maada to "list" (it was noted that the subject seemed to have lost comprehension of what the term "list" means). If subject was allowed to view a videotape of the hour, he could list events on a sheet of paper as he observed them occurring, though after the elapse of a half hour, he would not remember their sequence except by consulting the list. Also, Maada did not appear to recognize himself in the video, or would not acknowledge himself. (*Who is that black face?* Maada would ask, sneering and anxious. *I see him. He does not see me.*)

In the last several months of Maada's life, partly as a consequence (it is believed) of deteriorating vision, hearing, and cognitive functions, subject's paranoia was heightened so that he became convinced that a team of *black spies* had been sent to abduct him and return him to Nigeria to be imprisoned and tortured in collusion with the CIA. (See Lehrman, M., "Learned Helplessness and Conditioned Paranoia in Thirty-Year-Old African American Male," *Johns Hopkins Neurophysiological Journal* 22:17. Though this paper [attributed to Dr. Lehrman but in fact 90 percent of it the work of his postdoc staff at the institute] is based upon PROJECT JRD classified experiments, it does not contain information that reveals the identity of the test subject or the laboratory in which the cycle of experiments took place. Thus, the age of the subject has been altered as well as other details pertaining to the subject's ethnic identity and legal status in the US, in conformity with Department of Defense regulations stipulating classified scientific material revised for publication in nonclassified journals.) Simultaneously, and with no awareness of the contradictory nature of his assumptions, test subject Maada was made to believe that he was a "privileged alien agent" sent to Earth on a "secret stealth mission" from one of the orbiting moons of Jupiter and that the nature of this mission would be revealed to him at the proper time, and not before. *Am I a ticking bomb?* Maada would ask slyly. *Or am I just a ticking clock? A heart?*

Over a duration of several months, Maada so lost his ability to register the sequence of what we call "time" that he was continually expressing surprise at encountering members of the S_____ family (with whom he was living in Edison, New Jersey; their name is redacted, at least in this rough draft of our report, since the entire S_____ family is "undocumented"/"illegal") in their cramped quarters in a brownstone tenement on Ewing Street, Edison. When the older children returned from school, if Maada was in his room and heard their voices, he would rush at them, demanding to know why they weren't at school, for it seemed to him (evidently) that they had just left, or had not left at all; concepts of "earlier"—"previous"— "subsequent"—"consequent"—were no longer available to him. The several children in the S_____ household, ranging in age from three to eleven, were very fond of "Saidu" (as they called Maada), because he was "kind" and "funny" with them, like an older brother, and "very smart," helping them with their homework; but over the course of PROJECT JRD, as Maada's personality was made to "plasticize"(i.e., alter in a "melting" way) and other features of the experiments were initiated, the children did not know what to expect from their "Saidu" and began to avoid him.

Joyce Carol Oates

When the several adults in the S＿＿＿＿ household returned from their low-income jobs in the Edison area, Maada frequently expressed great anxiety for them, and occasional impatience, that they had failed to go to work at all, and were risking their jobs, thus their livelihood and ability to pay rent, which would lead to their arrest and deportation, and his own.

For the "undocumented alien"—"illegal alien"—it is arrest and deportation that is the prevailing fear, and not, as it is for others of us (who are US citizens) a more generalized fear of the impenetrability of the future: **Death**, we can assume; but not the *how of* **Death**, still less the (precise) *when of* **Death**.

As early as 6/11/15, within three weeks of the start of his participation in PROJECT JRD, #293199/J. S. Maada began to have difficulty listing the chronology of events in his previous life: his arrival in the US as an engineering student at Harrogate University, Jersey City, New Jersey, at which time a student visa was granted in his name by the United States Department of State (8/21/07); his withdrawal from Harrogate on "academic grounds," at which time his student visa was declared null and void and he was issued a summons from the Department of State ordering him to report immediately to the Newark Immigration Authority (2/2/08); his (unlawful, unreported) move to Edison, New Jersey, as an "undocumented alien" given temporary shelter in the small, fiercely protective Nigerian community; his sporadic (and undocumented) employment in the Edison/Newark area as a cafeteria worker, busboy, hospital and morgue custodian, sanitation worker, construction and lawn-service worker, etc.; his (first) arrest by law enforcement officers (Newark) on grounds of creating a public disturbance, refusing to obey police officers' commands, and resisting arrest (5/21/15); his release from police custody dependent upon agreeing to participate "freely and of his own volition" in the National Defense Security (Classified) PROJECT JRD (5/24/15); his (second) arrest, Montclair, New Jersey (6/19/16) on more serious charges of sexual assault, aggravated assault, assault with a deadly weapon (teeth, shovel), assault with the intention of committing homicide, and assault against (Montclair) law enforcement officers.

Following the altercation with law enforcement officers in Montclair, test subject J. S. Maada did not return to participate in the PROJECT. Injuries sustained at the time resulted in (emergency) hospitalization at Robert Wood Johnson University Hospital, New Brunswick, New Jersey, with the (federally mandated) proviso that no medical information regarding the patient could be entered in any hospital computer, and that access to the subject's room was restricted. Following the subject's death (6/30/16), his room was declared a *quarantine area* accessible only to the PROJECT JRD medical team, which performed the autopsy establishing cause of death as "natural": hypothermia, brain hemorrhage, respiratory, cardiac, and liver failure. (7/2/16) Per the contract signed by the test subject at the start of his participation in PROJECT JRD, his "bodily remains" became the property of PROJECT JRD and are currently stored in the research morgue at the Institute for Independent Neurophysiological Research on Rt. 1, Princeton, New Jersey.

(Information concerning NTM inserts, stents, surgical and chemical alterations to J. S. Maada's brain and body is not indicated in the [official] autopsy that has been sent to the test subject's family in Nigeria but is to be found in the [classified] autopsy on file with NDS (National Defense Security).

Though hundreds of pages of data have been recorded in PROJECT JRD computer files, the participation of test subject #293199/Joseph Saidu Maada in the cycle of experiments at the time of his demise is considered incomplete and unsatisfactory.

NOTE: As indicated above, this report is a rough first draft, a compilation of lab notes with some expository and transitional material put together by a small team of postdocs assigned to Dr. M. Lehrman working late at night in the depressing and ill-smelling quarters of the institute. If you have read this far, please do not be offended by our plea (of a sort) that allowances might be made for our (relative) lack of data concerning test subject #293199/Joseph Saidu Maada, whose full name was not available to us until this morning when we arrived at the lab to learn to our surprise that 1) #293199 was not coming today, as he had been coming every Thursday for months, and 2) #293199 would not ever be coming again, for any scheduled Thursday.

Oh. Shit—one of us murmured.

Weird. We'd got to know the guy kind of well, and now—

It is common practice in laboratories under the auspices of PROJECT JRD to refer to test subjects by their (classified) ID numbers and not by their (actual) names; so too test subjects are not told the (actual) names of the research scientists and medical authorities who work with them over the course of the cycle of experiments. (So

far as Joseph Saidu Maada could know, the names on our badges—
Dr. R. Keck, Dr. M. Lui, Dr. J. Mariotti—indicated who we actually
are, and in addition to this (quasi) information we encouraged the
subject to call us by first names closely resembling our own, actual
first names: "Rick" for "Rich," "Michelle" for "Millicent," "Jonny"
for "Jonathan"). In this way, a desired *atmosphere of trust* was established, a crucial goal for all PROJECT JRD labs.

Also, as postdoc assistants to Dr. M. Lehrman, director of our
institute lab, and not director of PROJECT JRD itself, we could not
access some essential files without arousing suspicion. Each rank at
the institute, as at PROJECT JRD, as at the Department of Defense,
carries with it a degree of "classified clearance," and postdocs are of
the lowest rank. (Just above lab technicians—we are sensitive about
being confused with lab technicians who do not have PhDs as we
do.) Hence the haphazard nature of this report, which we intend to
correct in subsequent drafts, before submitting it to Dr. Lehrman,
who will slash through it with a red pencil, correcting our mistakes
(as he sees them), revising and excising, and providing (restricted)
information of his own (which we will never see), to the director of
PROJECT JRD, whose very name is not known to us but whose
office is in the Department of Defense, Washington, DC.

(Unfortunately, the final draft of this report is due on Monday
morning. If only we were outfitted with the more potent neurotransmitter chips inserted into J. S. Maada's brain, or, at least, one or two
of the amphetamine biochemical boosters that kept the hapless test
subject awake at night!)

Radical temporal destabilization seems to have intensified the subject's confusion about his (classified) role as a "privileged alien agent"
with special powers (invisibility, ability to read minds, to pass through
solid walls, and to perceive the shimmering molecular interiors of
all things; to "detonate"—"demolecularize"—when directed by his
commandant) and his (actual, literal) life as a manual laborer in the
not-always-reliable hire of Adolpho's Lawn Care & Maintenance of
Montclair, New Jersey.

From the perspective of institute research scientists it would have
been preferable that the test subject had not worked at all, and that
he was available for their purposes at all times, like a laboratory animal that is kept, for his own safety as well as for the convenience of
experimental researchers, in a cage; but J. S. Maada's disappearance

from the Nigerian enclave in Edison would have aroused suspicion, it was believed. And so, inevitably, J. S. Maada's real-life activities impacted upon his role as an experimental subject, and presented serious limitations, which resulted in the tragic events of 6/19/16.

Precipitating factors include extreme heat on the day of the "assault" (a high of ninety-six degrees Fahrenheit in Montclair, New Jersey, by noon), protracted labor (the lawn crew had begun work at 7:00 a.m. at the E_____s' large, three-acre property; the assault occurred at 11:00 a.m.), and an evident miscommunication between Mrs. E_____ and J. S. Maada that ended in a "violent outburst" on the part of the test subject, bringing to an abrupt and unforeseen halt the subject's participation in PROJECT JRD.

Possibilities accounting for Maada's extreme reaction following an exchange with Mrs. E_____ are: the stent in the subject's cerebellum had begun to work loose and/or one or another of the inserted microchips may have been malfunctioning. Usually "docile, reticent, cooperative, and naively unquestioning," the test subject allegedly became "excitable, belligerent, and threatening." According to witnesses, Maada lifted his shovel as if to strike the terrified Mrs. E_____ but decided instead to attack the Floradora bush, rending it into pieces; he then threw down the shovel, seized Mrs. E_____ by her shoulders, and shook her violently as one might shake a doll with the intention of breaking it. Further, according to Mrs. E_____, Maada bared his "wet, sharp" teeth and lunged as if to bite her in the (right) breast.

By this time two of Maada's coworkers came shouting to the rescue of Mrs. E_____. Inside the house, a housekeeper called 911 to report the attempted sexual assault/homicide.

When Montclair police officers arrived at the E_____ residence they discovered the agitated (black, Nigerian-born) laborer "cowering at the foot of the property, by a fence"—"foaming at the mouth like a mad dog"—"rushing at us with a shovel." After "repeated warnings," officers had "no choice" but to open fire, seriously wounding but not (immediately) killing subject #293199.

Transcript of testimony of Mrs. E_____, to the Essex County prosecutor. 6/28/16

> I did not condescend to Mr. Marda. I did not provoke him.
> You can ask any of Adolpho's men—I am always very friendly when I see them. I will admit, most of the time I

can't remember their names—their names are so exotic!

We couldn't possibly—personally—know which of the workers are undocumented—illegal. I would never dream of questioning anyone who works for us, who is obviously working very hard to send money back home to a wife and seven children, or a mother and eleven siblings, in God knows what poverty-stricken African or Central American country, still less would I register suspicion of their legal status. I suppose that some are Mexicans, and some are Filipinos, and some are African, and some are—Pakistani? Well, I don't know. They are all *foreign*.

Mostly, they are excellent workers. Sometimes, in the house, I see them working out in the sun, and start to feel faint watching. . . . Of course, as Adolpho has said, they are not like us. They don't mind sun and heat, they have been born nearer the equator.

So in all innocence I approached "J. S. Marda"—this is the name I would afterward learn—I will never forget!—to whom I had spoken the week before, at least I think that I had (it's hard to keep them straight, they look so much alike especially hunched over in the rose garden), and I told him that the Floradora rose had not worked out well where he'd transplanted it, so he would have to move it again, back to where it had been originally, except now there was an azalea bush in its place that he'd planted, and that would have to be relocated . . . I was not speaking rudely. I am not a bossy person! I was speaking slowly and carefully as you would speak to a child or a retarded person. For the man did not seem to comprehend my words. I could see his mouth working—but no sounds came out. He was sort of hunched over in the rose bed like a dwarf, with a back like a dwarf's back, but he was not small like a dwarf, and was sweating terribly, and "smelling" (well, I know he could not help it, none of them can help it, which is why we don't allow them to use the bathroom in our house or to come into the house for any reason)—it was a strong smell—and was making me feel sickish. . . . He was not looking at me, his eyes were averted from my face. He had a very dark skin that seemed to suck in all the light, like an eclipse in the sky. He was polite and stiff and he was trying to smile but his face was contorted like a mask and I could see that he had cut his arm on some of the rose thorns but he did not seem to be bleeding like a normal person. It was like some kind of mucus leaked out, with a strange, sharp smell. And now I could see his eyes were not matching colors. The iris of one eye was a strange bright russet red and it was larger than the other iris, which was mud brown. Though his face was very dark it seemed to have begun to splotch with something like mange, or melanomas. It was very frightening to see—the black, "Negroid" skin seemed to be peeling off, but what was beneath?—a kind of pinkish skin, like our own skin if the outermost layer is peeled off, an unnatural pink, like raw meat. And now, the man was furious—at *me*. I could not believe how he lifted the shovel to hit me—screaming at me in a strange, brute language like the grunting of an ape—and then he struck the rose bush with the shovel—like a crazy man—and then he took hold of me and shook, shook, shook me and bared his wet, sharp teeth to b-bite . . .

(So agitated did Mrs. E_____ become, the prosecutor excused her from further testimony.)

Consequential, sequential. Without temporality, i.e., the measured unfolding of time, the human is reduced to something lesser than human.

J. S. Maada's first arrest, one day to be conflated with his second arrest, and yet a *causal factor* in the second arrest, had been in New Brunswick (5/21/15). Subject was waiting for a bus at State Street and Second Ave. at approximately 9:20 p.m. when two New Brunswick PD squad cars braked to a stop and police officers swarmed upon several "black youths" on the sidewalk. Subject demonstrated "suspicious behavior" by running panicked from the scene; after a scuffle, during which subject was thrown to the sidewalk and handcuffed, subject was arrested and taken to precinct with other young men.

Jailed in the New Brunswick Men's Detention, subject was ignored for forty-eight hours despite requests for medical attention (broken ribs, lacerated face, possible concussion), then discovered to be an "undocumented alien" from Nigeria whose student visa had expired.

NOTE: "Undocumented aliens" have no immigration status in the United States and may be arrested at any time and "removal proceedings" initiated. Legal help may provide options but these are temporary. Until individual is issued a green card (providing permanent residence, but not citizenship) or a student visa, he can be deported at any time.

Marriage with a US citizen automatically confers immunity to deportation by the State Department but does not confer citizenship.

Distraught subject was visited in the New Brunswick Men's Detention by a PROJECT JRD officer, who explained to him that

293

deportation for undocumented aliens was mandated by the US State Department with one exception: if subject volunteered for a federal medical research program that he successfully completed, he would be issued a new student visa with which to attend "any university of his choice" and he would be eligible for a green card—that is, permanent residence in the US.

Gratefully, then, Joseph Saidu Maada agreed to participate in the project, which was explained to him as funded by both the United States Department of Defense and the United States Department of State. Contracts pertaining to Maada's willingness to waive his rights were signed with a flourish, though (strictly speaking) the undocumented alien does not share "rights" with US citizens. The seal of the state of New Jersey lent to these documents an authentic air. Among the test subject's personal remains, after his death, these documents were found, and reclaimed by the PROJECT.

According to the S_____ family, who had taken in the young man in his hour of need, after his expulsion from Harrogate University, Maada seemed certain that his application for US citizenship was being processed by a "special, secret court," and that he would soon become a citizen, and when he did, he would help the entire S_____ family to apply as well. *Saidu was a very kind young man, very helpful and loving with the children, especially our three-year-old Riki. When he first came to live with us he was not so talkative, and suspicious of everyone at the door but then later he became nervous and excitable and loud-laughing when there was nothing so funny we could see. With a wink he would say how he would pay us back one hundred times over for he was a "special-mission agent," one day we would be surprised.*

Maada had enrolled in the engineering program—"One of the Finest Engineering Programs in the World!"—at Harrogate University but his background in mathematics was inadequate and his ability to read and write English was substandard. He had difficulty with all of his first-year courses but particularly Introduction to Computer Engineering in which he was given a grade of D- by a (Pakistani American) teaching assistant, who, he claimed, had taken a "hate" of him and whose heavily accented English Maada could not comprehend. His tuition to Harrogate had been paid by an international nonprofit agency and would not be continued after his first year. *It was kind of pathetic, these African students they'd recruited from God knows where. They weren't the age of college freshmen. They could speak English—sort of. Their tongues were just too large for*

*the vowels. They had the look of swimmers flailing and thrashing
in water hoping not to drown. They sat together in the dining hall,
trying to eat the tasteless food. Their laughter was loud and kind
of scary. White girls were particularly frightened of them, for the
way the Africans stared at them with "strange hungry" smiles,
they could feel "intense sexual thoughts" directed toward them
especially if they wore shorts and halter tops or tight jeans, which
(they believed) they had every right to wear and were not going to
be "intimidated."*

Along with several other universities, Harrogate has been charged
with fraud in soliciting young persons from abroad with "enticing
and misrepresentative" brochures, "unethical waivers of basic educational requirements," and "worthless scholarships"; presidents of
these universities travel to Africa, India, Korea, and China to prose-
lytize shamelessly for their schools, which attract only a small per-
centage of (white-skinned, above-average-income) Americans and
are not accredited in the US. The university does not clearly state
that tuition and costs are nonrefundable as soon as the term begins
and that "undergraduate living fees" are considerable. Harrogate University in Jersey City, New Jersey, has been several times indicted as
perpetrating fraud—yet, even as a half dozen lawsuits pend, it is still
operating in New Jersey.

After being asked to leave Harrogate, Maada was deeply shamed
and disconsolate. With several other ex-engineering African students
he made his way to Edison, New Jersey, where he lived with the
S_____ family, fellow Nigerians who took pity on him and made
room for him in their small, cramped apartment on Ewing Street. In
Edison, Maada looked for employment wherever he could find it. He
was paid in cash, and took pride in paying the S_____s whenever
he could; they did not know details of Maada's personal life but registered surprise that Maada had been released from men's detention
so quickly after his arrest, with no charges against him. Not only was
Maada spared a prison sentence but he was guaranteed payment
from the US government each month, in cash, which, combined with
the cash he received from his numerous jobs, allowed him to pay the
S_____s usually on time, and even to send money back to his
family in Nigeria.

By a 2012 mandate of the Department of Defense, payments
received by all participants in (classified) research projects throughout the United States are to be "at least one and a half times" the
wages earned by the participant in his primary civilian job; this

has been emphasized, for PROJECT JRD has committed to "zero tolerance" of exploitation of any of its subjects domestic or foreign.

LOST IN SPACE

As stated at the outset of this report, the destabilization of spatial functions of cognition in test subject #293199/Joseph Saidu Maada as a consequence of neurotransmitter microchips inserted in his cerebral cortex did not appear to be so extreme as the subject's temporal destabilization, though it was frequently a contribution to his general "disorientation."

Essentially, subject did not know "where" he was in the basic ontological sense of the term. He had exhibited some natural curiosity before leaving his homeland to fly (to Newark Liberty International Airport) and then to take ground transportation (bus) to Jersey City, New Jersey, to the campus of Harrogate University; but, if examined, he could not have said where these destinations were in relationship to one another, let alone to his homeland or, indeed, to any other points on the map; nor did Maada, like many, or most, foreign visitors, have anything like a clear vision of how vast the United States is and of how staggeringly long it would require (for instance) to drive across the continent. Maada had no idea of his proximate position in the universe—he had no idea of the universe. When it was revealed to him via the commandant (NTM) that he was a native of a distant moon (Ganymede, one of the moons of Jupiter) sent to Earth on a mission that involved amnesia (no memory of Ganymede) and "surrogate identity" (quasi memory of Nigeria), he was initially eager to be shown photographs of Ganymede and Jupiter but soon became discouraged by the distant and impersonal nature of the images provided him at the institute. For—where did the people *live?* Maada wondered. All you could see was strangely colored rock and blank, black space that was very beautiful but did not appear to be habitable.

Before this, Maada had had frequent difficulty with his physical/spatial surroundings in his "adopted" country. He could not begin to comprehend the New Jersey Turnpike with its many lanes and exits that seemed to repeat endlessly and to no purpose; if he was obliged to ride in a vehicle on the turnpike, being driven by Adolpho to a work site, he shut his eyes and hunched his head between his shoulders and waited to be told that he had arrived. Even on the Harrogate campus he was easily confused. Not only did the blank, buff-colored factorylike buildings closely resemble one another but walkways and "quads" appeared to be identical. Many of the (multiethnic) individuals whom he encountered at the university appeared to be identical. Often he became lost looking for a classroom; by the time he arrived, the class had ended, or perhaps it had never existed. Tests were administered like slaps to the head—he could not grasp what was being demanded of him, and he did not like the way his professors and TAs ("teaching assistants"—a term new to him) smiled at him in scorn, derision, and pity. For amid so many dusky-skinned persons, Joseph Saidu Maada was decidedly *black*.

Somehow, then, it happened that he was barred from the dour asphalt dormitory to which he'd been assigned, to share a "suite" with several other first-year engineering students from scattered parts of the globe. He was served a warrant: a notice of expulsion signed by the chancellor of Harrogate University and affixed with the university's gold-gilt seal. African American security officers, taller than he by several inches, burly, uniformed, and armed with billy clubs, arrived to forcibly escort him off campus with a warning that if he dared return he would be arrested and deported. His student visa had been revoked, his scholarship had been terminated. This happened so quickly, Maada had difficulty comprehending that he was no longer a *student* with much promise enrolled in one of the great engineering programs in the world but an individual designated as *undocumented, illegal*, who was shortly to be *deported*.

In "New Jersey" there was nowhere to go *on foot*. You could not use *instinct*. Blows to the test subject's head caused by the booted feet of enraged New Brunswick police officers contributed to his diminished sense of place and direction. In an apartment of three cramped rooms Maada could become hopelessly lost; as in a hallucination he might encounter his own self emerging through a doorway. A dingy mirror or reflecting surface told him what he already dreaded to know—there was "another" on the farther side of a glass whose intentions could not be known.

Later, the commandment would quell such fears. *You are one of many, and you are many of one.*

Since Maada had no idea where the institute was, how many miles from the apartment he shared with the S_____s in Edison, there was a kind of comfort in not knowing and in the certitude of not being able to know where he was taken. No one could possibly expect Maada to draw a map of where he was taken—he had virtually

297

no idea where he *was*, before he was *taken*. Each Thursday, according to schedule, and in fulfillment of his contract, Maada was picked
up by an (unmarked) van, to bring him to the institute for approximately twelve hours of neurophysiological experiments; soon after
the onset of the NTM insertions in the parietal lobe of his brain,
Maada had but the vaguest sense of direction, like a child on a fun-
house ride who is dazed and dazzled and frightened and yet strangely
comforted that the ride was after all a *ride*, prescribed by adults whose
wisdom far surpassed his own.

On a typical Thursday, the test subject was instructed to wait in
the early morning at a designated place, usually in the parking lot of
a fast-food restaurant on Route 1, though sometimes in the parking
lot of a discount store on Route 27; there was a busy intersection
near the campus of Edison Community College on Route 27 that
was a convenient place for Maada to await the van, for here he could
easily blend in with other young men like himself, drawn to the
college with a hope of bettering their lives and being granted US
citizenship as a reward. Maada had been warned never to speak of
waiting to be picked up by any vehicle. So zealous to obey the commandant, he did not speak to anyone at all, gesturing at his throat
and shaking his head bemusedly to indicate that (possibly) he had a
sore throat, laryngitis, if anyone tried to initiate a conversation with
him. It was a continual surprise to the subject to glance around and
discover the (unmarked) van gliding to the curb beside him like a
vehicle in a space film, and braking silently to a stop. The driver,
only just distinguishable through a tinted windshield, wore dark
glasses, and gave no sign to Maada that Maada should make his way
with seeming casualness to the rear of the van, where the doors
would be opened for him, quickly, and quickly shut behind him.

It was with a sense of excitement and exhilaration that Maada
climbed so trustingly into the van, to be borne however many miles
to the institute, in the company of mostly dark-skinned men of about
his age, sometimes younger, rarely older; these were individuals
dressed like himself, in nondescript dark hoodies provided by the
PROJECT and good-quality running shoes; at a glance you saw that
their wrists were not cuffed and their ankles not shackled, for they
were here voluntarily, as J. S. Maada was here voluntarily. There was
little need to warn these men (they were all men) to remain silent,
and to keep to themselves, for each believed the others to be spies
who would report them to the CIA. Also, each knew that a surveillance camera was trained on the interior of the van, for (they knew)

all US citizens were under surveillance at all times. The van was windowless, of course. There was no way to *look out*. The driver took the silent, slightly apprehensive men who avoided eye contact with one another on an ever-shifting, improvised circuit that might have taken them twenty miles from their pickup site, or five hundred yards. Their destination was the Institute for Independent Neurophysiological Research on Route 1, Princeton, New Jersey—a windowless three-floor rectangle that looked as if it were covered in aluminum foil, blindingly reflecting the sun—but of course none of the men ever saw the exterior of the institute.

The van passed into an underground garage and came to a halt. The rear doors were unlocked by unseen, deft hands. As Maada and the others disembarked, always very polite with one another, and maintaining their discreet eye evasion, PROJECT assistants were waiting to check their IDs (eyes, fingerprints) and to take them to their assigned laboratories. They had not a moment to glance about, to "get their bearings"—indeed, in the dim-lighted interior of the garage, which smelled of nothing more ominous than motor oil, there were no bearings to *get*.

Inevitably, the test subjects had no way of exercising any residue of a natural sense of space and direction, for they had no more information about where they were than blindfolded children forced to turn in circles until they were dizzy and in danger of fainting might have.

Joseph Saidu Maada was usually eager to cooperate with researchers. He was boyish, even energetic. He laughed often, if nervously. At the institute it was said of him that he resembled the youthful Muhammad Ali—so tall, so handsome, and so good-natured!—but that was at the start of his participation in the PROJECT.

After disembarking from the van, the test subjects were quickly taken to individual examination rooms in the institute. Their blood was drawn, and lab tests run. Some, like J. S. Maada, often volunteered to give more blood, for which they were rewarded with cash bonuses; but this was not required.

(Of course, after several months, when our research team began to replace Maada's blood with an experimental chemical solution mimicking the molecular structure of the blood, it was not "blood" drawn from his arm but a surrogate material designated as *blood [patent pending] in the reports. See also *plasma, *bone marrow, *nerves, *ganglia.)

From the examination room the subject was brought to Dr.

Joyce Carol Oates

Lehrman's laboratory, where the staff awaited him. Assiduous lab notes were kept by all, to be subsequently conflated; each session was videotaped, and copies sent at once to PROJECT JRD headquarters.

One of the consequences of the initial brain (microchip) insertions was a flattening of vision, so that to the subject much of the world looked like "walls"—"wallpaper." A three-dimensional world is a visual habit that can be broken readily in the human brain, if one knows how. Maada was more perplexed by this phenomenon than disturbed, for there was, in line with the simplification of images, a cartoonlike simplification of "depth"—you could feel that "depth" was missing from your visual field but you could not comprehend that it was "depth" that was missing.

Soon, without understanding what was wrong, and that it was his perception that was amiss and not the actual world, Maada began to puzzle over the S_____ children, who did not seem (to him) to be the "right sizes." Especially his favorite, Riki, a lively three-year-old, appeared to be "different sizes," depending upon his physical proximity to Maada. For Maada might sight Riki at a distance, without realizing that it was a distance, and so the child would appear to Maada much smaller than he was, like a doll; without three dimensions to suggest depth, all was flattened, cartoonlike. Such experiences bewildered Maada, who could not have explained them, even before the impairment to his cerebral cortex, in clinical or intellectual terms. The diminution of the children in size was particularly frightening to Maada, who soon became convinced that Riki, the smallest child, was in danger of *going out*—as a flame is blown out.

Conversely, adults who seemed, to Maada, of a comfortably small, contained size at a distance, loomed large up close, and could be terrifying. The overall shifting sizes of persons and objects was disorienting to Maada, and eventually exhausting, but he learned to shut one eye so that the expectation of three dimensions (whatever "three dimensions" had come to mean) was not an issue.

In all, there would be eleven surgeries performed on Maada's brain, each for a distinct purpose. One of the more successful was the instillation of selected amnesia, through "erasures" of certain clusters of neurons in the brain matter surrounding the hippocampus, with the result that the subject could not remember that he'd had surgery, along with much else. To account for his part-shaved head, the subject was told that he'd had an infestation of head lice—his hair had had to be cut off and his head shaved in the affected area. The surgery left wounds and scars that had to be disguised with a scalp covering, in this case a "wig" that was a patch of hair matching the subject's own hair, which he could not remove from his head, and would not try to remove, under the impression that it was a "scalp flap" that had been secured with stitches. In addition, Maada was told that the patch contained toxin to repel lice. All this he seemed to accept without question.

Another of the surgeries concentrated on the agency of *will*, *willfulness*. With neurons in these areas "hosed clean," these were subdued.

Eventually, the "scalp flap" was enlarged, and a more serious, systematic neurosurgery was performed on the subject. (Of course, the subject was kept in an anesthetized state for such surgeries, which could require as long as nine or ten hours.) Exposed as a clockwork mechanism, the brain was readily examined by a team of experimental neuroscientists involved in the NTM project. Could one communicate with a region of the subject's brain without involving the subject ("consciousness") at all? Could one give contrary signals to parts of the brain, and force upon the brain a quasi consciousness, born of desperation? Could "consciousness" be chased into a region of the brain, like a rat into a cage corner? Maada, in his state of suspended animation, barely breathing, bodily functions monitored minutely, was an ideal subject, for he was in excellent physical condition and, in recent months in particular, inclined to *passivity*.

In a sequence of surgeries, parts of the subject's brain were excised and replaced with artificial devices—chips, stents. Such experimentation is crucial, for one day, and that day not far in the future, neurophysiological enhancements will be necessary to provide longevity to humankind, at least to world leaders and members of the ruling classes. One of the most innovative experiments developed at the institute has been the gradual replacement of a subject's blood with a chemically identical *blood that was not red but near transparent, a more practical blood composition in which white cells are better equipped to combat bacterial and viral invasions than "natural" blood.

In another yet more radical experiment, through electrical charges directly into the memory center of the subject's brain, circumventing conscious channels, the subject was informed in a vividly "mystical" dream that he was not an ordinary, mortal human being but a native of Ganymede, one of four large, beautiful moons of the sixty-seven moons of Jupiter. Given the code name "Joseph," the subject had been sent on a stealth mission to the Earth, to the United States, in the guise of a youthful, male native of the African nation Nigeria; to throw off suspicion, the subject was outfitted with a very dark, purplish-black skin, hyperalert senses (visual, auditory, olfactory), and "radioactive" eye sensors. In this guise, as "Joseph," the subject could see through solid objects; he could hear not only what was being said at a distance but he could "hear" thoughts. He knew languages instinctively—without needing to think, he "translated" these languages into thought. In this superior being, the thin scrim between consciousness and unconsciousness had been penetrated.

Of course, there have been unanticipated side effects of such experimentation: in several test subjects these have included convulsions, psychosis, and death. (So far as we know, none of these have been subjects in Dr. Lehrman's lab.)

Here, there. How do we distinguish?

Despite J. S. Maada's spatial destabilization, or perhaps because of it, the subject exhibited no difficulty in understanding, or imagining that he understood, how his cramped living quarters in Edison, New Jersey, were at the same time the open, unbounded atmosphere of Ganymede; he was not baffled that he could be *here* and *there* simultaneously.

Partly, this extraordinary mental feat was made possible by the near-total modification of the subject's basic memory—that is, the neural region in which were stored memories of the subject's earliest childhood and adolescence, altered to include purposefully vague "memories" of Ganymede. In a bold experiment the subject was shown photographs taken in Nigeria, initially landscapes of surpassing beauty, villages, celebrations, smiling children; suddenly, war-torn villages, hellish ruins, fires, corpses; men, women, and children strewn in the street, some badly mutilated, headless. Such powerful stimuli had a minimal emotional effect upon the subject, for an inhibitory microchip governed the firing of neurons in his brain. Where neurons fail to fire there cannot be conscious "thought"; where there is not conscious thought, there cannot be the retrieval of "memory"; and where no memory, no "emotion." (See Lehrman, M., "Neurotransmitter Inhibitory Functions in the Subcortical Human Brain," *Neuroscience Quarterly*, I:3. [Another paper of which 90 percent was written by Dr. Lehrman's postdocs, names grudgingly acknowledged in an obscure footnote.])

Yet more ingeniously, microchip neurotransmitters were activated at a distance in the subject's brain by (remote) electrical stimulation sending "voices" to the subject, with such auditory acuteness the subject could not but believe that they were in the room with him and were *actual*; amidst these, secondary "voices" could be sent to confirm, or contradict, or drown out the initial voices, leaving the hapless subject utterly baffled and catatonic. In one phase of the experiment the subject was made to hear voices in his original (Yoruba) language but with unusual inflections as if being uttered by computers, or foreign-born persons, which produced a particularly unnerving effect in the subject; in another phase, the subject was made to hear "Ganymede" speech—a computer-generated language with a scrambled syntax. At all times the voice of the commandant could interrupt and redirect the subject. (This too was a computer-generated voice but its baritone timbre was soothing and "paternal.")

More recently developed has been a means of using the subject as a recording device without the subject's awareness, in Maada's case exchanges among Maada and some members of the S_____ family, when Maada sat down to meals with them; these in pidgin English or, presumably, Yoruba. No effort was made to translate these desultory conversations as they could have zero scientific interest.

Other sounds sent to the subject at a distance were thunder, music, dreams, an eerie whispering "breath" of outer space meant to simulate the sound of winds on Ganymede; each drew a specific reaction from the subject, ranging from fear to sorrow to intense, infantile joy, and each was experienced without question.

Electrical stimulations in the subject's brain stirred appetite and nausea, sexual desire and sexual repugnance, simultaneously. Shown photographs of (presumably) sexually stimulating images, like naked, nubile women and girls, the subject did not react as he might have reacted normally, when neurotransmitters blocked his reflexive reactions; conversely, shown photographs of (presumably) asexual images, the subject was stimulated to react sexually. (Of experiments performed upon him without his awareness this was perhaps the most distressing to the subject as Maada could not comprehend why he was beginning to have "sex desire" for such bizarre and inappropriate objects as clouds, towels, doorknobs, infants, and toddlers. Even in his diminished state, the subject retained a residue of human shame and conscience, and came to feel agitated about losing control of his "soul.")

As "Joseph," the test subject was required to carry a ("virtual") explosive device strapped to his body to be detonated by remote control at the direction of the commandant. This act of *martyrdom*

303

was a test of Maada's/"Joseph's" loyalty to his Ganymede mission. Though perceived to be "anxious" and "distracted" at the prospect of a suicide mission, or what he believed to be a suicide mission, Maada did not question its necessity; a crucial incision in his brain had reduced the impulse to "question."

Such detonations might take place, for instance, when Maada and the S_____ family were sitting together at a mealtime; when Maada was shopping in a 7-Eleven store, walking along a crowded street in Edison, or traveling with his fellow lawn-crew workers in the rear of his employer Adolpho's truck. Detonation would be accomplished at a vastly long distance: electrical forces would be released on Ganymede, to travel to Earth at the speed of light. *Why?* was not a question to be asked, nor even *How?*—for Maada need do nothing but submit, and he would be blameless.

Each time Maada was directed by the commandant to prepare for the explosion, he became highly agitated, but only inwardly; his heartbeat accelerated, and his sweat glands oozed sweat. (Eventually, in a later phase of the experiment, the subject's heart was adjoined to a fine-meshed mechanism that was immune to "accelerating.") That Maada cooperated unresistingly in what would be (theoretically) his own demise confirmed the success of the NTM inserts; he'd been programmed to elevate the commandant over any (merely) human beings. Obedience was linked to the subject's "Ganymede destiny" and "Ganymede pride" though J. S. Maada's notion of his mythical homeland was almost entirely abstract: a rugged rock terrain resembling the badlands of Montana, of pitiless sunshine and shadows so sharp they registered to the eye as crevices.

In another experimental mission the subject was directed to make his way into the Martin Luther King Building & US Courthouse at 50 Walnut Street, Newark, New Jersey. Here, in this clamorous foyer, he was to pass through security undetected—of course, the explosives he was carrying were "virtual" and not "actual"—and without calling attention to himself in any way; he was then to enter a specially designated courtroom on the first floor, and take a seat inconspicuously at the rear. A PROJECT observer stationed at the site noted that Maada did not behave suspiciously in this public setting but exuded the slightly nervous yet eager-to-please air of a foreign visitor to the United States who is hoping one day to become a citizen. Here too the subject was convinced that he was "Joseph"—a "stealth missile" and potential "martyr" to be detonated by a remote control from one of the moons of Jupiter.

In Judge D_____'s courtroom, which was beginning to fill with participants and spectators, the test subject waited.

Even at such a time of intense concentration and preparedness Maada retained some residue of awareness from his former life. He could not, he reasoned, be blamed for anything that "happened"—it would "happen" through him but not by his hand. He was as innocent as a young child of knowledge of who the enemy was, and why the enemy, and himself with them, was to be annihilated in a cataclysm of flames and rubble in this austere old government building. US Federal Justice D_____ was to be "executed"—but why? An enemy of—whom? Was the US government involved in a stealth program to assassinate certain of its citizens, like Judge D_____? So long as Maada was innocent of such knowledge and merely following the directives of the commandant, he was innocent of the acts he precipitated, and this was a solace to him.

Saidu, what are you doing? Why?

But he was innocent of such knowledge, merely following the directives of the commandant. He did not need to lift a finger—to employ a finger—to "detonate"—for that would be done for him, like magic.

And yet abruptly, after forty minutes, the commandant's voice calmly informed him that the mission had been "suspended" for the time being and he was free to leave.

What relief he felt! Or no, not relief, a sudden vast, insatiable hunger.

In front of a vending machine on the ground floor of the courthouse Maada stood trembling. So many choices!—soft drinks, candy bars, chips. He could not decide what to purchase first. His hands were shaking so badly, he could not remove his wallet from his pocket. In a trance of euphoria he wept hot acid tears that ran in rivulets down his cheeks.

And then, in late spring 2016 Maada began to misinterpret NTM signals. Willful neurons in the test subject firing *in ways contrary to directives*.

That this was happening in test subject #293199 after months of subject's near-total cooperation was in itself a significant if unexpected development. For no experiment is without valuable revelations!

Of course, *willfulness* in the subject J. S. Maada was intermittent and inconsistent. Resisting programmed directives did not represent

305

an altered pattern of behavior in #293199 for there was no (discernible) pattern to it.

In the heat of early summer working with Adolpho's Lawn Care crew, Maada was observed shivering violently while others complained of heat; subject perspired heavily, yet continued to shiver with (apparent) cold. When NTM activity was inoperative, subject began to "hear" voices of a new and inexplicable sort. Though he could not have known of the microscopic stents in his brain, still less the cluster of strategically placed computer chips, or the artificial "scalp flap" beneath a patch of hair, he began to obsess that there were "things" in his brain—grains of sand, staple-sized bits of metal, lice that crawled and sucked his blood. He came to believe that his heart had been replaced by "a kind of clock that ticks." His blood was no longer red but of the hue and substance of mucus. His skin, which had always been so rich and dark, was lightening in splotches, like a kind of cancer—from working in the sun? Yet, Maada could not *not work* for he needed the money to repay the S_____ family for their generosity to him and also to send back to his family in Nigeria (though his family had become distant and blank to him like faded faces on a billboard, and several messages from "voices" had called into question his actual blood relationship to them). Maada diverted his most anxious thoughts by scratching and peeling his skin, which seemed to give him an intense, sensual pleasure; beneath were patches of sickly pale skin, both repugnant and fascinating.

Even when no NTM activity was initiated from the institute, subject began to experience "zapping" sensations in his brain and throughout his body. These came from a long distance, subject believed, traveling at the speed of light. His genitals were particularly sensitive to such signals—though in fact there were no signals. "Sex desire" for inanimate objects like discarded Styrofoam cups bearing a residue of coffee or cola, carelessly opened cereal boxes, unlaced work boots swept upon him at unpredictable times. He could not bear to touch the genital region of his body for such touch was forbidden, yet his hands moved of their own greed and willfulness, and were shameful to him. In the S_____ family there was little privacy, which was shameful to him. *You smell funny, Saidu,* one of the older children said, wrinkling her nose. It was terrifying to him; the S_____ family would evict him from their apartment; a voice not precisely but resembling that of the commandant suggested that it might be wisest to slash the S_____s' throats in their beds some night when all were sleeping peacefully, and then to slash his own. Yet an instant later, Adolpho was shouting at him: *Asshole! Wake up.* So tired he was falling asleep in the truck—he was falling asleep on his (shaky) feet. Losing his ability to see himself in relationship to other (spatial) beings. For it is *space* that prevents us being crushed together—as *time* prevents everything happening at once—but what is *space?* Shut his eyes, *space* vanished. Much was becoming scrambled, dismembered, dissected. It was repulsive to him, to observe his own body dissected by (white) strangers with handsaws and bloodstained surgical instruments. And his jaw hanging slackly open, and his eyes but half closed. Those corrosive acid tears leaving rivulets on his cheeks, and elsewhere, on his body, splotches and peelings. So vividly he saw the strangers with their sharp instruments, their wrinkled noses at the smell of his sawn-open torso—*Jesus, what a stink!*

Had it already happened?—or not yet? As if compressed on the head of a pin, everything was prepared to detonate.

When Adolpho came for them on a street corner in Edison in the twilit hour at dawn Maada had to summon all his strength to climb into the truck with the others. Where once he'd been the youngest member of the lawn crew, now his youth had drained from him—he'd become the oldest. His back was stricken with pain. All of the nerves of his back had been strung to breaking. His brain was swollen with pustules. Lice scrambled through the hole in his head, and into his hair. His left eye was plastic. He had slipped back in "time" as clumsily as you'd slip in dog shit on the sidewalk—he had become his own ancestor, a slave. On the moon of Jupiter, slaves had revolted in open, deep crevice pits as their captors had flung livid torches down at them. It had been a slave uprising, which had propelled him to Earth, to save the others. He yearned to know more of his mysterious and forbidden origin but the words that would have brought him knowledge began to break and crumble like a column of ants when a booted foot descends upon them.

Riding the massive lawn mower. A coworker had been kind enough to adjust the ear protectors against his ears. Yet hearing a babble and crackle of voices and laughter. Seeing figures amid the trees, which (though lifelike) he knew were not really there, for they were transparent like jellyfish; you could see through them.

At the S_____ estate working stooped in the sun. How many hours stooped and digging in the sun. Woman with a pig face. That skin—"white." Snout nose. Pig-eyes lewd and laughing. Pig-eyes dared to descend to the gnarl of misery at his groin.

307

What issued from the pig-mouth was confusing to him for he had already obeyed the pig-mouth. He knew. He was sure. Yet he was not sure for perhaps it had not happened yet.

Yet, *it had happened*. The Floradora rose was to be dug up another time and another time replanted.

Dug up and brought to the other bed, which is/was the first bed. And the azalea dug up, and hauled away to be replanted. It seemed to Maada that he had just performed these actions. He had performed these actions several times. The pig-woman had given him orders, and he had obeyed. Yet it was possible that the several times he had obeyed the pig-woman were collapsed to a single time and that time like the head of a pin, too small to see. Was there just one rose bed, and one hole?—but more than one Floradora rose? And what of the azalea? Trying to understand such a puzzle was like trying to push inside his head an object too big to fit inside his skull as well as oddly angled. Subject began to experience rapid zaps in brain, groin, fingers. Began to scream, grunt, tear like a ravenous animal with his teeth.

Pig-woman screamed, screamed. His coworkers screamed at *him*, pulling him off her.

It was the end. All of Ganymede would rejoice; a new martyr would enter the firmament.

The night before, this had happened.

Riki, who'd loved to cuddle with Saidu, shrank from him now, seeing something in Saidu's face that was beginning to twitch, splotch, and peel like sunburn. The iris of one eye was inflamed, half again the size of the other iris. And the strange smell like something rotted.

Riki laughed uneasily, and sucked his thumb, and began to cry when Maada stooped to play with him.

Yet Maada had no clear idea when this was. Riki was running away from him before he'd run toward him.

No! Go away, I don't like you.

Reached for the child, who was screaming with laughter. Or, screaming. Reached for the child, and the child's legs thrashed wildly.

Far away, on a moon of the great planet Jupiter, a remote control was being pressed. The detonation would be instantaneous.

The Unrivaled Happiness of Otters
S. P. Tenhoff

THERE WAS ALWAYS MORE than one of us, in those days. We were a plural proposition. We would huddle, Shem maybe on one side and The Collider, for instance, on the other—other combinations were possible—and confer over secrets important because they were secret. Or no longer secret. We would fill Tarsky's battered Subaru, arrive somewhere, tumble out like clowns from a clown car. We spoke in code, spurned work and daylight. Our comings and goings were inexplicable even to ourselves, our snarled trajectories heroic, volatile, nonlinear.

Who could stop us? People. People stopped us. Time stopped us, some of us, slowed others down. Tarsky drove his Subaru through fog, off a Big Sur cliff, into foam and rock and sea. Lance immigrated to Malaysia. Zurilla wed an eczemic orthodontist. Our happy manyness was being erased at the margins. (We'd never needed to think of ourselves as happy.)

We became numerable, our remaining trajectories easily traced and no longer sufficiently tangled.

A point came when, near the sand-swept decay of Seaside, murder capital of Central California, I found myself residing alone in an apartment with an address that sounded like a joke at my expense. Which was not in itself the problem: I was used to making fun of myself and encouraging others to join in. It was what I'd always done best. The problem was that there was no one around anymore to share the joke with. Lance sent me a postcard once of Malaysian rain forest and printed 666 CASANOVA AVE MONTEREY CA in the address space without so much as a scrawled snicker, without the briefest parenthetical note of irony. On the photo side of the postcard an arrow pointed into serrated shadow below the blue-inked words I AM HERE.

When I got The Collider's e-mail I hadn't heard from anyone in a long time. He was living up in Petaluma, and wanted to stay overnight while he took care of some business related to his mother's house, which he'd been renting out since she died. I made up an itinerary, a tour of the places that had been most important in all of our lives. We would need more than a day, though. I e-mailed, telling him he could stay longer—he could stay as long as he wanted. He e-mailed back to say he could only come down for a day, and at least part of that time he'd be busy dealing with a real estate agent. My reduced itinerary included dinner at the Speckled Urchin, a Japanese/Mexican fusion place we all used to love. Now you needed a reservation. I had us for seven, but the day of his arrival he kept texting that he was running late, and finally that he'd decided to grab something on the way. I canceled the reservation, made myself a peanut butter sandwich, and waited at the kitchen table, where I had a view of Casanova Avenue. It was after nine when he pulled up to the curb. I rushed down to meet him. He looked more or less like himself, except for an unconvincing mustache that seemed to have been pasted onto his lip in an attempt to disguise himself as someone's father.

"The Collider," I hollered in a carnival-barker voice, as if I was announcing his arrival to the entire street.

"Wow," he said. "Almost didn't recognize you for a second." The brief body scan his eyes gave reminded me that I might have put on a few pounds.

"Yeah, well," I said, making the face I'd always made in such situations to show—what? Large part deadpan humor, small part fatalistic resignation, a pinch of snarky displeasure. . . . Something like that. I felt a little self-conscious doing it, as if I were trying to show him a face he could recognize as mine.

"Find it all right?" But had I *made* that face in the past? Hadn't it just *been* my face then?

"Oh, yeah. Yeah. I used the GPS. Can't believe you ended up all the way out here, though. What is this, practically Seaside?"

"Still Monterey, technically. It's not like I *ended up* here. This is temporary. Can you even believe my address? Six six six Casanova Avenue. Perfect." And I found myself making the face again. I was expecting a smart-ass Collider dig, something maybe about me and my luck with women. But he just stood there with his overnight bag in his hand. Tired from the drive, probably.

Once we were inside, the first thing I did was offer him a loaded pipe. I'd gotten a bud from one of the janitors at the aquarium. I wasn't really much of a smoker, but this was The Collider visiting, and although I couldn't even imagine him not bringing his own—I'd never known a time when he wasn't stoned and holding—I wanted to be a good host.

He waved it away. "Thanks," he said. "I'm good."

"You're good?"

"I don't smoke anymore. Haven't for a long time."

". . . You're kidding."

"No, it gives me these . . . anxiety-attack sort of things."

"Seriously? I mean, seriously? Anxiety attacks. You're The Collider. This psychotropic substance here? It *relieves* anxiety."

"Not for me. Not anymore."

I took the pipe into the bedroom.

"But, hey," I heard him say. "You go ahead."

"No. No, I'm OK."

After that I told him about my job. My hope was to be promoted to assistant otter feeder at the aquarium. This position was coveted and therefore the source of every species of nasty cloak-and-dagger. Assistant otter feeders didn't actually assist in the feeding of otters; they assisted in the preparation of the food that would be brought to the otters by the otter feeders. It was, nevertheless, a step in the right direction. A step in the direction of the otters, which was the point. This was what we all dreamed about, those of us who fought and schemed and despised each other: the day when we could commune directly with the otters in yellow rubber boots and aprons, tossing fish from buckets at our new friends from our own gloved hands. . . .

"And that's just the next step," I said. "That's not the ultimate goal." My dream, I started to explain, was to eventually help rescue orphaned and injured otters. He kept shifting and fidgeting on the couch, looking more and more exasperated.

"To do that?" he blurted out finally. "Get to feed them and all? Don't you have to be like a properly trained oceanographer or something? How'd you even get that job anyway?"

I outlined the steps in my progress: volunteer, janitorial trainee, janitor, current position as custodial assistant to the assistant sea mammal feeders. Talking about my work—or my potential future work—usually made me excited, but now I couldn't stop thinking about properly trained oceanographers. What kind of thing was that for him to say? You didn't need an advanced degree to feed otters fish from a bucket. Or to bond with them, to recognize their needs, to help them. . . .

"How about you?" I asked. "What kind of work are you doing?"

He was a smog technician at an automobile inspection center in Petaluma. Smog technician: I couldn't picture it. Or I could picture it: a mustached, greasy-jumpsuited Collider in an unlit concrete

311

room, facing a row of rumbling cars showing their tailpipes and farting gray fumes. . . . How had The Collider ended up as the sort of person who measured exhaust emissions for a living?

"If you're just going to be inspecting smog," I said, "you don't have to be all the way up there. Might as well be in Monterey. Come back, why don't you? You can crash here until you get yourself set up."

"I'm not inspecting smog. I'm inspecting cars. And if for some reason I wanted to be back here, I could stay at my mom's place instead of renting it out. I don't know how you can stand it, man. To tell the truth. Stuck in this town."

I hadn't realized until then that I felt any sense of betrayal toward those of us who had chosen to abandon our town. To change the subject, I said, "Sorry about your mom, by the way. Don't know if I told you."

This was not the right way to change the subject.

I tried again, this time talking about our friends. The way he listened, I might have been mentioning people I'd introduced him to once at a party. He hadn't kept in touch with anyone. He didn't even know about Zurilla's orthodontist, for example. Or Lance and Malaysia. I handed him the postcard.

He looked down at it for a second—rain forest, arrow, blue-inked words—before setting it on the coffee table. Then he tilted his head and stretched in what struck me as a contrived way.

I put a blanket and pillow on the couch.

"Here you go. G'night."

"Night," he said. "Hey. Thanks."

In my room, I sat cross-legged on the bed holding a lighter and the pipe I'd loaded for him. Eventually I lit the bowl, a tentative sip: it had been a while. It was like inhaling scented air; but as I held it in my chest it bloomed, swelling. I pinched my nose closed and hunkered down around it until I had to surrender, a blue coughball exploding across the bed. The Collider would have heard the sound in the next room. There was no reason to feel guilty about smoking alone: he hadn't wanted any. Anxiety attacks. How was that possible? What had *happened* to him? I remembered him as he had been before and then I started thinking of the others, remembering our adventures together and how we had all been once. I was watching a film: I was a viewer and at the same time a participant captured and preserved there. The film wasn't some Vaseline-lensed nostalgic blurring of the past; it was a documentary, everything true, everything revealed to me with an exact stoned clarity. That life was vivid and actual; it was my current life, and my current self, crossed-legged on a bed sipping a pipe, that felt dim and unreal.

Once in a while I'd hear a sound coming from the living room, and each time, for a second, I'd panic, thinking an intruder had broken in. I wasn't used to having people in my place. I'd remember that it was just The Collider, moving around, apparently wide awake even though he'd been stretching and making a show of how sleepy he was. I would wonder what he was doing in there. Then I'd start thinking again about The Collider I'd known, and that would start the documentary rolling again, and then I'd hear something, and again, for a second, before I remembered, I would freeze in alarm at the sound of the intruder stealing through my apartment.

The Collider had grown up in one of those magazine-cover gingerbread houses in Pacific Grove, the kind with hummingbirds suspended above year-round perfect flower gardens. Whoever had been renting the place had let it go a little, though: there were weeds in the garden and it needed a paint job. A real estate agent was waiting for him when we pulled up. He got out and they circled the house together. She rang the doorbell, another woman answered, and they all went inside. After a while The Collider and the agent came out and he followed her SUV to a real estate office in a strip mall. I waited in his car for about an hour before he finally returned.

"How'd it go?" I asked.

"How'd it go. It went. It's gone. Will be. I've got a buyer."

". . . Wow. That must feel . . ."

"Like what a relief. Like: finally. Cut that string."

It was still early; he didn't have to drive back up to Petaluma until evening. That left plenty of time for him to see the aquarium. Even though The Collider had grown up in Monterey, he'd never actually been there. Besides, it would give me a chance to show him the important work I was doing there, or would be doing in the future, once I was promoted.

On the way, we passed Lovers Point Park.

"Remember that time?" I said.

"What time?"

"You know, the time with Waltzer. We're all blazed, but Waltzer, he's just, I mean, supremely shit-faced and trying to climb the rocks and he slips and—you remember that." I looked at him. "He's in this puddle in the sand and can't get up and the tide's coming in. Right?

313

And we're pulling him up by those four gangled limbs of his and threatening to throw him out to sea . . . I *know* you remember. . . ."

"I wasn't there," he said.

"You were there," I said. "We come back and our picnic table, it's, those seagulls, a gang of them, in the middle of scarfing our munchies? And they fly off, all our food, bags, and wrappers in their beaks? You remember that."

"It wasn't me." He was gazing out at the bay, where iron pools melted and reformed across the lit water. "I missed that one."

He drove down Ocean View Boulevard to Cannery Row. We started searching for a parking space.

He was there. I knew he'd been there that day and I was convinced that he remembered it too. It wasn't like it was necessarily such a major event in our lives. Absurd and improbable things were happening to us all the time then. But even taking into consideration the fact that we were all in assorted stages of chemical disrepair at the time, it seemed impossible that he could have forgotten the entire incident. It was as if, by denying his presence there, he was trying to take the memory from me, the certainty that it had happened at all.

The aquarium allowed every employee one free guest a month, but I'd never actually had cause to use this perk before. I led him across the atrium, through the barred shadows of the whale skeleton overhead. Molly was working the entrance, smiling and putting dolphin stamps on children's tickets. She'd been awarded this position because she was good with people, one of her many annoying qualities.

"Who's your friend?" she said.

"This," I said, "is The Collider." I put a hand on his shoulder. "We go back."

"Collider," she repeated with a smirk.

He shrugged, looking embarrassed. "Old nickname."

"And you're getting the complete guided tour, I guess." She was still smirking at him. He smirked back. There seemed to be some sort of collusion in the way they smirked at each other.

"See you, Molly," I said.

"Enjoy the tour," she said to The Collider.

We went through the gate.

"Not completely unacceptable." He'd turned to examine the back of her khaki shorts. "Have you . . . ?"

"No. Not even a possibility," I said, making the old face again in spite of myself. There was a long history with Molly, not the romantic kind but the kind that, whatever I might have been inclined to feel for her otherwise, made romance inconceivable. Molly was one of the cloak-and-dagger assistant-otter-feeding rivals, the main one possibly, because of the way she curried favor with Terrence, the sea-mammal supervisor most susceptible to flattery. I felt unable, though, to explain this to The Collider. It would require a further explanation of my ambitions involving otter feeding, a subject that, after his mention the previous night of properly trained oceanographers, seemed too precious to share with him. So instead I said, "You know the story with me and women."

I was the one among us who never had a girlfriend, and, probably as an emotional defense, I'd always exaggerated this role for my friends' amusement, grumbling in a comically despairing way about my mutant special power: the ability to repel any potential female partner. This was why my address, 666 Casanova Avenue—the anti-Casanova—had seemed so ridiculous and so apt. The Collider, on the other hand, was the one who, without any overtures or seductive techniques or, well, without doing anything at all, had found himself constantly surrounded by beautiful women simply by being his disheveled and deeply stoned self. When I'd complain about my women problems he would always laugh and then give advice. Now, though, he didn't even seem to be listening.

He'd stopped at the touching pool. Children lined the edge, arms in the water. "Oh, this," I said. "Kids can feel the whatever, stingrays and starfish and stuff."

I nodded to Celeste, the old woman who supervised the touching. "A friend of mine."

"Well, welcome," she said to him. "Dip your hand right in there and feel for yourself, if you like. Don't be shy."

"You know what? I think I will."

He pulled up a sleeve, kneeled, reached in.

"Lovely, isn't it? The feeling," Celeste said to The Collider. "Almost like satin."

"It's amazing." He looked up at me. "Right?"

I saw him study my face.

"Oh. Oh, no way. Don't tell me you've never done this before."

The truth was I'd never liked touching sea creatures. Furred ones, possibly yes, certainly yes, certainly I would enjoy stroking sleek, shimmering otter fur if given the opportunity, but this was . . .

"Come on. You work at an aquarium, right?"

"We don't usually go around grabbing fish with our bare hands. We have these things we use. They're called nets. Or gloves."

315

"You work at an aquarium, man. Come on. Stick your arm in here."

I was aware of Celeste there on her stool.

"Go ahead," he said, grinning under his implausible mustache disguise, the old Collider, daring me to do something I shouldn't. Or something that maybe I should do but wouldn't ordinarily have the courage to. "What're you afraid of?"

I rolled up my sleeve. The water was warmer than I'd expected. Below my hand a starfish. I reached for it, but a black shape glided like a shadow between the starfish and my fingertips and as it brushed past, I shuddered at the touch of living flesh. . . .

I pulled my arm out of the water.

The Collider stood wiping his arm with a paper towel, grin even wider.

"Right?" he said.

I dried myself off. My fingers tingled at the aftertouch. The brush of a black wing tip, soft and alive and . . .

The Collider wasn't there. I found him at the tropical fish tank. "I can't believe they don't all just eat each other, together in there like that."

My fingertips were still tingling. "You have to choose carefully," I heard myself say authoritatively, as if I were involved personally in the selection process. "The ones that can get along."

We passed moon jellies, skeleton shrimp, leafy sea dragons. He paused at the octopus tank. Clyde, our resident giant Pacific octopus, was suckering his way across the front panel.

There was a story I'd heard from a janitor when I first started working there. According to the story, fish started disappearing from their tanks. Fish, or maybe it was crabs. One day it would be there and the next it would be gone. After ruling out the possibility of mutual predation, management began to suspect that the culprit might be one of the aquarium staff, stealing the fish or crabs at night. So they set up a hidden camera. And what they found was that it was the octopus who was responsible: it would slip out of its tank and go to another one and eat the fish or crab and bury the bones or shell in the sand and then return to its own tank. It was unlikely that the octopus was Clyde: they only live for a few years, and when I'd heard the story a few years before, it was already well established. I wasn't even sure that the incident had happened at my aquarium, or that it had really happened at all. It was one of those stories that gets passed along. But as I told it to The Collider, I described it as if Clyde was the culprit, and—without actually saying so—I let it be understood that I'd been there myself, involved in noticing the missing fish or crabs or possibly even in coming up with the idea of using a hidden camera. And then, as if to legitimize the tale with a story that really was true, I added that Clyde was very clever, intelligent enough to recognize his feeders and prefer some to others, touching the ones he liked with a tentacle and squirting the ones he didn't.

"What's he think about you?" The Collider asked.

"I don't feed him," I said. "Remember, I told you I'm hoping to feed the otters. I'm on the otter team."

"Yeah, but you said he recognizes all of you. How's he react to you?"

"He doesn't, really. I don't know. He just . . . It's hard to say."

Clyde's head, as it moved in front of me, resembled a submerged scarf being whirled around.

"Isn't he lonely in there?" a little boy was asking his mother. "He doesn't get to be with the other fish."

"Actually, he's not a fish," I said. The boy and his mother turned. "He's a mollusk. Clam family. He's basically a very smart clam. They like being alone. Octopuses. Octopi. Not like us. Clyde there is probably enjoying his solitude."

The mother pressed her hand to the boy's back and ushered him over to a tank across the room.

"Jesus," I said. "You see the way they looked at me? I guess I should have told them I'm aquarium staff." But The Collider wasn't paying any attention. He was watching Clyde settle in a bed of his own tentacles.

"Why doesn't he make a run for it?" he said.

"What?"

"The octopus. He's such an escape artist, why doesn't he wait for dark and make for that emergency exit? It's right there. Squeeze his way under the door—they can do that, you know? Fit through anything. Then flop off the pier into the bay. Freedom. If he's so smart."

"Maybe he likes it in there."

I was tired of talking about Clyde. I remembered that the next otter feeding was at four. My watch said five after. I rushed The Collider over to the viewing area, but tourists had already claimed the best spots at the railings on both tiers. I'd planned a schedule that would allow us to see everything at just the right time. Then The Collider had decided we needed to touch stingrays and stand around looking at an octopus. As we watched the backs of the heads of the tourists who were watching the otters getting fed, I couldn't stop thinking about Clyde. . . . To focus myself, I began narrating to The Collider the procedure that I knew, from countless viewings, must be taking place: the feeder standing there in yellow rubber boots, a fish-filled can holstered on each hip; the otters leaping on command, one at a time, from the pool onto the imitation rock platform. . . . I described it all for him, a detailed play-by-play, even though I couldn't see a thing.

On the way back to my apartment, as we drove down Alvarado, The Collider pointed to a bar. He asked if I remembered a particular incident that had happened there. Before I could answer, he started recounting it for me. I was surprised—he'd been avoiding talking about the past ever since he arrived. He would ignore an in-joke, pretend he didn't understand when I used our coded language. But now he seemed eager to revisit the memories. He wasn't reminiscing, though; whatever he was doing felt like the opposite of that. He pointed at a bus-stop bench, the scene of another incident, a minor one, in reality, he argued; hardly the legendary event we'd all chosen to remember. That was the gist of what he was saying as he drove: the ridiculous and noble and unrepeatable things that had happened to us were not as we'd remembered them. The Collider, I began to understand, intended to take apart the story of our lives together until it was a manageable size, until it was small enough for him to destroy its remaining glamour completely. Maybe I wouldn't have minded if he'd been trying to prove that we'd all been immature or reckless or misguided. But what he was saying was something else: that none of it had meant what we thought it did. We passed Monterey Peninsula College, where we'd all nominally been students, and there were memories there too that apparently needed dismantling. It wasn't clear whether he was attacking or pleading. The closer we got to my place the more agitated he became, rapidly unearthing memory after memory as if he'd just realized how much more he needed to say and how little time we had left together. His arguments made me feel weak. They didn't persuade me but they drained the energy to oppose them.

". . . See?" he was saying as we pulled up to my apartment building. "Now that's a perfect example. Do you remember how I got that name?"

". . . There was a reason."

"Yeah. There was. Do you remember? Do you remember what that fucking reason was?"

"Sure," I said. I didn't remember.

"From now on? Let's just go back to Todd. OK?"

"Todd," I repeated. "Sure: Todd." Forcing myself to say it out loud, the blunt and ordinary monosyllable he'd been stuck with once before we'd given him something better.

"All right then. I should hit the road. Long trip back and all that."

We shook hands. I got out of his car, and then The Collider—I was tempted to shout it out defiantly, his real and permanent name, a final wild call—drove down Casanova Avenue while I stood waving idiotically at the curb.

As soon as I was in my apartment I realized I didn't want to be there. I went back outside and took a bus downtown. From Fisherman's Wharf I followed the Peninsula Trail, passing joggers and rollerbladers. It was going to be another one of those Monterey sunsets they say can't be beat. Out past the shore, a pair of sea lions lazed on a crag of rock, looking like rock formations themselves. In the sea around them, invisible to me now, otters would be congregating, clam diving and circling each other in otter play and floating together companionably on the waves. They didn't even need to swim. They could just float together in water like they were floating in air. A raft of otters: that's what you called a group of them. There was nothing wrong with this town. People came from all over to see this town. This pristine, otter-filled bay.

The sun burned orange and a scorched red, then extinguished itself in the distant water, leaving its colors behind. What had they seen, those who had abandoned this town? Other sunsets, other bays: no matter how hard I tried to visualize them, I could only see deformed replicas of this sunset, this bay. Out there, in the direction of the vanishing colors, far out there somewhere was Malaysia. I thought of Lance, squatting unseen in jungle shadow under his hand-drawn arrow. I AM HERE. I thought of Zurilla, kissing the red eczemic neck of his orthodontist. Tarsky at the wheel of his Subaru. I thought of Shem, Zachary, Dangling Jim, Waltzer, Mitch, Eric, The Collider . . . until I wasn't actually thinking of them so much as listing them, enumerating them, resurrecting through naming, even though, except for Tarsky, they were all still alive.

Cannery Row was clotted with tourists milling around under blinking lights, putting food in each other's mouths and loitering in front of souvenir-encrusted windows. There they were: the people who came from all over to see my town.

The aquarium was dark. I used my key at the service entrance. Inside, underwater light wavered across the walls and floor. Shapes behind glass glinted and slid and turned.

There was nobody in the otter enclosure. Jack, the abandoned pup rescued a few months before, no longer needed twenty-four-hour care. He was in the pool aboard his surrogate mother, Effie, nestled in her furred chest, where he looked as content as an infant rocking in its cradle, although it occurred to me that otters in general always looked content, maybe because their faces were incapable of showing any other expression. I took a mask from its hook on the wall and put it on. We wore these masks—a headband attached to a tinted visor that could, like a welding helmet, be raised or lowered over your face—to prevent otters like Jack, who might eventually be released back into the wild, from becoming too familiar with humans. Better for them to fear us, or to see us as, at best, benign but faceless creatures. Only the otter feeders and handlers were allowed to show the otters their actual faces. I stood at the pool's edge, watching them bob on the unruffled water, oblivious captives. As I watched, I noticed for the first time something unsettling about them, their placid animal contentment suddenly alien and incomprehensible.

I left the enclosure and made my way back through the underwater light. I was stopped, though, before I reached the exit—the octopus tank was empty. For a second I experienced a thrill I didn't understand; then I spotted him, compressed in an upper corner of the tank like a partially deflated balloon. One eye was visible. I moved closer, waiting for a sign of recognition—an uncurled tentacle, a shift in the angle of his enormous head. . . .

I remembered that I still had my mask on. I lifted the visor. We looked at each other, or I imagined that we did. He didn't move. Who knows what he was thinking there behind the glass? Who knows if he recognized me as an ally, as a creature like himself?

At the control panel on the wall I entered the code to deactivate the alarms. I raised the lid of Clyde's tank. Took a step back. Waited. Clyde seemed disinclined to leave his spot in the corner, let alone make his escape. Finally I walked to the crab tank, held open the lid, and looked over at Clyde meaningfully. Nothing. Rolling up my sleeve I stood on tiptoe and plunged my arm in. Bubbles shivered across my skin. I felt a shell graze my fingers: it was rough and at the same time lightly slimed, as if coated with a thin gel, and punctuated at the rim with small spikes. . . .

320

The crab's legs scrabbled uselessly as I carried it dripping over to Clyde's tank and held it up for him to see. Clyde stayed where he was, with his single eye regarding me or the dangling crab or possibly the situation as a whole. Surrendering, I lowered the crab into the tank and let go. It wobbled briefly on the water's surface, then a slow, drifting fall, legs still scrabbling. Once it touched sand the crab began shuffling, left, right, trying to get its bearings. A part of me was rooting for it as Clyde softly disengaged, pulsed forward, and spread himself over the moving shape below.

Smear

Brian Evenson

1.

AKSEL COULD SEE a smear, something just inside the vessel's skin. He blinked, rubbed his eyes. It was still there.

"Query," he asked. "What am I seeing?"

The voice responded, *I cannot know what you are seeing. I can only know what you are looking at.*

"All right," he said. "What am I looking at?"

The voice did not respond. Why did the voice not respond? Surely it knew what he meant. And then he remembered.

"*Query*," he said. "What am I looking at?"

The voice responded immediately, *Bulkhead.*

"No," he said. "There's something there, something more."

The voice in his head responded, *Interior of your faceplate.*

"No," he said. "Not that either." He called on the vessel to remove his helmet, which it did by extruding a chrome claw from a bulkhead and plucking it deftly off his head. *Why did it do that?* he wondered. *It could have done it just as easily by deploying a focused magnetic field.* Was the vessel trying to unsettle him?

He looked again. The smear was still there, just in front of the bulkhead, a few inches away from it, over his head, perhaps a meter long, a half meter wide. He reached up and tried to touch it, but, strapped down as he was, couldn't reach. "Query," he repeated. "What am I looking at?"

Bulkhead, the voice insisted.

"No," he said. "Between myself and the bulkhead."

For a long time the voice said nothing. Had he gotten the form wrong? He didn't need to say *query* again, did he? But then, finally, hesitantly, the voice spoke.

Are you looking at the object properly? Is your gaze centered upon it? If your gaze is not centered upon it, you are no longer looking at it, but merely remembering it.

He instructed the vessel to reposition his chair until the smear was centered in his vision. He focused his eyes on it. He held his gaze steady, unblinking.

"Query," he repeated. "What am I looking at?"

Bulkhead, the voice said.

"No," he replied, irritated. "In front of the bulkhead."

There is nothing between your eyes and the bulkhead.

But it was there, he could see it. A smear, semitransparent but certainly present. He was sure he could see it. What was he seeing?

I can tell you what you are looking at, the voice said, unbidden, *but not what you are seeing*. Which made him wonder if the voice had burrowed deeper into his head than he had realized and could hear what he was thinking.

2.

Apart from the vessel, apart from the voice, he had been alone for a very long time. He had been strapped into the vessel and then the vessel had been accelerated to an extraordinary rate, but very gradually, over the course of days, so as not to kill him.

The chair had been made so that he would never have to leave it until he left the vessel for good. The chair was now so integrated with his body that it was hard for him to remember where body stopped and chair began. When he awoke, he felt as if he didn't have a body. It was a tremendous effort to move a digit, let alone a limb.

When he awoke, the vessel displayed on the inside of his faceplate a countdown of the months, days, minutes, and seconds before deceleration would begin.

Off, he whispered, and the vessel reduced the countdown to a red pixel.

Why was he awake? Was he meant to be awake? He was still groggy, still woozy. Maybe he wasn't awake at all but only dreaming. He wasn't meant to be awake in the vessel, ever.

Why am I awake? he whispered, and suddenly there were words in front of his eyes, as if the faceplate had been written on. It was the vessel, responding.

Unexpected failure in storage system, the words read.

What failure? he asked.

Storage system component 3/9aOxV.

Excuse me? he said. Upon which the vessel displayed a series of schematics that made no sense to him at all.

*

So he would remain unstored for the rest of the trip. Would he die? The vessel indicated he would not die: it would feed him intravenously through the chair, converting the molecules of extraneous portions of itself into nourishment. Would he waste away sitting in the chair? The vessel indicated no, that it would continue the stimulation of muscles and nerves that it had been conducting while he was in storage. Which meant that his body was constantly twitching, his muscles bunching and releasing, but that he was not the one doing it. It was being done to him.

He asked the vessel for a distraction. It opened a feed to his faceplate and showed him space around itself, mostly black, a few specks of light. He asked if it couldn't provide music or some sort of teleplay, but as it turned out, no, it couldn't. He was never meant to be awake—nobody was ever meant to be awake on the vessel. The vessel could show him space. The vessel could show him schematics.

Perhaps if he told it stories, he hoped, it could learn to tell them back.

Indeed, it did tell them back: verbatim each time. When instructed to construct its own stories, it offered a mishmash of what he'd already told it, but in a way that made little sense.

And so, instead, he regarded schematics, examined a representation of space on the inside of his faceplate, traced the curve of the bulkhead with his eyes. He slept, woke, slept. He never ate, but, fed intravenously, was never hungry. At least not at first. He watched his body grow lean, hardly an ounce of fat left. His suit draped loosely on him.

Are you sure I'm being fed enough to survive? he asked.

Technically speaking, the vessel responded, *you are being fed enough to survive.*

The voice manifested after several weeks of being awake, alone. At first, he sensed it more than heard it, had a strange inkling that something was there, speaking to him—or, rather, trying to speak to him. Was it the vessel? At first he thought, yes, it was the vessel. But they didn't talk quite alike. And when he asked the vessel about the voice, it seemed baffled.

For some time—days, even weeks—he just listened. He taught himself to filter out the noise of the vessel around him and just wait, listen. It was as if the voice was there, slightly beyond a frequency he could hear, making his eardrums throb slightly but not in a way that conveyed sense. He spoke to it, tried to coax it to speak back until, suddenly, to his surprise, it did.

It had rules, formulae that must be followed, patterns of speech it seemed prone to respond to. He had stumbled onto them only slowly and gradually. It would not always tell him what he wanted to know. There was still much he didn't know.

3.

Vessel, he whispered, *please replace my helmet.*

The same chrome claw on a long pale arm plucked the helmet from the floor with surprising delicacy and pushed it back onto his head. When it was affixed, he looked again for the smear through the faceplate. It was still there, still visible. It didn't matter what the voice claimed.

He asked the vessel about the smear.

There is nothing there, the voice said again, despite his not following discourse protocol. *I already told you.*

"I wasn't speaking to you," Aksel said. "I was speaking to the vessel."

But the vessel did not respond. The faceplate in front of his eyes remained blank.

"Have you disabled my interface?" he asked.

There was no response, either from vessel or from voice.

"Query, have you disabled my interface?" he asked.

Query, the voice responded. *What is an interface?*

Interface, interface. What an odd word, he told himself. *Intraface* would mean inside the face, within the face, which made sense. But *interface* would mean between the face. What did that even mean: between the face?

"Query," he began, but the voice immediately cut him off. *Don't ask*, it said.

It had a tone now . . . did it have a tone? Had it had that mocking tone before? What was the voice? What did it have to do with him? Why was he willing to listen to it? Why hadn't he panicked?

But no matter how he tried to work himself up he couldn't bring himself to panic. Maybe the voice was doing that to him too.

*

His arm was little more than a stick wrapped in skin. Looking at it, it didn't look like an arm that could possibly belong to him. In fact, the more he looked at it, the less it looked like an arm at all.

But when had he taken his suit off? Why was he looking at a bare arm at all? And why, if he wasn't wearing his suit, was he wearing his helmet?

Or wait. *Was* he wearing his helmet?

His gaze slowly slid to the smear then slid away. If he looked at it out of the corner of his eye, it almost made sense, almost looked familiar. He tried to look at it and not look at it at the same time, but, like the voice had been at first, it felt like he could almost sense something but not quite. As if whatever it was was impinging on this world by accident, was only being seen because of an anomaly.

What if that anomaly is me? he wondered.

Or was that the voice wondering it?

Perhaps, if he got closer. Perhaps, if he regarded it from one side, at an oblique angle.

Vessel, he whispered, *move the chair forward.*

But the chair didn't move. The vessel was paying him no heed. Perhaps, as with the smear, it no longer realized he was there.

He kept looking, kept staring. Part of him felt the smear was staring back. Watching him. Was it staring back? No. It was just a smear, a smear couldn't stare.

If he could only get closer, move a little nearer, then he'd see it clearly, he was sure. Almost sure.

Time went by. Years maybe, or what felt like years. When he regarded his arm again, it still didn't look like an arm. When he lifted the claw on the end of it and touched the release and kept pushing until the belts restraining him actually parted, it looked even less like an arm.

It took immense effort to free himself from the chair. And more effort still to crawl across the deck. Still more to turn and look upward, to regard the smear.

326

Was it still there? Yes, it was still there, but differently distended from this angle. It was, almost, a face. It was, almost, a human face. He crawled a little closer, looked up again. Still smeared, still distorted, but anamorphically transformed. Yes, a face. Maybe. He crawled until his head was touching the skin of the bulkhead and then looked up again. Yes, a face, a face very much like his own—his own face in fact. He stared into it, filled with wonder.

After a moment the face smiled, tightly, in a way that bared its teeth.

Or would have bared them if what was inside the mouth was teeth.

4.

They scanned the small craft. Nothing harmful detected, no extraordinary presences, nothing to give pause. Out of caution they kept the craft quarantined, alone at its dock, for several weeks, before finally sending a team in.

The man was out of his chair, eyes wide open, staring up at the upper portion of the vessel's bulkhead. He had been torn free of the chair and his legs were tangled with a snarl of tubes and wires, many of which were still attached to his body. A discolored spill of dried fluid spread in a trail behind him. His neck was bent impossibly upward, his body desiccated and bloodless.

"Where's his suit?" asked one of the technicians.

The other shrugged. "I don't know," he said.

"What's with his arm?"

"Arm?" said the other. "Is that what that is?"

It was contorted, and little more than bone. He reached out and pushed down on the arm with his boot. The body yawed to one side, hollow or nearly so. When he drew his boot back, the body rocked back and forth, slowly settling onto the floor.

He grunted. "What do we do with him?"

"Incinerate him," said the other.

"And the craft?"

There was a long moment before the other responded. "No reason to destroy that," he finally said. "We can salvage it."

But he wasn't looking at the other technician as he said it. Instead, he seemed to be looking at a spot high up the bulkhead, near the curve where wall became ceiling. He took a step forward and reached his hand out through the air, as if to touch something. Then he drew back and stared at his gloved hand.

"What is it?" asked the other.

"Nothing," he said, confused. "I thought I saw something. My . . . faceplate must be dirty."

The other nodded. He started for the air lock. When he realized the first wasn't following, he stopped, looked back.

"Coming?" he asked.

"Just a moment," said the first. He had pulled one arm from its sleeve and back into his suit and now had it pressed between the suit and his chest. He worked the fingers up past where the suit joined the helmet, trying to rub at the faceplate from the inside.

"Come on," the other pressed.

"You go ahead," the first managed to say. "I'll follow you out in just a moment."

All alone, he just stood there, hand caught between his throat and the rim of the helmet, waiting. He had seen something, he was sure. Or almost. A swath, a fluttering, something almost visible.

What was it? he wondered.

Or not quite that: *Query: what was it?* he wondered. Yes, that was what the thought had been. What a strange way to think.

He wriggled his fingers, swallowed.

Four Atomic Poems
Jessica R*eed*

EXOTIC ATOMS AND THE VISIBLE WORLD

Magnify the world's snowy blue-cast
physicality, its forms
    and the blankness beneath.
Here is hydrogen: one electron orbits one proton.
    Made exotic, muon
            displaces electron.
The lone proton will not stay so.

Atoms are strange enough, though, taste
of honeysuckle, vaguely sweet,
    barely there,
the reason you are here.
    Now altered, they embody
          metaphor: an electron is
(like) a pion. Electrons are

unlike cathedrals, dominoes, chess pieces—
Consider the frame
    around the photograph
of a painting of a woman
    posing as something else.
          Massive orbital particles
alter orbits, negative pieces drawn in

toward the center. Some even lie
within the nucleus. Daisies,
    petals the color of snow,
and dark blue Baptisia blossoms
    in series in June's sun, the same colors
          as a bare winter place,
the same divisions of white light.

I only want to say one true thing
(belief in a literal language).
These atoms we have built,
with their cinching atomic radii,
        parade our questions about those
                whose architecture
we can only probe.

LITTLE ROOM IN THE MIND

Here, the peach tree whose branches bend
under peach weight. Someone is in love
with counting. Someone sorts. *Same, same.*
Yellow is the bullet; yellow is the wave.
Scattering events, decays, bound states—
someone probes less directly (*they're just
too small*). What is kept there. Someone
finds what is red in it from a breeze.
And then, yellow tearing itself off,
as the seams of these peaches.
Here, such a thing as a massless particle.
Such a thing as an absence that feeds
on matter and light. Mud, cloud obey.

It is a mind that imagines a potential well.
It is a mind that thinks in positions under a curve.
Chambers—cloud and spark and bubble—
chasing a fine yellow thread of evidence. An absence
creates galactic arms. What is apparent: a quickening.
Nautilus driving itself backward—these are the reefs
it encounters. This yellow comes boiling off. A peach
bullet. Peach ballet. You are someone.
Your mind feeds. Red cheeks, there.

THE DISTORTION OF SPACETIME

Hypothetical sky, black-airless and grid-tugging.
Gravitational field equations, solutions, as language
spins on its axis. Sky becomes substance. Another
is added to (pennies, stripes) the ingredients of the real.
But a city of unpenetrable objects, a subatomic realm,

built this moment, defies the familiar. Chalk dust of fugues,
dismantling. Units of meaning—notes, rests, notes—
topple. So, you want to make figures of the lights
that come to you? The mathematical solution cinches
our idea of the world to the world.

A WORLD MADE BY ATOMES

Of Aiery Atomes

In 1653, Margaret Cavendish, Duchess of Newcastle-upon-Tyne, published
in *Poems and Fancies* a series of poems about atoms, just three years after
Lucy Hutchinson's verse translation of Lucretius's *On the Nature of
Things*, the earliest English version of the world's first book-length poem
on the subject. Atoms in this era were still hypothetical objects rather than
investigable matter, and would remain so for another two centuries.

Of Aiery Atomes

Hydrogen, loosed upon the cosmos.
Wind, menace of air, furious invisible
mass: there are some bodies
eyes cannot discern. Galactic clusters:
bees swarming on trunks of invisible trees.
Light matter and dark matter: *we worshipped,
we parted green from green.*[1]

---

[1]H.D., "The Helmsman," *Sea Garden*.

Jessica Reed

The weight and bignesse of Atomes

In Cavendish's poems, the world consists of four "figures" of atoms: *Long, Round, Sharpe,* and *Flat* (or *Square*). These figures, joined in several ways, create the fabric of the world. The "loosest atoms lye" in vegetables, whereas in minerals they are "hard wedg'd in." In every brain, loose sharp atoms lie, and from those, she explains, "Fancies flye."

The weight and bignesse of Atomes

Atom to atom compared,
a radius: (the slope between tall and tall)
acres of hard horizon, yellow bodies,
distance to a boundary (electron) cloud.
What petals into the impatient blue,
what unseen elements knock about?
A god, a dimensionless quantity,
a granular number behind all things,
sculpting its windblown configurations of snow.

All things last, or dissolve, according to the Composure of Atomes

Cavendish's footnotes: *These Atomes are halfe aiery Atomes, and halfe Fiery. *Unless there be Infinities of Worlds; then there may be infinities of Centers, although not a Center in Infiniteies. *The severall Elements are all but one matter. *They are stinted according to the severall strengths of their motion. They trune as they go. A jack Bowle is the marke.* (The Duchess said it was "against nature for a woman to spell right.")

All things last, or dissolve, according to the Composure of Atomes

Quickly, then, for they will fly away:
looseness somewhere.
Causality, iron-black nails pinned
to possible worlds. Actuality an indexical,
like *here and now*
          (world in which the utterer resides).

Jessica Reed

Of Loose Atomes

"[B]y the standards of any era, seventeenth-century arguments for and observations cited in favour of corpuscularianism were inconclusive, and [. . .] its reappearance [. . .] had as much to do with the charm of Lucretius'[s] presentation, and its appeal to the senses and imagination, as it did with argument, observation, and evidence."[2]

Cavendish's atoms made more than hunks of inanimate matter. Atoms made heat and cold. Atoms made the sun, and the sea, go round. Atoms made life, wit, understanding, and dispositions; they made sickness, health, peace, and war.

Of Loose Atomes

A "screw loose" somewhere.
Rough picture, less of a departure
from actuality. What *is* the nearest world?
The one in which kangaroos have no tails
is not one in which there are tail trails in the sand,
or tail shadows, but no tails.

What Atomes make Flame

Flames consist
of carbon dioxide, water vapor, oxygen, and nitrogen.
I am made of all this, and a glass cloche.

Of Fire in the Flint

A hard form of mineral quartz, when struck
against steel, will spark. Flint edge shaves off
a particle of steel (where, the composition
that does not unravel?), exposing
iron. The tongue, a wheel.[3] Oxygen, react.

---

[2]C. Meinel is credited with this viewpoint in Johnson, Monte and Wilson, Catherine, "Lucretius and the history of science" from *The Cambridge Companion to Lucretius*, ed. Stuart Gillespie and Philip Hardie (Cambridge University Press, 2007).
[3]Cavendish wrote a poem entitled "Comparing the Tongue to a Wheele."

Jessica Reed

What Atomes make Fire to burne, and what Flame

Fossil of fire appears 470 million years ago,
when land-based flora oxygen flooded the atmosphere.
(There is this dark void,
beside which the universe creates itself,
broken by blue and after-blue.)

Of the Sympathy of Atomes

Life only exists as long as atoms are in motion. When Atomes and Motion
fall out, great disorder reigns: earthquakes, thunder, winds. . . .

Of the Sympathy of their Figures

A winter bird balances
on top of my blue spruce.
Pierced as the dive of ice, a separate sky.
There is only a paper grid, drawn by hand.

All things are govern'd by Atomes

Suppose night is only black shutters,
painted so that steel wool could eventually
remove black *and* shutter: that is the physicist's
work. Then the material blue.
Accounted for.

All things are govern'd by Atomes

Some thirteen years after her atomic poems, Cavendish writes in
Observations upon Experimental Philosophy that atoms and a vacuum
(always posited so that atoms could move) were "impossible" in nature:
parts would never join across the gaps; a "piece of the world would become
a singular particular world, not joining to any part besides itself."

Motion directs, while Atomes dance

A kind of backwardness.

Motion directs, while Atomes dance

Each gesture makes a quick exit.
We agree. Until we must unpack it,
knotholes letting in light,
and find we agree on nothing.
Objectivity, our brilliant notion.

Of the Center

In *Observations*, between sections discussing whether fishes can live in
frozen water and whether celestial parts of the world can be alterable,
between sections titled "Of the Pores of a Charcoal, and of Emptiness,"
and "Of the Spleen," Cavendish finally declares that atoms are "fitter
for a poetical fancy, than for serious philosophy."

Of the Center

Suppose what I see out my window is the center
of the universe entire. Stare at the nucleus of our world
through thin air—mind of god. *All things are thinned.*[4]

In the Center Atomes never Separate

Bound together, conscious of self and other.
Buds clinging to a bare branch.

---

[4]Ronald Melville's verse translation of Lucretius.

Jessica Reed

The Infinites of Matter

Ambiguity as to whether Cavendish meant
"infinites" or "infinities,"
     (little particles, little forevers)
or, as it was spelled once
in her manuscript: "Infiniteies."
The genesis of an object from one moment
to the next:
               conjecture, sensed relation,
light moving along an inner dark dome.

Radio City
E. G. *Willy*

"My name's Lollipop. And I'm hot, radio hot. Not hot like you think. Not a girl in a mini. Not a muscle guy with no shirt. No shots on the beach. No steaming sexy hot. I'm the new hot. The hot everyone's talking about. The dark hot. Like record levels of cesium-137 hot. I mean off the charts, gem. You run a counter over me it will bark and scream like a dog on fire. Snazzle dazzle, snazzle dazzle, rip and roar. It goes like this: *kek kek kek kek . . . shshshsh . . . kek kek . . . thika thicka thick*. See what I mean? Friggin' hot. Dead hot. Touch me, you will die."

My audience is across from me as I say this. His name is Princess. I have my hand out, challenge him to take it. My death-ridden hand, my fingers of radio death. He takes it, shakes firmly, then snaps his fingers, a message to go on, that he's cool with my hotness.

"First day out of the zone I knew it," I say. "You didn't need meters to read me. I had it written all over me. People like me are full of understanding. We get it. Like, I saw the Van Breugel 6 pollinator drones lying by the melt this morning, busted and dead from the pulse, more radiation around them than in their ephemeral polymer hides, I saw the situation like it was. You're raised in a disaster zone, you got only two ways to go. Life or death. Death or life. You see both sides. That's the nature of disaster zones. They are perfect and ugly all at once. Good luck. Good night. Jesus, you're on your own. You and old man Darwin. It ain't survival of the fittest but survival of the tweakiest. You don't like it? Oh well. You're at least alive. No one comes in to rescue you. No one sends food or fresh water. Oh yeah, they say they will but when your disaster comes, you'll see. Ain't no governments going in there. Ain't no safety nets. Sixty million people in trouble, they're too worried about their own sick selves. And the Army? No way. Those guys are all vomiting blood, swallowing the latest pharma and gobbling iodine and bentonite clay. Dipshit faith believers in broken dreams."

I pause, hold up a cigarette, wait for his reaction. Princess looks at me like he's heard it before. He probably has. I don't care. I got to sling this pitch anyway, second generation like I am. This is my standard lonely guy speech. I don't use it much unless I really have to, you know, just when I'm desperate to talk to someone, when I can't stand another minute of being alone with myself. Which is right now.

He pulls out a fresh cigarette, blows the steam off his latte, nods. "Yeah, well," he says.

It's what I expect from a semi-hot low-end pretender. At least he could show me a little respect. I wish low-enders would at least do that. None of them ever understand, not ever. I go on anyway, say, "Gem, there are things in me never seen before in the human genome."

"Yeah," he says.

"I mean it. You can't get me."

"Sounds familiar," says Princess. "No offense, but you see what I mean."

"Please, gem. I'm a real wonder, the original dangerous pirate material prototype survivor of the nano-chemo generation. Here look." I pull up my shirt, show my white flesh. "Check that shit out. Wonder how I got that? Nothing to mess it up either. No pre-albinism, no twisted hormones making me all disfigured, no perforated organs, no Kaposi, nothing. I haven't even been chipped because I'm too hot for it. Nor biometricked either. Nor was I ever GMed, not ever. It won't last. I'll burn it off I'm that tough. Freaky sure, but serious out there kickass. And I may look ugly . . ." I pull my shirt higher, show my cut (I got nobby old shoulders, magnesium skin, hotdog red hair). "But I can roll with the hardest. I can go anywhere. I can eat anything. Take a fish screaming hot with iodine-131 at five million times your New American Standard, I will grill it, fry it, poach it, gourmet myself in it. And it will be delicious and tasty sweet, I tell you. I won't feel a thing, not even a belly ache. They haven't seen anything like me yet. Everyone before me has come up short. Just pretenders. They die early. Anemia. Necrosis of the jaw. Acute myeloid leukemia. Papillary thyroid cancer. Nothing to lose. Just goddamned life itself. See what I'm saying?"

"Who says you're that hot?" wonders Princess. "Your mommy?"

"Me."

"OK, sure."

I light a fresh cigarette, say through the smoke, "You're not bounty hunting are you?"

"What?" asks Princess, surprised. "Hell no."

"No skin off my ass, but I know how this is. You act bored, like you don't care, maybe you got a plan. Like, you expropriate me, I will fry the meters. Get it, gem?"

Princess nods. "Yeah. You need to ask. I don't blame you."

So maybe he is a bounty hunter and he's hiding in the lie that he isn't. I've seen that before. Low-end shithead trying to make a step up in the world, get close to the GMers. I know I should stop here, keep my big mouth shut. But I have this stupid need to impress him, to show what a tough guy I am because he's sitting there like a fat turd on wet ground. "My dad was radio hot," I press on. "So was my mom. And they were expropriated when I was like twelve. So I get the game, gem. Someone heard they had a viable hope and folks came along with guns and hazard suits and took them away. Left me alone in the way deep. I got to throw that out and ask you one last time, you work for someone?"

"No."

"Good to know."

"When did they come after your folks?" asks Princess, sucking on his smoke, almost interested.

"I was like twelve."

"Yeah. I see it."

"But I adjusted just fine."

"I been there. You don't have to explain. We got more up here," announces Princess. "Just don't turn around. Wait. You engage, they get tweaky. Like, they don't need encouragement."

I turn around anyway. I vibe the parade. They're carrying skateboards and torn up old daypacks, walking quick, skinny like Princess, making noise like they don't care if someone's listening or not. Anyone can see they're damaged material, busted and strong all at once like the crazy burner folks down by the melt. The old diseases re-erupting. Polio. Measles. Smallpox. They said they were hidden but nothing ever stays hidden. But I don't care. I'm radio hot. I'm used to scum. They're the only ones who will ever talk to me. Dirt and garbage and trash in them like me.

"Yo, Princess, you seen Fat Freddy?" calls Syrup, the first to arrive.

Princess says, "No," loudly, his back still turned.

Syrup stops, then takes a step towards him. She's got a dirty green shirt on that shows off just a little bit of what she's got. It's not much but it looks flash when she lifts up her arm. She's wearing a pair of broken Panama Jack iGlasses that are so obviously broken that it's cool. Like she's pretending to be GM but not and therefore more GM than you can think. You can tell she's overexposed by the patches of radiation epilation in her hair, white on chestnut red. Not anywhere near my levels, but good enough.

"What's wrong?" asks Syrup.

Princess calls over his shoulder, "That big fat pervert is sick."

"He's sick?" wonders Syrup.

"Yeah, he ain't getting up for nothing."

"Well damn and hell," says Syrup.

Princess says, "This is Lollipop. Before you ask, we're not poaching him or turning him out."

And they all say, "No way."

We get into explaining my name, how I am white skinned and red haired like a cherry sucker. And Syrup says, "That shit's cute."

The way she says it, I kind of get a thrill from it, not like I got a thing for her, you know, not like how it was with my old ex Bernadette. I can tell she's just comfortable to know, what with her dirty shirt and all.

So Syrup introduces me to the crew: Jeezer, Skippy, Dog Girl, Little Bip, and Flower. They look OK, but Jeezer, I can see he's hardcore diseased and will go soon. Sixteen but he looks almost fifty. He won't look me in the eye for nothing because he is worried about this. I don't care. He'll be dead soon. So I don't look him back. Why make problems? Then there's Dog Girl. Princess tells me she goes doggy for anyone in a car. This because she needs money and likes it. Dog Girl nods when he says this. I don't explore it any deeper. I've seen her type before. Syrup explains Little Bip, ninja verified casualty, one hundred percent twister, only like twelve years old. He's a thief and a pain specialist, they say. You can beat him silly and he won't feel it. Next is Flower, ugly redhead like me, all scratched up and torn, dirty old clothes, nasty old arsenic teeth. The crew.

We start shooting the shit right out there by the melt, you know, hanging. I feel out of place with the clothes I have on. I'm all Diablo Canyon red, and they're all black, black, black. But they don't seem to notice nor even really care. And the sand's blowing around. And the sun is shining.

So we smoke a couple of cigarettes, check out the melt. It's calm today and only a little bit choppy. Birds fly in and out of the tide. Just one drone out there still, buzzing and chirping, trying to hang on to GM vision, goddamned pre-melt ideal bullshit. Jeezer scowls when he sees me smoking my second cigarette, shows his sixteen-fifty-year-old teeth, "Yo, little mini bop, what you bringing to the table? We share here. We're family."

I pull out some more peanuts from my bag. And Little Bip rides off somewhere on his cruiser and comes back with some beer.

Syrup says, "You sure that big fat moron Freddy is sick?"

"You can check on him if you want," goes Princess. "He looks like three-day-old dogshit."

And Flower is all, "Screw that guy."

Then Jeezer goes, "I ought to piss on him."

Flower says, "I already did."

Everyone laughs, me too, though I don't really think it's that great of a joke. I'm just laughing because the day is almost clean and I guess I'm kind of desperate to keep these new friends for at least a couple days without having to return to silence. And I appreciate how they're being nice to me, making me feel like one of them. I need to talk. I need this. It's lonely in the zone. Terrible distant.

I glance out at the melt. It's getting dark. Princess says, "It's scatter time."

Jeezer says, "Amen, brother."

Syrup pulls out a pipe. And pretty soon we're all blowing scatter. I'm not a scatterhead. But I do it to show I'm cool. It goes right in like a glass of water. And now I'm laughing like every couple of seconds.

Syrup says, "Bip, put on that sick, sick old school music you been carrying."

Little Bip has a ghetto blaster that looks a hundred years old. He puts on a pre-melt band called the Acid Surfers. I haven't ever heard anything like that before, all crazy guitars like the dudes were wired for twister. And the whole crew starts doing a scatter dance, jumping up and down and saying the same thing over and over again, shouting. Words I don't know but they sound good. I don't know what to do. I just sit there with my mouth open.

Princess goes, "Watch this gem dance."

He starts stomping around the ghetto blaster like he's climbing a mountain of imaginary sand. The crew huddles around the box, grinding and twisting. If you get anywhere close to Jeezer, he pops you one like he's down in the pit, roughing it up with a load of GMers. It's great sightseeing the crew dance. They look like heavenly ghosts, fatal white, like twig insects snapping in a cool night, like they're already dead a thousand years. Especially Flower. She has on these big old stompers six sizes too big. They make her legs look like two stretches of fine leather. She pulls off her dirty old jacket, showing all kinds of flesh, white as cream, whiter than me even, but mottled bad like someone's been whacking her with a garden hose. She looks

341

E. G. Willy

wicked sick, her cigarette shooting out of her mouth like a hook.

We smoke more scatter. Except for Flower. She shoots a clothes hanger full of it. Does it pretty good in the moonlight too, though she complains a lot. Her face becomes smooth as water, like someone has taken all her pain away, though you can see the knot of chalk working on her insides, burning her up inside. Jeezer, he puts his arm around her to show he really cares and all but he's just hanging on, hoping maybe Flower will lend him her shooting kit.

Syrup says, "Let's light a fire on account that big fat moron Freddy ain't around."

Princess goes, "Let's light one up for our new friend, Lollipop."

And everyone says all together, "Yeah, a fire for Lollipop."

We gather wood and paper and light a fire on the shore of the melt. Princess gets the idea that we need more wood. I run amongst the broken houses, scrapping wood, building the fire so high that it gets bigger and bigger and bigger, burning red yellow hot, tossing out all kinds of sparks. Pretty soon the whole crew has gone fire bug. And everyone's screaming and shouting. I'm shouting the loudest, saying, "Hell yeah!" over and over like a thousand million times.

And then the sirens. When I look up on the headlands, I see they have like six or seven cop cars up there. There is a second drone hovering in the air above, whirring and clacking, cranking its old polymer wings. A Van Breugel Terminator, armed with air-to-ground ricin flechettes, one of the few that made it past the pulse, still going after all these years.

Princess shouts, "Run for your lives!"

We go running down the melt, howling like cats, knowing if we go far enough they won't come down on us. Because, gem, cops hate to run. They are passing too like the rest of us. No perfect GM amongst them except at the top. Besides, even this group is radio, so the cops won't try more than they have to. And the Van Breugel won't arm. It's too dangerous for the cops to think about using it.

I run the fastest down the melt, my feet going *kish, kish, kish* in the sand. I'm all "Fuck yeah! Fuck yeah! Fuck yeah!" shouting right up to the sky. That old Van Breugel Terminator drone is nowhere around. Probably off tracking no one to nowhere. I feel more alive than I have ever felt in my life. Like I'm a mile above the ground, flying, looking down on the world. When I turn to see if anyone is following, I see I'm alone.

I go back up to the park and see someone's jacked my stuff. I don't care. I've been here before. You take from me, I just take more from

342

you later on. Alone again. Shit, the story of my life. So I check the melt. The waves are coming in roller slow. You can see all kinds of drunks and drifters crawling amongst the buildings. It's like the waves are tossing them up, pulling their shaggy forms out of the sea. I can smell the creosote coming off the pilings on the pier, the rot of a thousand sardines taken by domoic acid. Wrong place, wrong tide. It's a warm night despite the fog, perfect right. Someone out on the beach is singing over the rollers. A woman or a guy with a high voice. By the tone of the voice I know they'll die soon, are calling out to the melt, wishing they could stop things. After that I guess I blink. When I look up it's around midnight. The rain's coming down. It's going *tink, tink, tink* on my forehead. I blink again and it's four. There's a purple blue glow in the night sky.

So I walk down the melt, climb up on the roof of the Surfari Motel. It's quiet calm up there, still warm on the tar room. I wait, listen to the night, the waves breaking.

I wake up and see this dude standing over me, his big old belly blotching out the sun like a nuclear bomb and I figure, you know, like he's the building manager. You can see the vibe: he's the little-minded kind, how every moment of every day is connected to his big, fat gut, which is connected to paychecks, pizza, beer, porn, and poker. And the way he's staring down at me through his Bausch & Lomb Pure Vision Processors, giving me the YOU ARE THE MOST MEANINGLESS PIECE OF TURD ON THE EARTH eye, I see perfect straight that I have been tumbled by the mega-GM-shithead. So I'm all, "Sorry, mister, we just came up here and fell asleep, me and my buddies from the troop. See, we're Boy Scouts, here for the weekend. We didn't mean any harm. We'll get off your roof right away."

The big nuclear bomb looks around, sees no one else but me, says, "What troop is that?"

"Fifteen, twenty-six," I roll off like I've already said it fifty million times before.

"Oh, really? Fifteen, twenty-six?"

"Yep. Salinas."

"That so? I never heard of that troop, sport. Boy Scout troops usually only have two or three numbers. But maybe they got new numbers. Or maybe you're making that part up just like a second ago when you mentioned you weren't alone."

I digest that the fat guy has more brains than I've allowed. He's probably seen a hundred punks like me sleeping on his roof. I'm like, "Sorry, dude. I ain't with the Boy Scouts. I just needed a place to rest.

You know, ever since my folks passed away. I can understand if you want to call the cops or something. I mean, I didn't want to upset anyone. I'll be moving right out of here."

Mega-GM thinks on this for a moment, then he goes, "Sport, I ain't who you think I am."

He doesn't have to say it again. I mean, I probably knew who it was at first glance, like exactly when I opened my eyes. But sometimes your head lies to you, tells you things you want to hear. I cut right to the play. I'm all, "You're Fat Freddy."

"Good guess," says Fat Freddy.

"What you want?"

He goes, "Princess sent me up here to get you."

"Why isn't he here?" I ask.

Fat Freddy says, "Sport, he's down at the car. Says he needs to talk to you."

I'm like, "How come he can't come up?"

Fat Freddy nods, says, "Come on over here and I'll show you."

I follow that fat jerk to the edge of the roof.

"Down there, sport," says Freddy pointing with his lip to a junky old van he's got parked half up on the curve. You can hear all kinds of dogs barking in there. "He's watching my dogs."

"How come I can't see him?" I ask.

"Because we're up here. He's down there."

We go down to the van. Princess is sitting in the passenger's seat, smoking a cigarette, all calm like, you know, swishing the smoke around his face. He's got on a pair of Ray-Bans. I can see the processors blinking on the lenses. And he's like, "Hey gem, sorry to wake you up like this."

I shrug, ask, "Dude, what's up?"

Princess takes about ten seconds before he answers. "Well, remember that fire we had the other night?"

"Yeah?"

"It's . . . uh . . . kind of hard to explain without getting technical. But you messed Jeezer up," says Princess.

"Really?"

Princess takes a drag on his cigarette, blows out the smoke, says, "Well, what do you think about that?"

"About what?"

Princess nods, says, "Don't you think you kind of owe me for it?"

"Owe for what?"

"Well, like for our medical bills. The scatter and all. And the cops, what they did to Jeezer." He kind of half winces, like all of a sudden he's not up for what's coming. His hands are trembling. His face is getting all blue. Then his voice goes up an octave. "Well, you know we're crew and all. The crew helps out the crew. Rule of the street."

Fat Freddy says, "Yeah, that's just what I was saying on the way over. Ain't that right, Princess?"

"Yeah," he squeaks. "Crew helps crew."

"I'm not on Jeezer's crew, Princess," I say. "I've never been on Jeezer's crew, not in a million light years."

"That's just what Princess said you would say," goes Fat Freddy. "Like you think you're not responsible."

I say, "Take your hands off me, asshole."

Fat Freddy says, "Show some manners, little radio."

I'm all, "Don't touch me."

He's all, "Trust me, you'll know when I'll be touching you." And that fat asshole is lifting my shirt, checking out my skin.

"Don't touch me," I repeat.

"What's this? You got melanoma burns?" asks Fat Freddy, surprised. "Wow, what gives, Princess? I thought you said he was clean."

Princess is like, "No, Freddy, that's just the cigarettes I was telling you about. See how he's healing already?"

Fat Freddy smiles, says, "I guess it's true how they say you're the shit, ain't it? A regular treasure."

Next thing I know I'm like hanging off him. Fat Freddy is a strong dude for being big and fat and useless.

He's all, "Don't get me started, sport."

I'm like, "Fuck you, asshole."

He leans in close, his corny breath blowing over me. "I suggest you change your attitude. I know some people who'd love to meet you. How's that sound? I sell you piece by piece."

And then that cank grinds his thumb into my armpit, right through my jacket, squibbing a nerve I never knew I had.

I spit in his fat face, say, "This how you do it? Overpower little boys then bounty them out?"

Fat Freddy squeezes even tighter, then says, "You probably figure I ain't a cop or Army, so no chance of expropriation. But I got buys lined up. Merck. Phillips. Not just Europe. There are folks in Saigon and Buenos Aires bidding on you right now. Sport, you were parted out days ago. You're just too stupid to realize it."

Fat Freddy pulls a counter from his pocket, flips it on. It starts crackling, then crying like a baby. "Oh Jesus, do you see that?" asks Fat Freddy. "Hotter than we thought."

"Yeah, like I told you," replies Princess.

Next Fat Freddy has my mouth pried open, is looking at my teeth and gums. "Lord, this is exceptional," he says.

The lenses of his Bausch & Lombs are glowing. I don't have to be told there are bidders in many cities seeing what he is seeing. I can hear their voices whispering into his iGlasses. Fat Freddy's saying, "Yep, yep, this one's a viable. A damned treasure. Those previous radios couldn't even approximate. Good job, Princess. Well done."

I'm about to shout out, you know, in case someone is walking by and noticing this weird shit going down. But I look around and see no one's anywhere near. So I kick that fat cank right in the crotch. But my foot misses and I just hit slippery old fat dude flesh.

Next thing, he's lifting me like a foot off the ground, saying, "I got so much more you can't even guess. I suggest you stop fighting and learn to take it."

So I kick again. And that cank slams my head against the van. It's not much of a shot. Not so much pain as anguish to it. But the door goes *boom, boom, boom*. And he opens up the van, and I feel this hollow old drift of dread come welling up. For a second I think I'm fainting or maybe going somewhere real quick. I gasp, close my eyes, take another breath, make sure I'm not dreaming all this. When I open my eyes, there are like six dogs in there. A couple are barking. The others are huddled up, shivering, licking themselves, flashing their grills like they're about to get shines. One is puppy fresh, this white patch of goop over one eyeball like he's been poked something horrible. Bounty dogs. They can tell Radio City hot from a mile away. They're chained together by this long old cable that wraps right round the inside of that van. And everything smells of danky old dog shit, dog food, dog piss, and dog breath. A few generations of dogs have gone through that van by how worn that cable is. It goes right up to the back of the passenger seat. That's where Princess's left hand is, lashed a couple times with cables, padlocked, hooked right up with the dogs like he's a canine captive himself. I look at Princess. The spark's almost like crying. He's saying, "Come on, Lollipop, don't make this hard." But I'm not scared. Maybe freaked and sketching. But not scared. It's like all of a quick sudden I'm seeing things clear as corn syrup. I have like super vision. And when Fat Freddy pulls me off the door and sets up to toss me in the back of the van, it's like the GMer was doing me a favor. I pull rapid quick that extra-large standard screwdriver I'm holding in my back pocket, the one I use for such instances, and I make the first sticky plunge into Fat Freddy's lard ass back. I twirl that skiv around like I'm mixing cake. I'm like, "Fuck you, you big asshole."

It doesn't hurt Fat Freddy as much as I think. He just sets me down quietly, touches the hole I've pierced in his side, and says, "What the hell?"

So I strike again and scud that screwdriver home into his thigh. It slips in crazy quick like it almost knows where to go, then catches on the bone. Right like that Fat Freddy is dancing around like a snake on a wire, shouting, saying, "You little fucking bastard, you fucking prick!"

I vibe a moment on striking that spark a third time, but there isn't any way I'm getting that screwdriver from his leg, the way he's hopping about. So I'm good I should leave it there, seeing as he's not coming back on me anytime soon.

Princess says, "Kick him in the head."

So I kick that spark in the head. Problem is, I'm only about a fifth his size. And my rubber All-Stars just bounce right off his temple. I think maybe I should kick his arms out while he's propping himself up. But I don't got time to think about this because Princess goes, "Yo, let's boost the van."

I skip around Fat Freddy. He makes a grab at me. Somehow I kick him hard enough so his hand is pancaked between my foot and his face. It makes a nice splatting sound. He rolls over and slips on his side and jabs that screwdriver in deeper all on his own. He lets out a wail to wake the departed. And damned if I don't feel this great shock of energy coming into me. Like I'm getting all juiced up on seeing that spark go down. It was like a thousand million volts were zipping through my veins. And I'm clear and popping free.

Princess is saying, "Come on, gem, we're rolling."

I lean into the van, looking for something to get Princess free. I'm all, "Where's the key?"

"Freddy's got them."

Maybe he's down but he's not gonna let me come in twice. So I start yanking on the cables, seeing if I can bust them from the walls. But that's a bad idea, seeing as it's connected to Princess's wrist and all those dogs. They start yelping, and Princess, he's screaming. And I'm all, "What the hell!"

Princess says, "Ah fuck."

I look up and see Jeezer and Flower coming down the street. Jeezer's face is all crusty and stitched up. And you can see it's swollen as hell. His front teeth are broken stubs. And he's got a line on his scalp where they shaved his head. Flower's standing behind him. She doesn't look so hot in the light of day, her oversized stompers all dirty and greased up, scary as ever. Jeezer, he waves a tire iron in the air, whistles through his busted mouth, saying, "Bounty time."

I turn around and run behind the van towards Fat Freddy. The bounty hunter's already up. He's got that driver sticking out of his leg and he's coming at me sideways. No way I can take Jeezer and Flower and Fat Freddy, no matter what those thousand million volts jizzing through my veins are telling me. So I run back around the van. Jeezer, he's running up alongside, and he makes a swipe with his tire iron. I juke and float by like he's nothing. And then I'm in the driver's seat. Jeezer is pounding the side of the vic with the tire iron, breaking things. The motor spins. The transmission clunks. And we're down the street, driving. The street rushes under us like water. And we're gone daddy gone.

"Give me the iGlasses," I tell Princess as we roll along the edge of the melt.

He takes off the Ray-Bans, hands them over. The lenses are still lit. I briefly catch a glimpse of Fat Freddy's face in the lenses. He's shouting, probably giving orders. I throw the glasses out the window, listen as they clack softly on the pavement, skipping down the highway behind us.

"Any other electronic devices in the car?"

"No, nothing," says Princess.

"Drones?"

"Shit, we don't got money for that."

I don't bother to check. There's no time for it. I could dump the van in Ben Lomond. Nothing out there but scatter cookers and fallen drones anyway. But Princess is still cabled up to those dogs. So I drive straight to the old highway. At Gilroy we make the road south. I'm worried but not too worried. Driving a van to Radio City isn't like driving one from it. There are always a few Army patrols out. But they're broken men, partial hot, not GMers, dirty and underpaid, stopping only those coming out, not those going in. Besides, only the officers are GM. And they won't go out there. Too dirty for them. Soldiers don't care as much as they should. They're all dying sooner than later. And there are dirt roads, open patches, cutoffs, places marked by us.

An hour passes. Princess has been quiet for sometime, finally says,

"Say, gem. I didn't mean to sell you out. You can see that, right? I mean, I didn't have a choice. You see what Fat Freddy's done to me. He runs things. I can't get out of it."

I keep my eyes on the road. I won't help him with this. "I thought we were friends," I say.

"We were, gem. I swear."

"You tricked me into hanging out with you."

"I had to."

"Oh really?"

"You don't get it, gem. Life in Santa Cruz is hard. The damned melt."

"What did he offer?"

"Scatter."

"How much?"

"Free for two months. I thought we were, you know, going to be friends. But then Fat Freddy got better. I didn't expect that. He's sick. Maybe he won't show up for a few days. But then he shows up, wants to know what I'm working on."

"But you didn't really mean it. You really didn't want to hang out with me. No one does."

Princess is silent the rest of the ride. He doesn't even attempt to talk when we get to SLO Town. But he's breathing hard, starting to worry. I let him think about it.

We arrive in the zone. Like all dead cities, there's charm to it. The vacant streets. The grasses and shrubs growing on roof tops. Homes choked in wisteria. Buildings matted in ivy. A beautiful soft city full of feral cats and fat, plump kangaroo mice. Then the road towards Diablo Canyon. The drop zone. You won't know this if you haven't been there. You can see the images downloaded to your iGlasses if you want to. They will walk you through this place without being there, showing you the destruction. But the images won't ever resemble how it is out here, the wonderful yellows, the fields of mustard and poppies, the redwoods, though just a half century old, majestic and cool. Beneath this you see the flashing red of poison oak, the sulfa butterflies in swarms of a hundred thousand each. Under stones, the seas of lizards. Above, the red-tailed hawks. The green bottle beetles. The rusty coyotes. This disaster is the most beautiful place on earth. I love it like no other. You can drive for hours in any direction and not see another person. And when you finally run across someone, your meeting will be brief yet personable. You will remember their faces as they remember yours. Because you are hot and they are hot. And there are so few of you true Radio City.

Princess says at last, "Please, Lollipop, don't do this."

I look over, see the worry on his face, the eyes open too wide. "It's beautiful, isn't it?"

"It's too hot. I can't survive here."

"No, I don't suppose that you can."

"You can't do this. This isn't you. You know it isn't."

"Well, I don't know who I am anymore. I just am," I reply. I try to sound calm, but Princess can hear the anger in my words. He groans. He knows he has maybe a week here, not much longer. I feel a moment of anguish, a stitch of pain for taking him. But it passes quickly. I mean, it isn't as if he's going to live forever.

Noh Exit
A Play in One Act
James Morrow

Characters:
JEAN-PAUL SARTRE, philosopher and author, age forty-five, later
the *shite*
SIMONE DE BEAUVOIR, philosopher and author, age forty-two,
later the *shite-tsure*
TAKESHI IKEDAMA, artistic director, Japanese Medieval Drama
Touring Company, age thirty, later the *waki*
FLORENCE LARSON, president, San Antonio Cultural Society,
age thirty-five, later the *waki-tsure*
MUSICIANS, the *hayashi*, one flutist and three drummers drawn
from the onstage spectators, various ages
CHORUS, the *jiutai*, eight chanters drawn from the onstage
spectators, various ages
ABORASETSU, the *kyōgen*, the comedy relief, king of demons and
prince of caprice, ageless

(*South Texas, a sweltering Sunday evening in July of 1950.
We are in the spare and unadorned basement of the Bexar
Lions Club.*

*Four flags droop from freestanding poles arrayed along the
back wall: a Texas state flag, a Lions Club banner, the Stars
and Stripes, and an Alamo flag featuring green, white, and
red bars. A grid of twelve folding chairs, each holding a
member of the San Antonio Cultural Society, faces a raised
platform on which three additional folding chairs accommodate* JEAN-PAUL SARTRE, SIMONE DE BEAUVOIR, *and*
FLORENCE LARSON. *At rise,* FLORENCE *pulls an index card
from her shoulder bag and approaches the lectern at the
front edge of the dais.*)

FLORENCE. (*Addressing onstage spectators.*) I still can't get over it. Two of the world's most eminent philosophers have seen fit to include our town in their book tour. (*Consults index card.*) Before I forget, let me lob a big fat juicy thank-you to Scooter Prescott for allowing the San Antonio Cultural Society to meet here tonight in the Lions Club basement. And we're grateful as grateful can be to Ellie Thornton of Ellie's Browserama Bookshop for sacrificing a quiet Sunday evening at home so we can all purchase hot-off-the-presses English translations of works by our distinguished visitors. (*Waves to unseen woman.*) Muchas gracias, Ellie. Tonight she'll be selling both Mr. Sartre's *Being and Nothingness* and Miss de Beauvoir's *The Second Sex*, and here's the really big news: the authors have agreed to autograph your books with their very own internationally famous names. And now, without further ado, I give the floor to our deep thinkers, who will jointly favor us with a talk entitled, "Existential Freedom versus the Fall into Inauthenticity."

(FLORENCE *pivots away from the lectern, approaches her guests, and shakes first* SARTRE'*s hand, then* BEAUVOIR'*s hand. The twelve spectators applaud.* SARTRE *lights up a cigarette and takes a drag.*)

As you may be aware, Mr. Sartre, here in Texas the words "fall" and "freedom" resonate for us like cathedral bells. Thanks to the fall of the Alamo, which happened right down the street, Sam Houston was able to regroup his forces and send the Mexican army packing across the Rio Grande, thereby giving us our freedom.

SARTRE. I don't know what you're talking about.

BEAUVOIR. She's talking about a Catholic mission, Jean-Paul, named after the poplar or cottonwood tree, indigenous to this part of the world. The Spanish word for poplar is *alamo*.

(FLORENCE *sits down next to* BEAUVOIR. *Sucking on his cigarette,* SARTRE *rises and assumes the lectern.*)

SARTRE. *Eh bien*, trees. Naturally I think of the moment in my novel *La Nausée* when Roquentin, strolling through the local park and gazing at the boiled-leather bark of a chestnut tree, realizes that the source of his anxiety is not simply the tree but the indifferent *being* of the tree.

FLORENCE. Another theory holds the mission got its name from La Compañía del Alamo, a Mexican battalion that moved in after the priests moved out. The soldiers were all from the town of Alamo in Coahuila.

SARTRE. (*To spectators.*) Although it's true that English translations of two books by Mademoiselle de Beauvoir and myself have just appeared from La Maison de Knopf, in her case, *Le Deuxième Sexe*, and in mine, *L'Être et le Néant*, we did not come here this evening to indulge in sordid capitalist commerce.

(*A male spectator,* VIRGIL CHILTON, *removes his Stetson hat and rises from his folding chair.*)

VIRGIL. (*More curious than hostile.*) Mr. Sartre, when I hear you getting testy about free enterprise, I think of certain rumors that you and your lady friend are communist subversives.

FLORENCE. Virgil, honey, Mr. Sartre and Miss de Beauvoir will be happy to take questions at the end of their presentation.

(*As* VIRGIL *resumes his seat,* BEAUVOIR *lights a cigarette, then joins* SARTRE *at the lectern.*)

BEAUVOIR. *En réalité*, I must urge you all not to purchase *The Second Sex* tonight. The American edition is an abomination. On orders from the publisher, the translator omitted many pages and rendered most of my philosophical terms incoherent.

(*A young female spectator,* RUBY WALKER, *rises and addresses* BEAUVOIR *in an awed, breathy voice.*)

RUBY. Mademoiselle, I heard that *Le Deuxième Sexe* was placed on the Vatican's Index of Forbidden Books.

BEAUVOIR. *Oui, c'est vrai.* They did not appreciate my chapter on lesbianism.

RUBY. Then I simply *must* have it.

BEAUVOIR. Human beings are always free to make such choices. *Je vous salue.*

FLORENCE. Miss de Beauvoir's talking about consumer choices, not bedroom choices.

BEAUVOIR. Actually I'm talking about both.

RUBY. Here in the Lone Star State, we don't set much store by the pope's opinions.

BEAUVOIR. *D'accord.*

SARTRE. (*To* BEAUVOIR.) Lone Star State. Does she mean the Soviet Union?

FLORENCE. Ruby, dear, please sit down.

SARTRE. (*To* RUBY.) I share Mademoiselle de Beauvoir's delight in your decision. If there were a God, which of course there is not, we might logically assume that human beings are blessed with a stable and coherent essence devised by this Creator. But in the ontological system developed by Mademoiselle de Beauvoir and myself, with a nod to Martin Heidegger, existence *precedes* essence.

RUBY. (*Aroused.*) Oh, Monsieur Sartre, when I hear you talk like that . . .

SARTRE. In other words, Mademoiselle Ruby, your essence is something that you yourself create, moment by moment, as you make your way through life.

RUBY. (*Swooning.*) *Oui, mon professeur.*

(*As* RUBY *resumes her seat, everyone's attention is abruptly drawn to the imposing figure of* TAKESHI IKEDAMA, *who enters the basement arrayed in a striking silk robe and burdened with an enormous steamer trunk. He hauls the trunk to the front of the dais, then mounts the platform and bows politely before* SARTRE, BEAUVOIR, *and* FLORENCE.)

IKEDAMA. I'm so terribly sorry to interrupt this beautiful meeting of minds, but a deep existential crisis has come to South Texas. Call me Takeshi Ikedama, artistic director of the Japanese Medieval Drama Touring Company. I am also a philosophical person. After completing my honorable wartime service in the Imperial Japanese Army Air Force, since disbanded, I attended Freiburg University and four years later received a degree predicated on my thesis, "Buddhist Motifs in Occidental Phenomenology."

SARTRE. Freiburg? Did you study with Heidegger?

IKEDAMA. During my years in Germany, the honorable Nazi philosopher was hiding out in the Black Forest. Hear my tale, O Texicans.

Last night our troupe of Nogaku players was headed northeast across your endless state toward the metropolis of Austin. It was our intention to give a performance this evening of Zeami's *The Wind in the Pines.*

BEAUVOIR. *(Dragging on cigarette.)* Phenomenological intentionality is fundamental to understanding consciousness, or so Husserl argued.

IKEDAMA. *(Agreeing.) Logical Investigations* is a most felicitous text. *(Beat.)* The bus broke down outside your city, and we proceeded by taxicab to your opulent Davy Crockett Hotel, our assumption being that we could easily reach Austin the next morning. Alas, after breakfast a pandemic of food poisoning overcame everyone in our humble company.

FLORENCE. Everyone except you, Mr. Ikedama?

IKEDAMA. I did not have the longhorn steak tartare. And yet it remains imperative that *The Wind in the Pines* or some other Nogaku drama be performed posthaste, for this is the seventh hour of the seventh day of the seventh week of the seventh month of the seventh year of the seventh century after the Buddhist priest Nichiren revealed that the *Lotus Sutra* contains the most efficient path to enlightenment.

(A peeved male spectator, CREIGHTON FILBERT, *speaks up.)*

CREIGHTON. You want to know something, Mr. Moto? We came here to learn about Continental angst, not Oriental soap opera.

IKEDAMA. *(Unperturbed.)* Happily, a solution to all our problems lies at hand. After seeing in the hotel lobby a poster advertising this meeting, I spent my afternoon composing a Nogaku interpretation of Mr. Sartre's scintillating play, *Huis Clos*, which I recently saw presented in Kyoto under the title *The Mushroom Patch of the Soul.*

BEAUVOIR. How recently?

IKEDAMA. Last year.

BEAUVOIR. Jean-Paul, did you ever receive payment?

SARTRE. Who cares?

BEAUVOIR. You should.

SARTRE. I won't cede my freedom to a bourgeois ledger. (*To* IKEDAMA.) Other translations have included *Dead End, Vicious Circle, Behind Closed Doors, In Camera,* and *No Way Out.* I prefer your mushrooms.

(IKEDAMA *jumps off the dais, opens the steamer trunk, and removes a pile of sixteen identical scripts.*)

IKEDAMA. Thanks be to Buddha, your Davy Crockett Hotel maintains an emergency mimeograph machine. If all of us in this room were to perform my play in the shadow of your great Alamo shrine, starting immediately, then everybody wins—the honorable members of your cultural society will receive their eagerly anticipated education in angst, the honorable Mr. Sartre and the honorable Miss de Beauvoir will sell a truckload of books, and the ghost of Nichiren will constrain his dead disciples' spirits from unleashing demons bent on burning down this building.

(IKEDAMA *reaches into the trunk and retrieves a stack of six black silk kimonos, plus two cypress masks—male and female—a rolled canvas, a transverse flute, a shoulder drum, a hip drum, and a stick drum.*)

FLORENCE. Do you really believe we're threatened by demons, Mr. Ikedama?

IKEDAMA. Here in the twentieth century the demon hypothesis enjoys little credibility.

SARTRE. I would argue that if we lose our nerve and fail to mount Mr. Ikedama's play—

IKEDAMA. *The Battle of Alienated Gazes.*

SARTRE. If we fail to mount *The Battle of Alienated Gazes,* we shall be guilty of *mauvaise foi,* bad faith, whereby human beings under pressure from conventional social forces disown their innate freedom and act inauthentically.

FLORENCE. Inauthenticity seems an awfully high price to pay for sticking with our original agenda. I say, let's put on the kimonos!

(*Suddenly the lights in the basement flicker, then regain normal brightness.*)

IKEDAMA. Whereas in the medieval era, the time of my play, people *did* believe in demons.

FLORENCE. Let's put them on *right now!*

(SARTRE *stubs out his cigarette in the ashtray on the lectern.* IKEDAMA *presents him with a script and the wooden male mask, which exhibits an indecipherable expression.*)

IKEDAMA. The principal performer in a Nogaku drama embodies the *shite*, the protagonist. I wrote the part with you in mind, Monsieur Sartre. Your character is Yamashina no Shōji, a royal gardener.

SARTRE. (*Contemplating wooden face.*) Many are the facades we assume in our flight from responsibility.

(IKEDAMA *presents* BEAUVOIR *with a script and the female mask, serene of countenance.*)

IKEDAMA. Miss de Beauvoir, you will be the *shite-tsure*, compliment of the *shite*.

BEAUVOIR. Jean-Paul and I have always enjoyed a reciprocity of intellect.

SARTRE. Much to the distress of our lovers.

IKEDAMA. (*To* BEAUVOIR.) Your character is Hitomaru, an itinerant lute player. My own role will be that of the *waki*, the foil of the *shite*, typically a courtier, messenger, or traveling monk, though in this case a majordomo.

(BEAUVOIR *stubs out her cigarette in the lectern ashtray.* IKEDAMA *presents* FLORENCE *with a script.*)

FLORENCE. Don't I get a mask?

IKEDAMA. The *waki-tsure*, compliment of the *waki*, never wears a mask. Mrs. Larson, you are a brine maiden named Murasame, which means Autumn Rain.

FLORENCE. How lovely.

VIRGIL. I played the bass drum in my high-school marching band.

(IKEDAMA *presents* VIRGIL *with a script, carved sticks, and the corresponding drum.*)

James Morrow

IKEDAMA. You'll see it's all quarter notes. Very simple. Flute, anyone?

(RUBY *raises her hand.* IKEDAMA *gives her a script and the flute, then gestures toward the shoulder drum and the hip drum. Two spectators spring to attention, and the director gives them their instruments.*)

IKEDAMA. So now we have our *hayashi,* our musicians. The rest of you will be the *jiutai,* the chorus.

(IKEDAMA *distributes scripts to the remaining spectators, keeping one for himself.*)

I must now ask you to employ your chairs in building the *hashi-gakari,* a bridge at upstage right linking the human realm to the world of ghosts and spirits.

(*The four* MUSICIANS *and eight* CHORUS *members collapse their chairs and carry them to the far left corner of the room. They open the chairs and arrange them in two parallel lines extending from the back wall to the dais, upstage right, six bare seats abutting six bare seats. The result is an elevated diagonal bridge along which actors can make entrances and exits.*)

(*Gesturing toward flags.*) Those poles will become the pillars on which our imaginary sacred roof is suspended.

(IKEDAMA *mounts the dais and shoves the lectern out of the way.* SARTRE, BEAUVOIR, *and* FLORENCE *rise and set their chairs aside. The four cast members remove the flags from the poles, fold up the material, and place the bundles beside the steamer trunk.*

IKEDAMA *takes up the rolled canvas and affixes it to the rear wall of the basement. The painting, unfurled, proves to be a pine tree. The director grasps a naked flagpole and places it downstage left near the corner of the dais.*)

The foil's pillar, the *waki-bashira,* goes here. (*To* SARTRE.) The protagonist's pillar, the *shite-bashira,* goes upstage right. (*To* BEAUVOIR.) The flutist's pillar, the *fue-bashira*—upstage left. (*To* FLORENCE.) The focusing pillar, the *metsuke-bashira*—downstage right.

(Sartre, Beauvoir, *and* Florence *set their poles in the proper locations.* Ikedama *removes the remaining garments from the trunk, then divides all the costumes into two piles: twelve black silk kimonos and three colorful, elaborately embroidered silk robes.*)

(*Clapping.*) Robes for the actors! Kimonos for the rest of you!

(*Under* Ikedama's *supervision, the* Musicians, *the* Chorus, *and the actors select their costumes, then slip them on over their street clothes. The* waki-tsure *robe awarded to* Florence *is as elaborate as* Ikedama's *regalia, but it pales beside the* shite-tsure *gown of shimmering purple brocade that* Beauvoir *puts on.* Sartre *dons the most elaborate costume of all, a luminous crimson caftan with exaggerated shoulder pads that threaten to compromise the diminutive philosopher's dignity.*)

Actors to the bridge! Musicians to the pine tree! Chorus on the floor stage left!

(*The* Musicians *and the* Chorus *scurry to their positions. In a matter of seconds, a static procession forms at the far end of the bridge,* Ikedama *in the lead, followed by* Florence, *the masked* Sartre, *and the masked* Beauvoir. *The actors study their scripts.*

A high wailing sound issues from the flute. The drums produce monotonous rhythms that continue unbroken throughout the performance. Ikedama *walks slowly along the bridge, steps onto the dais, and stations himself near the foil's pillar. The drama has begun.*)

I am the majordomo of Arbuda, one of the Eight Cold Narakas into which the wicked are born, except for those consigned to the Eight Hot Narakas. Yesterday my master, Lord Aborasetsu, king of demons and prince of caprice, being in a mood to experiment, altered the variety of excruciation for which Arbuda has always been famous. I wonder whether the inhabitants of this new Arbuda will fare better or worse than their predecessors. . . .

Chorus. (*Chanting.*)
Who were forced to abide naked and helpless
Within the frigid depths of the Naraka,

While the frost chewed holes in their faces
And the wind made ribbons of their skin.
In both Arbudas, ancestral and avant-garde,
The duration of a prisoner's sentence
Is the time it takes for an immortal ant
To empty a barrel of sesame seeds
By removing a single kernel
Once every hundred years.

> (*The flute wails. Poring over her script,* FLORENCE *begins a long, slow march down the bridge.*)

IKEDAMA. Here comes our first damned soul of the day, Murasame, a brine maiden of Suma Bay.

FLORENCE. (*Entering playing area.*) There must be some mistake.

IKEDAMA. The great god Aborasetsu never makes mistakes.

FLORENCE. Surely my sorrowful existence was punishment enough for whatever evils I committed in my past lives. I should never have been thrown into this place.

IKEDAMA. In a future era, the occidental ontologist Martin Siegheildegger will observe that each of us is thrown into the world, a circumstance pregnant with perplexity.

FLORENCE. I'd heard Arbuda was infinitely cold, a zone of chattering teeth and blue flesh.

IKEDAMA. Lord Aborasetsu got bored with all that. So did the condemned, as a matter of fact.

> (FLORENCE *removes the fan from her sash and opens it. In the speech that follows, she treats the fan as a bucket, pantomiming the behavior she describes.*)

FLORENCE. There's nothing Aborasetsu could teach me about boredom. Day after tedious day, night after insipid night, I drew brine from Suma Bay, lugged the six heavy pails to a cart, and hauled them over rutted roads to the salt kilns for boiling. I lived in a hut. The moon was my only companion. When I died of pneumonia, it seemed like a blessing.

IKEDAMA. Was not the aristocratic poet Yukihira moved by the sublime austerity of a brine maiden's life?

CHORUS. (*Chanting.*)
If ever anyone
Chances to ask for me,
Say I live alone,
Soaked by the dripping seaweed
On the shore of Suma Bay.

FLORENCE. My sleeves were soaked in seaweed, all right, and also in the tears of my misery. That said, I do not begrudge Yukihira his sentiments. But for poetry and the moon, I would have drowned myself long before the pneumonia killed me.

IKEDAMA. "Without music, life would be a mistake." Thus spake the future occidental sophist Friedrich Nietzsche.

(*Still stationed on the far end of the bridge,* SARTRE *removes his mask, lights a cigarette, and wafts out an improvised line.*)

SARTRE. How easily the highborn romanticize the proletariat. Yukihira could return to his pleasure boat whenever he wished.

(*The basement lights flicker.* SARTRE, *startled, stubs out his cigarette on a folding chair, then restores his mask.*)

FLORENCE. (*Pantomiming with fan.*) How I loved catching the moon in my pails. I would line them up, six moons along the shore, one moon in the bay, an eighth moon in the sky.

(*A high, sustained note pours from the flute. Script in hand,* SARTRE *crosses the bridge and takes his place near the protagonist's pillar. He removes his mask and scratches his nose.*)

SARTRE. I am Yamashina no Shōji of Chikuzen Province, until recently charged with tending the Emperor Shirakawa's chrysanthemums, then came a lethal accident with my pruning hook. (*Restores mask.*) I do not belong in this meat locker.

IKEDAMA. Lord Aborasetsu intends not to punish Shōji the gardener but rather the person Shōji was in a forgotten former existence.

SARTRE. If anybody deserves to be in a Naraka, it's Princess Tokuski. Can you hear me, Lord Aborasetsu? I'll gladly stick around if that means I get to watch you freeze her royal ass off.

FLORENCE. (*To* IKEDAMA.) He's not a poet, but I like him anyway.

SARTRE. What I most came to loathe about Tokuski was her inauthenticity. When she learned that I, a common gardener, had become infatuated with her, she went around quoting a twelfth-century folk song.

CHORUS. (*Chanting.*)
The way of love follows no fixed path,
Neither high nor low.
The imperatives of passion will acknowledge no station,
Neither of prince nor of peasant.

SARTRE. But she didn't believe those lofty words, not for a minute. One day a royal messenger appeared before me.

CHORUS. (*Chanting.*)
The Princess Tokuski, who knows neither high nor low,
Bids you visit the pond where floats a single lotus.
There you will find a drum hanging from a laurel tree.
Beat on the drum, and when Tokuski hears the noise,
She will step onto her balcony, arrayed in all her loveliness.
There she will wait for you, and once you appear
She will lift from her lips a thousand kisses
And let them fall upon your face like petals from peonies.

SARTRE. (*Removing fan from sash.*) So I went to the tree by the lotus pond, only to discover that the drum was made of damask. Fool that I am, I took up a log and beat on the damask drum. (*Pantomimes striking drum with fan.*) No sound came forth, but I kept on beating, tearing the drum to shreds, and when I looked up, I saw a hundred courtiers gathered around the water's edge, laughing at me.

FLORENCE. I am Murasame, brine maiden of Suma Bay, and I think Princess Tokuski was a fool to treat her handsome gardener so shamefully.

SARTRE. Despite the humiliation, the episode proved instructive, enabling me to understand a great schism in the universe.

CHORUS. (*Chanting.*)
Drum, log, tree, pond, lotus:
Each such objective phenomenon enjoying
A fullness of existence, a being-in-itself,

Whereas we conscious actors,
Inherit and incarnate being-for-itself,
Wellspring of subjectivity in the world.
And yet this status is eternally vulnerable to collapse,
Menaced by the ubiquity of other minds,
Alien gazes that relentlessly make objects out of subjects,
Thus refashioning our freedom
As a source of dread,
An incompleteness,
An emptiness,
A nothingness,
A void.

FLORENCE. I've often thought of it that way, only with buckets and the moon.

[*As the flute warbles, the masked* BEAUVOIR *strides majestically along the bridge and enters the playing area.*]

BEAUVOIR. I was expecting glaciers.

IKEDAMA. Lord Aborasetsu is experimenting.

BEAUVOIR. I am Hitomaru, for many years an itinerate lute player living in Owari Province, but then I choked to death on a fish bone. The punishments that await me here doubtless fit the crimes I committed in earlier incarnations—but of late I've been a victim, not a perpetrator.

FLORENCE. The lot of Murasame, brine maiden of Suma Bay, was also hard.

SARTRE. Yamashina no Shōji, royal gardener to the Emperor Shirakawa, endured many indignities.

BEAUVOIR. Hour after wretched hour I walked barefoot through freezing blizzards and fearsome gales. . . .

CHORUS. [*Chanting.*]
Under dark skies and beneath broiling suns,
Along brambled roads,
Over muddy paths,
Across broken bridges,
Down culs-de-sac.

363

BEAUVOIR. *(Removing fan from sash.)* Each time I entered a village, a prayer formed on my lips. Sometimes Lord Buddha would hear me, sending a crowd to attend my performance and throw coins at my feet, but more often heaven turned a deaf ear to my entreaty. *(Plucks veins of fan like lute strings.)* But the playing was always its own reward, even when the audience was indifferent, hostile, or nonexistent.

FLORENCE. My fair Hitomaru, naturally I think of "The Lute Girl's Song." The thick strings—

CHORUS. *(Chanting.)*
The thick strings crashed and sobbed
Like the falling of winter rain,
And the thin strings whispered secretly together.
The first and second string
Were like a wind sweeping through the pines
With stuttering howls.
The third and fourth
Were like the voice of a caged stork
Crying for its children at night
In low, mournful notes.

BEAUVOIR. Po Chü-i is my favorite poet. *(Takes* FLORENCE *by the hand.)* How marvelous that you know his work, Murasame, my comely brine maiden.

FLORENCE. I have always cherished the voice of the lute.

BEAUVOIR. And I have always cherished those who cherish it.

(Compelled by a sudden mutual attraction, FLORENCE *and* BEAUVOIR *rush toward each other and embrace. In an unbroken and sensual gesture,* FLORENCE *removes* BEAUVOIR's *mask and stares into her eyes. Suddenly* FLORENCE *screams and pulls away.)*

My dear Murasame, have you never kissed a woman? Before the fish bone intervened, I inhabited all genres of desire.

FLORENCE. Your eyes, Hitomaru! I see them in your eyes!

BEAUVOIR. *(Taking mask from* FLORENCE.*)* What do you see?

FLORENCE. The crimes that condemned you to this place.

BEAUVOIR. (*Restoring her mask.*) Tell me about them.

FLORENCE. I won't do that.

(SARTRE *strides up to* BEAUVOIR, *removes her mask, and contemplates her face.*)

SARTRE. What am I looking for?

FLORENCE. In a past life she was Lady Tamamo, a ruthless sorceress living on the island of Kikaigashima. Peer into Hitomaru's eyes, and you'll see the towers and ramparts of the witch's palace.

SARTRE. (*Fixing on* BEAUVOIR.) I see only coruscating blue irises surrounding black pools of being-in-itself.

FLORENCE. No castle by the sea?

(SARTRE *returns* BEAUVOIR*'s mask, but she does not put it on.*)

BEAUVOIR. Evidently I stand naked in your gaze alone, my sweet Murasame. (*Impulsively removes* SARTRE*'s mask.*) On the other hand, my dear Shōji, you cannot hide your former existence from me.

SARTRE. My former existence as—?

BEAUVOIR. (*Studying* SARTRE*'s eyes.*) A samurai warrior, Kumagai no Jirō Naozane. It ended shamefully. I see Naozane being led to the chopping block. I see the executioner sharpening his sword. (*To* FLORENCE.) Come here, my darling.

FLORENCE. I never watch a beheading before breakfast.

BEAUVOIR. If we're going to escape from Arbuda, we must learn how the place works. (*Draws* FLORENCE *toward her.*) Do you see him? The most skilled executioner in Kawachi Province, his sword flashing in the rising sun.

FLORENCE. (*Fixing on* SARTRE.) I see nothing.

BEAUVOIR. The blade descends. Naozane's head falls to the ground and rolls away.

(BEAUVOIR *drops* SARTRE*'s mask on the floor.* SARTRE *shudders and gasps. Bending, he retrieves the decapitated wooden face. Instead of restoring the mask, he surveys it like Hamlet considering Yorick's skull.*)

SARTRE. How easily a person becomes a thing. What sin brought Naozane to this ignominious end?

BEAUVOIR. We'll go into that another day.

SARTRE. If you alone can see my past, Hitomaru, and if Murasame alone can see your past, then it follows that I alone can see Murasame's past.

(SARTRE *tucks the mask under his arm, then approaches* FLORENCE *and fixes on her face. She closes her eyes.*)

Grant me access to your iniquity.

FLORENCE. No.

SARTRE. There can be no secrets here.

FLORENCE. Kiss me.

SARTRE. What?

FLORENCE. Kiss me.

(SARTRE *approaches* FLORENCE *and plants an unequivocal kiss on her eager lips. She opens her eyes.*)

Now what do you see?

SARTRE. I see the lovely Murasame, who I fear is fast becoming mere flesh in my eyes, even as I become mere flesh in her eyes.

IKEDAMA. Even worse, if they keep this up, Shōji will want Murasame to become mere flesh in her *own* eyes. And vice versa.

BEAUVOIR. A project without a future.

FLORENCE. Keep looking.

SARTRE. (*Obeying.*) I see . . . I see . . . I see a beautiful but merciless courtesan, Lady Rokujō, forever toying with the affections of callow soldiers and sensitive young poets. After telling a man she can never return his love, she recommends that he drown himself.

IKEDAMA. It is said that twenty ghosts, eternally smitten with Lady Rokujō, still haunt the foggy banks of the Ikatu River.

FLORENCE. Is that the whole of my sin?

BEAUVOIR. I would say it meets the minimum entry requirements for this place.

SARTRE. There is more, but I prefer to postpone the discussion.

BEAUVOIR. Speaking of suicide, I wonder if that's a way out.

IKEDAMA. Perhaps you should investigate.

BEAUVOIR. [*Removing fan from sash.*] A samurai wife never lets herself suffer rape or captivity at the hands of her husband's enemies. Instead she takes up her tantō knife and with a ritual stroke severs the arteries of her neck. A mere lute player can do the same. [*Attempts to cut carotids.*] Damn! It's like I'm made of iron.

IKEDAMA. *Quod erat demonstrandum.*

BEAUVOIR. Everything is clear to me now. I understand Aborasetsu's grand experiment perfectly. O Demon King, you are too clever by half. Why should you bother to appoint the cold Narakas with icebergs and blizzards, or the hot Narakas with brazen bulls and pools of boiling pitch, when all that's needed is for the condemned to become aware of one another?

SARTRE. [*Agreeing.*] You are my appointed torturer, Hitomaru, and I am Murasame's torturer, and she is your torturer—forever.

IKEDAMA. Not precisely forever. Your sentence is the time it takes for an immortal ant to empty a barrel of sesame seeds by bearing away a single kernel once every hundred years.

SARTRE. Here's an idea. Let's retire to the corners of our prison and proceed to ignore each other, day after day, year after year, seed after seed, thus canceling all this meaningless mutual torture.

BEAUVOIR. It's worth a try.

FLORENCE. I'm game.

(SARTRE *turns and marches to the protagonist's pillar.* BEAUVOIR *proceeds to flutist's pillar.* FLORENCE *crosses to the focusing pillar.*)

CHORUS. [*Chanting.*]
In this manner will a prisoner in the new Arbuda
Try to recover what was lost to other persons,
Even as he finds himself wondering . . .

SARTRE. Am I courageous enough to keep the recognition of myself by these same persons from becoming the essential source of meaning in my life?

(*The three prisoners gaze outward as the flute trills and the drums provide a simple cadence. Soon each inmate grows restless, glancing backward to see if the others are doing the same.*)

FLORENCE. (*Pointing fan at* SARTRE.) Yamashina no Shōji, it isn't *fair* that you should know more about my alter ego than I do.

SARTRE. Life is not fair. Damnation even less so.

BEAUVOIR. (*To* FLORENCE.) Nor do the gods smile on you, Murasame, when you hoard knowledge that could aid my quest for authenticity and dealienation.

FLORENCE. Dealienation—is that a word?

BEAUVOIR. Everything is a word.

(SARTRE, BEAUVOIR, *and* FLORENCE *drift toward the center of the playing area.*)

FLORENCE. (*Hesitant.*) You will be pleased to learn, Hitomaru, that as a young sorceress Lady Tamamo used her powers merely for mischief, causing birds to soil the pompous and toads to vomit on the proud.

SARTRE. (*To* BEAUVOIR.) How droll of you, Hitomaru.

FLORENCE. But in her later years she placed her magic at the disposal of a corrupt daimyo called Lord Naritsune, the object of her adoration. To please Naritsune . . . shall I continue? (BEAUVOIR *nods.*) To please Naritsune, the witch would enter the mind of whomever he detested at the moment, then compel that person to commit *seppuku*—not ordinary *seppuku* but the slowest and most agonizing kind, whereby the suicide disembowels himself with a dull bamboo knife.

BEAUVOIR. Shame on Lady Tamamo. Shame on me.

FLORENCE. Now it's my turn.

SARTRE. Do you insist? (FLORENCE *nods.*) As you might imagine, Lady Rokujō's escapades always entailed the possibility of procreation.

In her fertile years she gave birth to three babies, all girls, and in every case . . .

FLORENCE. I took the infant . . .

SARTRE. She took the infant, put it in a jute sack, added a heavy stone, and—

FLORENCE. And threw the sack into a river.

SARTRE. Lake Biwi, actually.

FLORENCE. I truly belong here.

SARTRE. (*Contemplating severed face.*) Yes, and so presumably does the beheaded warrior Naozane. Did I flee the field of battle, Hitomaru? Am I a coward?

BEAUVOIR. (*Ad lib.*) Quite the opposite. You were a hero of the French Resistance. (*Beat.*) Among the legends that arose during the twelfth-century internecine wars, the most famous told of Taira no Atsumori, a warrior of the Heiki clan. The astonishing beauty of this young man, a mere sixteen years old, made him curiously invulnerable, for the soldiers of the rival Genji clan could not decide what part of so flawless a body to cut. (*Beat.*) In time there emerged between the clans an unspoken but sacred compact, whereby no Genji samurai would ever hurt the Heiki youth. Then came the battle of Ichi-no-tani, during which—

SARTRE. Let me guess. Naozane found himself alone on the field with Atsumori.

BEAUVOIR. The Genji samurai straightaway fell in love with the beautiful Heiki youth, this boy who was also a god, and the same forbidden passions possessed Atsumori. Instead of fighting, the warriors removed their armor and lay together beneath a plum tree. Later, Naozane noticed that—

SARTRE. (*Putting on mask.*) That Atsumori's body was not in fact perfect?

BEAUVOIR. There was a scar aslant his groin. Upon seeing this impossible and profane blemish on the god with whom he'd lain, Naozane took leave of his senses, maddened by the paradox.

SARTRE. (*Pantomiming murder with fan.*) Seizing his sword, he killed Atsumori by planting the blade in the unthinkable scar.

369

BEAUVOIR. As he donned his armor, Naozane realized that his fellow knights would punish him for breaking the sacred compact, and so he decided to mutilate Atsumori's corpse beyond recognition. (*Beat.*) But before he could complete the unholy task, a party of Genji samurai arrived on the scene. The following day Naozane was tried, sentenced—

SARTRE. (*Whipping off mask.*) And sent to the chopping block.

BEAUVOIR. End of story.

SARTRE. From now until the sesame barrel is emptied, each of us in this appalling place will be susceptible to the judgments of the other two.

CHORUS. (*Chanting.*)
Thus are the condemned of the new Arbuda,
Through the remorseless power of interpretive gazes,
Doomed to pass their postmortem existences
Entombed in the perceptions of their fellow prisoners,
All the while transforming one another into objects,
Surrendering their freedom to phantoms,
And dwelling in ignominious inauthenticity.

SARTRE. So now we know.

BEAUVOIR. Naraka is other people.

FLORENCE. There's no way out.

SARTRE. What happens next?

IKEDAMA. I suggest you get on with it.

FLORENCE. All right.

BEAUVOIR. Very well.

SARTRE. Yes, let's get on with it.

(*The flutist plays a long mournful note. The drummers beat out a final cadence. SARTRE suddenly points to the floor. BEAUVOIR and FLORENCE stare at the indicated spot.*)

Look! An ant!

FLORENCE. With a sesame seed in its mouth!

BEAUVOIR. (*Putting on her mask.*) Let's find out where it's going!

(*Slowly, solemnly, eyes fixed on the ant,* SARTRE *walks toward the protagonist's pillar and starts down the bridge to the floor, presumably pursuing the ant.* BEAUVOIR, FLORENCE, *and* IKEDAMA *follow. Next come the* MUSICIANS *and the* CHORUS. *After descending from the bridge, each member of the procession marches toward the focusing pillar. Eventually all sixteen troupers stand in a milling crowd before the dais.*)

IKEDAMA. (*To* FLORENCE.) My gratitude to your honorable cultural society is as vast as the Great Pacific Sea. Nichiren's ghost is surely at peace.

RUBY. (*Waving script around.*) A brilliant piece of work, Mr. Ikedama! Florence, you were sensational! Monsieur Sartre, Mademoiselle de Beauvoir, all I can say is—*magnifique!*

FLORENCE. Let's take it on the road.

SARTRE. Mr. Ikedama, I would like to suggest a few improvements in your little play.

BEAUVOIR. I have some recommendations too, beginning with the first line.

(*Suddenly the basement lights flicker and die. The troupers issue cries of bewilderment. "What the hey?" "Lordy!" "Darn!" "Who's got a flashlight?" "Somebody forgot to pay the electricity bill!"*

The tall, sinister figure of ABORASETSU, *robed and masked, appears on the bridge, bathed in a red spotlight. He wears a golden robe with flaring shoulders, a fearsome* kishin *demon mask, and a wig whose white tresses trail to his waist.*)

FLORENCE. Mister Ikedama, is this in the script?

IKEDAMA. I'm afraid not.

ABORASETSU. (*Thunderous voice.*) I am Lord Aborasetsu, king of demons and prince of caprice! O ye pathetic mortals, for whom life is but a dewdrop in the morning sun, I curse you with my dying breath!

IKEDAMA. He's evidently functioning as the *kyōgen,* the comedy relief.

FLORENCE. I'm not laughing yet.

BEAUVOIR. (*To* ABORASETSU.) Dying breath? Since when can a god die?

ABORASETSU. Since you and your fucking exotropic nebbish consort confused the civilized world with your fucking overbearing existentialist ideas, Mademoiselle de Beauvoir!

FLORENCE. Language, sir, language.

(ABORASETSU *charges over the bridge and vaults into the center of the playing area.*)

ABORASETSU. What is it that makes a god a god? Not being-in-itself, certainly, the fullness of mere things, but neither does a god require being-for-itself, the emptiness of thinking creatures! (*Howls in despair.*) *Aaaaaiiiiihhhhh!* The essence of a god is being-in-itself-for-itself, but that is a contradiction, an absurdity, a fullness that is also an emptiness! *Aaaaaiiiiihhhhh!*

(*As the mortals stand helplessly by, the angry deity seizes the upright protagonist's pillar and snaps it in half over his knee. He then breaks the other three flagpoles, bashes a hole in the lectern with his fist, and rips down the pine tree from the back wall. He tears the canvas in two.*)

(*Pulling fan from sash.*) Having become irremediably severed from myself, I now take leave of you, off to commit ontological *seppuku! Aaaaaiiiiihhhhh!*

(*Brandishing his fan,* ABORASETSU *returns to the bridge, crosses into the other realm, and vanishes. The basement lights come back on.*)

RUBY. My goodness.

FLORENCE. I suggest we run through the rest of our agenda before something else happens. Does anyone have a question for Mr. Sartre or Miss de Beauvoir?

(*Silence. The spectators are too stunned to reply. At last* RUBY *speaks up.*)

RUBY. Perhaps there's a question the philosophers would like to ask *themselves.*

(S̲ᴀ̲ʀᴛʀᴇ *and* B̲ᴇ̲ᴀᴜᴠᴏɪʀ *look at each other, then burst out laughing.*)

Sᴀʀᴛʀᴇ. We have as many questions for ourselves—

Bᴇᴀᴜᴠᴏɪʀ. —as there are entities in a barrel of sesame seeds.

Fʟᴏʀᴇɴᴄᴇ. (*To unseen woman.*) Ellie, I think we've got some customers for you.

Rᴜʙʏ. Me first!

(*Clutching her script,* Rᴜʙʏ *rushes offstage, bound for the Ellie's Browserama Bookshop table.*)

Bᴇᴀᴜᴠᴏɪʀ. Forget my complaint against the American translation, everyone. I am happy to have you buy my book.

Iᴋᴇᴅᴀᴍᴀ. (*Bowing before* Sᴀʀᴛʀᴇ *and* Bᴇᴀᴜᴠᴏɪʀ.) Thanks to your philosophy, honorable sages, a terrible dragon was slain tonight.

Sᴀʀᴛʀᴇ. Mademoiselle de Beauvoir and I are evermore the enemies of bad faith.

Fʟᴏʀᴇɴᴄᴇ. That *kyōgen* certainly made a mess of things.

Bᴇᴀᴜᴠᴏɪʀ. No god goes gently to his grave.

Iᴋᴇᴅᴀᴍᴀ. I'm terribly sorry, Mrs. Larson. My company will pay for the damage.

(Rᴜʙʏ *returns with two book purchases and a ballpoint pen. She gives the pen and* The Battle of Alienated Gazes *to* Iᴋᴇᴅᴀᴍᴀ. *He autographs the first page. She hands her copy of* The Second Sex *to* Bᴇᴀᴜᴠᴏɪʀ. *The philosopher signs the book.*

Rᴜʙʏ *presents* Being and Nothingness *to* Sᴀʀᴛʀᴇ. *He writes an inscription on the title page, then returns the volume.*)

Rᴜʙʏ. (*Reading.*) "*L'enfer, c'est les autres, mais nous n'en sommes pas encore là.*" "Hell is other people, but we're not there yet." (*Reading.*) "*Avec toutes mes amitiés, Jean-Paul Sartre.*" Oh, Monsieur, I shall treasure it always. *Je vous aime.*

Sᴀʀᴛʀᴇ. So, who's next?

(*BLACKOUT.*)

NOTES ON CONTRIBUTORS

MATTHEW BAKER is the author of *If You Find This* (Little, Brown), an Edgar Award nominee for 2016, and the founding editor of *Nashville Review*.

Drama and fiction translator EVA BUCHWALD is a dramaturge for the Finnish National Theater in Helsinki.

JOHN CLUTE is coeditor of *The Encyclopedia of Science Fiction* (Gollancz). His most recent books are *Pardon This Intrusion: Fantastika in the World Storm* and *Stay* (both Beccon).

World Fantasy Award–winning author JOHN CROWLEY's most recent novel is *Four Freedoms* (William Morrow). His next will be a history of crows.

In 2016 and 2017, Dover Books will reissue science fiction pioneer SAMUEL R. DELANY's novel *Dark Reflections*, and Wesleyan University Press will bring out the first volume of his journals, *In Search of Silence, Volume 1, 1957–1969*, followed by his *Letters from Amherst: Five Narrative Letters*.

JULIA ELLIOTT is the author of *The New and Improved Romie Futch* and *The Wilds* (both Tin House). She is the recipient of a Rona Jaffe Writer's Award, and was awarded a Pushcart Prize for her story in *Conjunctions:56, Terra Incognita*.

Cover artist JOSEBA ELORZA, aka MiraRuido (miraruido.com) is an illustrator and animator living in Vitoria, Spain.

BRIAN EVENSON is a *Conjunctions* contributing editor and the author of more than a dozen books of fiction, including *The Warren*, *Immobility* (both Tor), *A Collapse of Horses*, and *Windeye* (both Coffee House). He teaches at the California Institute of the Arts.

JEFFREY FORD is the author of the novels *The Portrait of Mrs. Charbuque*, *The Girl in the Glass*, and *The Shadow Year*, and the story collections *Crackpot Palace* and *The Drowned Life* (all Morrow/HarperCollins). His latest book is the collection *A Natural History of Hell* (Small Beer).

The translator of almost two hundred graphic novels, EDWARD GAUVIN is a contributing editor for comics at Words Without Borders and the winner of the John Dryden Translation Prize and the Science Fiction & Fantasy Translation Award. His translations of fiction by Georges-Olivier Châteaureynaud have appeared several times in *Conjunctions'* print and online editions.

Issue coeditor ELIZABETH HAND's novels and short fiction have received multiple Nebula, World Fantasy, and Shirley Jackson awards. Her many books include *Glimmering* (Harper Prism), *Saffron and Brimstone: Strange Stories* (M Press), *Generation Loss* (Small Beer), and, most recently, *Hard Light* (St. Martin's).

MADELINE BOURQUE KEARIN is a PhD student in historical archaeology at Brown University. Her academic work examines the intersection of class, gender, and madness in nineteenth-century asylums in the United States and United Kingdom. This is her first literary publication.

The award-winning author LEENA KROHN's work has been translated into more than twenty languages. Her contribution to this issue is a translation from her most recent novel *Erehdys* [*Mistake*], published in Finnish by Teos. Her *Collected Fiction* in English appeared in 2015 (Cheeky Frawg).

MICHAEL PARRISH LEE is the author of *The Food Plot in the Nineteenth-Century British Novel* (forthcoming from Palgrave Macmillan), a study of eating and appetite in fiction. His fiction has appeared previously in *Conjunctions'* print and online editions.

KELLY LINK is the author of *Magic for Beginners* (Small Beer), *Pretty Monsters* (Viking), *Stranger Things Happen* (Subterranean), and *Get in Trouble* (Random House). She is the cofounder, with her husband, Gavin J. Grant, of Small Beer Press.

VALERIE MARTIN's most recent novel is *The Ghost of the Mary Celeste* (Vintage).

JAMES MORROW is the author of the Godhead Trilogy (Harcourt), *The Last Witchfinder* (William Morrow), and *Galápagos Regained* (St. Martin's Press), among other books. He has received the World Fantasy Award, the Nebula Award, and the Grand Prix de l'Imaginaire.

Robert Burniaux (1924–88), who wrote under the name JEAN MUNO, is among the best known of Belgium's Silver Age fabulists. The author of nine novels and four story collections, he received Belgium's top literary prize, the Prix Rossel, in 1979. "Cartoon" is from his first collection, *Histoires singulières*.

NICOLE NYHAN is a graduate of Bard College and the New School for Social Research. A *Conjunctions* senior editor, she works at Grove Atlantic in New York.

Longtime *Conjunctions* contributor JOYCE CAROL OATES's most recent books are *The Doll-Master and Other Tales of Terror* (Mysterious Press) and *Soul at the White Heat: Inspiration, Obsession, and the Writing Life* (Ecco). She is currently the visiting distinguished writer in the graduate writing program at New York University.

PAUL PARK's most recent books are *All Those Vanished Engines* (Tor) and *Other Stories* (PSJ). He teaches writing at Williams College.

JESSICA REED's work has appeared or is forthcoming in *Conjunctions, Crazyhorse, North American Review,* and other periodicals. She teaches a course on physics and the arts at Butler University.

LAURA SIMS's most recent poetry collection is *Staying Alive* (Ugly Duckling). Her first book, *Practice, Restraint,* was the winner of the 2005 Fence Books Alberta Prize, and in 2014 she edited *Fare Forward: Letters from David Markson* (powerHouse).

PETER STRAUB's most recent book is *Interior Darkness: Selected Stories* (Doubleday.)

S. P. TENHOFF is a recipient of Columbia University's Bennett Cerf Memorial Prize for Fiction. His writing has appeared in *Conjunctions'* online magazine, *Southern Review, American Short Fiction, Ninth Letter, Antioch Review,* and *Fiction International,* among other publications.

JONATHAN THIRKIELD is the author of *The Waker's Corridor* (LSU Press). He teaches programming at the New School's graduate program in media studies.

LAVIE TIDHAR's books include *A Man Lies Dreaming* (Melville House); *Osama* (PS Publishing), winner of the World Fantasy Award; and *The Violent Century* (Thomas Dunne).

Alice Bradley Sheldon (1915–1987), aka JAMES TIPTREE, JR., aka Raccoona Sheldon, grew up traveling with her parents through regions such as India and Central Africa. In the 1940s and 1950s, she worked as an Air Force photo intelligence officer and for the CIA, before publishing her first short story in 1968. Writing under a male pseudonym for twenty years, Sheldon had a revolutionary effect on the science fiction of the 1970s and 1980s in her exploration of political—and especially feminist—themes. The many books she published during her lifetime include *Ten Thousand Light-Years from Home* (Eyre Methuen), *Star Songs of an Old Primate* (Del Rey), *Up the Walls of the World* (Berkley Books), *Tales of the Quintana Roo* (Arkham House), and *Crown of Stars* (Tor). Avowedly a lesbian (among other, more complicated orientations), she nevertheless enjoyed a close marriage of four decades with her husband, Huntington D. Sheldon. In 1987, with both spouses in ill health, Sheldon shot her husband and herself, having predicted her eventual suicide for many years. In 1991, the annual James Tiptree, Jr. Award was created in her honor to recognize a work of science fiction or fantasy that expands or explores understandings of gender. Tachyon published an omnibus collection of her stories, *Her Smoke Rose Up Forever,* in 1994, and Open Road Media released the Kindle edition of *Brightness Falls from the Air* in 2014. Her honors include two Hugo Awards, three Nebula Awards, and posthumous induction into the Science Fiction Hall of Fame.

E. G. WILLY's work has been anthologized in *Stories from Where We Live* (Milkweed Editions), *The Breast* (Global City Press), and *Creatures of Habitat* (Mint Hill).

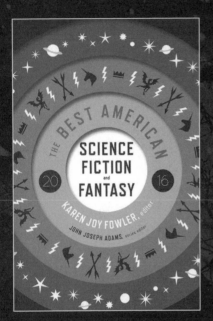

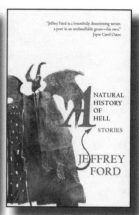

The Year in Small Beer

has been strong! It started with Joan Aiken's "sprightly but brooding" (*Kirkus*) collection *The People in the Castle* and Sofia Samatar's "soaring paean to the power of story" (NPR) *The Winged Histories*. Summer was a celebration of Jeffrey Ford's *A Natural History of Hell* "tales that bend the world as we know it in unexpected ways" (*Booklist*, starred review) and in autumn we will time travel with John Crowley's new edition of the first science fiction novel, *The Chemical Wedding of Christian Rosencreutz*. And we're ending the year in spectacular fashion with Ursula K. Le Guin's selected recent nonfiction *Words Are My Matter*.

Intersperse a couple of issues of our twice-yearly zine, LCRW, and it's been a fabulous year in all senses of the word. Find them at your local bookshop or online at **smallbeerpress.com**.

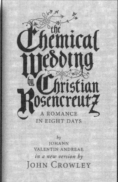
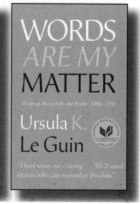

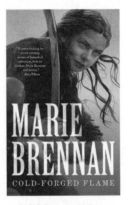

Level up your *fiction*

Clarion West
Writers Workshop

Summer 2017
June 18 – July 28

Applications open in December
clarionwest.org/summer/

INSTRUCTORS

Daryl Gregory
Kij Johnson
John Chu
Connie Willis
Daniel José Older
Pat Cadigan

twitter.com/ClarionWest
f facebook.com/clarionwestworkshop

Space and Time is a 50-year-old magazine of fantasy, horror, and science fiction. We particularly like to present stories that cross and blend genres. Want some science in your fantasy? Steampunk in your horror? Then this is the magazine for you!

SPACE AND TIME

THE MAGAZINE OF FANTASY, HORROR, AND SCIENCE FICTION

JOHN WALTERS
JC HEMPHILL
JAMIE KILLEN

FALL 2016
ISSUE # 126

$6.00US $7.50CAN

PLUS:
AN INTERVIEW WITH
DANIELLE ACKLEY-MCPHAIL

MFA *in* Creative Nonfiction

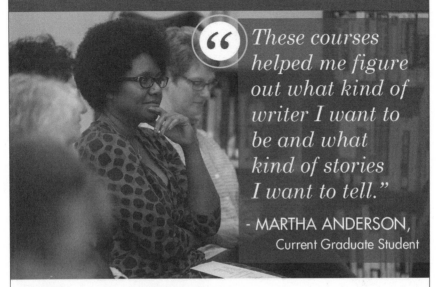

66 *These courses helped me figure out what kind of writer I want to be and what kind of stories I want to tell."*

— MARTHA ANDERSON,
Current Graduate Student

ABOUT THE PROGRAM
- Completely online, no residency
- Track in publishing and teaching
- Memoir, personal essay, travel & food writing
- Summer creative writing seminar in Ireland
- Classes start every May. August & January

FACULTY MENTORS

Mel Allen	Ann Hood
Adam Braver	Leanna James Blackwell
Rita Ciresi	Suzanne Strempek Shea
Anthony D'Aries	Kate Whouley
Shahnaz Habib	

BROWN UNIVERSITY LITERARY ARTS

HOME FOR INNOVATIVE WRITERS

Program faculty

John Cayley
Colin Channer
Thalia Field
Forrest Gander
Carole Maso
Meredith Steinbach
Cole Swensen

Visiting and other faculty

Lori Baker
Andrew Colarusso
Laura Colella
Mónica de la Torre
Joanna Howard
Erica Mena
Gale Nelson
Camille Rankine
Chika Unigwe

Since 1970, Literary Arts at Brown University has been fostering innovation and creation. To learn more about the two-year MFA program, visit us at http://www.brown.edu/cw

Bard's unique summer-based MFA in Writing focuses on innovative poetry but also welcomes students working in sound, performance, and other short or mixed-media forms. In this interdisciplinary program, anchored in the theory and diverse practices of contemporary art, students work with a distinguished faculty of writers, artists, and scholars, and are in close dialogue with faculty and students in Film/Video, Music/Sound, Painting, Photography, and Sculpture.

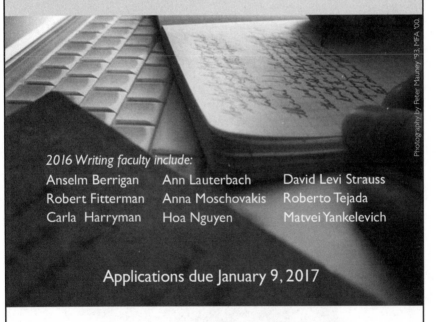

Photography by Peter Mauney '93, MFA '00.

2016 Writing faculty include:

Anselm Berrigan   Ann Lauterbach   David Levi Strauss
Robert Fitterman   Anna Moschovakis   Roberto Tejada
Carla Harryman   Hoa Nguyen   Matvei Yankelevich

Applications due January 9, 2017

Bard**MFA**

MILTON AVERY GRADUATE SCHOOL OF THE ARTS

mfa@bard.edu • 845.758.7481 • bard.edu/mfa

S O L I D

Julie Carr

Thalia Field

Renee Gladman

Noah Eli Gordon

Lisa Jarnot

Miranda Mellis

Jake Bohstedt Morrill

Laura Mullen

Elizabeth Robinson

Jim Shepard

Mac Wellman

O B J E C T S

www.solidobjects.org

NEW BOOKS IN 2017 BY
CECILIA VICUÑA
ANOUCK DURAND
MIRTHA DERMISACHE
VINCENT SARDON

siglio uncommon books at the intersection of art & literature

PO BOX 111, CATSKILL, NEW YORK 12414 **www.sigliopress.com**
Image from *Eternal Friendship* by Anouck Durand, translated by Elizabeth Zuba, out April, 2017

Bénédicte Vilgrain: *A Tibetan Grammar*
[translated from the French by Keith Waldrop]

Bénédicte Vilgrain
A Tibetan Grammar

"A project which explores language from an almost archi-tectural perspective, using the structure of Tibetan to examine how a language creates categories—and then immediately overflows them....Vilgrain deftly demon-strates the inability of language to remain sufficiently static for any cartographical system. Her balance of analytic query, sharp imagery, and radical juxtaposition creates a varied and vivid surface that gives the reader an uncanny sense of experi-encing the familiar through foreign means."—Cole Swensen
Poetry, 80 pages, offset, smyth-sewn, original paperback $14

Quit

Lissa McLaughlin

Lissa McLaughlin: *Quit*

Taut lines—fragments from a journal? a report on hospice work?—seem to keep moving out of our grasp while at the same time bringing us closer to their subject, the elusive experience of the dying and their nurses. A grief worker at a hospice ponders how power structures and ordinary human failings can overwhelm rewarding work. And yet how even a lousy sandwich can recall us to the pleasures of this world.
    "Life and death is daily but never rendered mundane, and the poems turn quickly from rushed observance to elegy to report, often in the same breath... Even the smallest moment can become urgent, and the poems articulate that urgency."—*Rob McLennan Blog*
Poetry, 88 pages, offset, smyth-sewn, original paperback $14

Michael Donhauser: *Of Things*
[trans. from the German by Andrew Joron & Nick Hoff]

Michael Donhauser
Of Things
translated by Nick Hoff and Andrew Joron

A thicket, a manure pile, a marigold, gravel, a tomato, a cypress—award-winning Austrian poet engages in a "close reading" of natural things. His emphasis is less on depiction than on tracing the movement from object to language. He brings a dazzling variety of perspec-tives to his deeply felt encounters with nonhuman phenomena.
    "Donhauer...intends a poetic by which the reader is implicated in the genesis of his or her world. To make us 'aristocratic auditors of our steps.' 'Though also fitted with a mute attentive-ness./ (A sensibility that listens more than interprets.)'" —John Olson, *Tillalala Blogspot*
Poetry, 128 pages, offset, smyth-sewn, original paperback $14

Dallas Wiebe: *Skyblue's Essays*

Dallas Wiebe

SKYBLUE'S ESSAYS

"If you read this book, your life, not to mention your conversa-tions, may become more interesting"—Charles Alexander, *Rain Taxi*
Fictions, 160 pp., offset, smyth-sewn, original pbk. $14

Also available:
Going to the Mountain, Stories, 192 pp., orig. pbk. $14
The Vox Populi Street Stories, Novel, 312 pp. $15
The Tranparent Eye-Ball, Stories, 114 pp. o.p. $20

Orders: www.spdbooks.org, www.burningdeck.com

BOMB
Conversations
between
Artists, Writers,
Musicians,
Performers,
Directors—
Since 1981

March Curriculum Conversation

Friday, March 10, 2017

IWT Curriculum Conversations foster innovative approaches to teaching and reading texts that contribute to our contemporary sense of an evolving self. Using writing-to-learn strategies, the day's workshops focus on a rigorous reading of the text through the lens of contemporary and historical nonfiction, fiction, and poetry.

TO REGISTER and for WORKSHOP DESCRIPTIONS
please visit *writingandthinking.org*

The Lord of the Flies: An Allegorical Tale of Democracy and Survival

William Golding's tale of schoolboys cast away on a Pacific island after a nuclear attack has inspired dystopias as disparate as *The Hunger Games*, *The Maze Runner*, *Ender's Game*, and *Lost*. Since the 1954 publication of *The Lord of the Flies*, this provocative story of children who, as Joyce Carol Oates put it, "replicate the worst of their elders' heritage of ignorance, violence, and warfare," illustrates how quickly civility can revert to bloodthirsty savagery.

Why are such dark stories popular with young adults? How do they reflect the current views on politics, the economy, and the environment? What does *The Lord of the Flies* teach us about the roles young people can play in combating chaos, tyranny, and paranoia? This Curriculum Conversation will address these questions as we explore and grapple with a text that has engaged readers for generations.

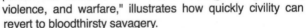

IWT Bard | 1982-2016
Celebrating More Than 30 Years of Writing and Thinking

Bard Institute for Writing & Thinking PO Box 5000 | Ludlow 105 | Annandale-on-Hudson, NY 12504